HORTICULTURAL SCIENCE

A Series of Books in AGRICULTURAL SCIENCE

Plant and Soil Science

Editors: IVER JOHNSON AND M. B. RUSSELL

Horticultural Science

JULES JANICK *Purdue University*

W. H. FREEMAN
AND COMPANY
San Francisco

© Copyright 1963 by W. H. Freeman and Company

The publisher reserves all rights to reproduce this book, in whole or in part, with the exception of the right to use short quotations for review of the book.

Printed in the United States of America

Library of Congress Catalog Card Number 63-7192   (C6)

To Shirley and Peter and Robin

Preface

Horticulture is concerned with those plants whose cultivation brings rewards, whether monetary profit or personal pleasure, sufficient to warrant the expenditure of intensive effort. This art—which entails judicious timing and many skills—has an ancient tradition. But modern horticulture involves the integration of many natural phenomena with man-made effects and so is a scientific discipline in its own right. The primary purpose of this textbook is to examine the scientific concepts on which horticulture is based. A comprehension of the science gives meaning and scope to the art and enables the improvement of centuries-old practices.

Part I introduces the biology of horticulture; horticultural problems are biological problems. The plant, the basis of all horticultural activities, must first be considered as a living entity. A knowledge of plant relationships, structure, growth, and development is necessary if the technology and industry of horticulture are to be understood.

Part II deals with the technology of horticulture. Rather than the techniques being considered as they relate to specific crops, they have been treated in terms of their broader horticultural implications. Thus, it is hoped that the information will become more meaningful and transferrable. Specific practices should be discussed by the instructor, since they will vary with geographical location.

Part III describes the industry of horticulture. The industry is analyzed on the basis of location and specialty, thus emphasizing its distinguishing characteristics and special problems. In recognition of their importance, a discussion of the esthetic aspects of horticulture has been included.

This book has been designed primarily as a university level text for the beginning horticultural student as well as for those students whose interests may be only incidentally associated with horticulture. Although the book assumes no large familiarity with botany, it would be to the student's advantage to have completed some prerequisite study or to be simultaneously enrolled in a botany or plant science course. The text is divided into 14 chapters, which should be adequately covered in a semester's time. The skills associated with horticulture can be reviewed in a laboratory in a sequence similar to that used in this text. Key references are provided at the end of each chapter to facilitate further study by the student.

It is a pleasure to acknowledge my colleagues who have been so generous with their time, their information, and their support. Among the many are K. M. Brink, Professor N. W. Desrosier, Professor Dominic Durkin, Professor F. H. Emerson, Professor A. T. Guard, Professor C. E. Hoxsie, Professor Jerome Hull, Jr., Professor K. W. Johnson, Professor A. C. Leopold, Professor N. W. Marty, C. L. Pfeiffer, Professor E. C. Stevenson, Professor R. B. Tukey, Professor G. F. Warren, Professor G. E. Wilcox, and Professor Milton Workman. Professor C. E. Hess and Professor A. H. Westing, who have each contributed a chapter, have been of inestimable help. I would like to thank Professor J. R. Shay, Professor W. H. Gabelman, Professor M. N. Dana, and Dr. I. J. Johnson for their critical reading of the entire manuscript.

January 1963   JULES JANICK

Contents

CHAPTER 1

The Impact of Horticulture

The origins of horticulture are intimately associated with the history of mankind. The term *horticulture,* however, is probably of relatively recent origin and first appears in writings in the seventeenth century. The word is derived from the Latin *hortus,* garden, and *colere,* to cultivate. The concept of the culture of gardens (Anglo-Saxon *gyrdan,* to enclose), as being distinct from the culture of fields—that is, *agriculture*—is a medieval concept, indicative of the practices of that period. Agriculture now refers broadly to the technology of raising plants and animals. Horticulture in its present concept is that part of plant agriculture concerned with so-called "garden crops" as contrasted with *agronomy* (field crops, mainly grains and forages) and *forestry* (forest trees and products). (See Fig. 1-1.)

Horticulture deals with an enormous number of plants. Garden crops traditionally include fruits and vegetables, all the plants grown for ornamental purposes, as well as spices and medicinals. Many horticultural products are utilized in the living state and are thus highly perishable; water is a necessary constituent of quality. In contrast, the usable products of agronomic and forest crops are often utilized in the nonliving state and are usually high in dry matter. Custom has delineated the boundary line for some crops; for example, tobacco and, in some locations, white potatoes, are considered agronomic crops in the United States. In the main, however, horticulture deals with crops that are intensively cultivated; that is, plants that are of high enough value to warrant a large input of capital, labor, and technology per unit area of land. Pine trees grown for timber or pulp are an example of extensive agriculture. Although the per acre value of a pine grove may be large if harvested at once, the yearly increment of value is relatively small ($20–80/year in current dollars). The importance of our forest industries is due to the tremendous acreage involved. When pine trees are grown more intensively, as are Christmas trees (Fig. 1-2), they are usually considered as a horticultural crop. Pine trees grown as nursery

1

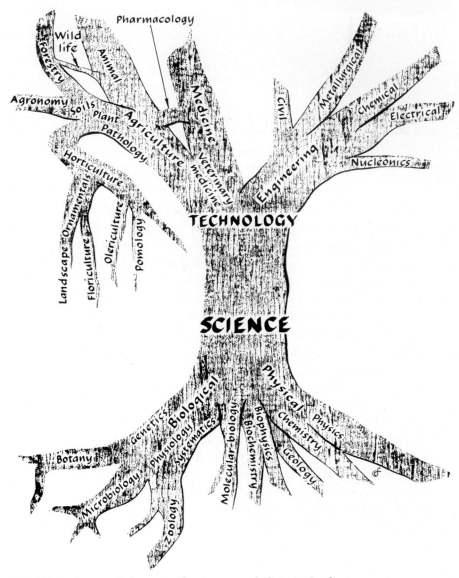

Fig. 1-1. *A tree of the natural sciences and their technologies.*

stock for use in ornamental plantings assume sufficient value to justify large expenditures for fertilization, pruning, harvesting, and marketing, and therefore become a true horticultural crop. (The value of good nursery land may compete with suburban real estate!) Similarly, the presence of a sugary gene in maize increases its value enough to warrant using more intensive cultural methods (the use of better seed—single-cross versus double-cross hybrid—spray programs, and expensive harvesting procedures) and transforms it into the horticultural crop, sweet corn.

Horticulture thus can be defined as the branch of agriculture concerned with intensively cultured plants directly used by man for food, for medicinal purposes, or for esthetic gratification. The industry is usually divided on the basis of crop and plant use. The production of edibles is represented in *pomology* (fruit culture) and *olericulture* (vegetable crops); the production of ornamentals is represented by *floriculture* and *landscape horticulture*. These terms are not mutually exclusive. For example, many edible plants (apples) are used as ornamentals, and many plants often classed as ornamentals (poppy, pyrethrum) have pharmacological and industrial uses (Fig. 1-3).

Fig. 1-2. *Applying insecticide to young Scotch pines being grown for Christmas trees.*

[Courtesy D. L. Schuder.]

Fig. 1-3. *The dried flowers of pyrethrum* (Chrysanthemum cinerariaefolium) *are the source of a natural insecticide. Ornamental forms* (C. coccineum) *are known as painted daisies.*

[Courtesy E. R. Honeywell.]

The esthetic use of plants is a unique feature of horticulture, distinguishing it from other agricultural activities. It is this aspect of horticulture which has led to its universal popularity. Paradise means garden! In the United States ornamental horticulture is undergoing a renaissance brought about by an increased standard of living coincidental with the development of suburban living. The satisfaction of this bent in the American family has created an expanding industry out of that part of horticulture that had been mainly confined to amateurs and fanciers. This has not, of course, been true for the older portions of the world. The hanging gardens of Babylon (one of the seven wonders of the ancient world) and the awesome seventeenth century gardens of Versailles are spectacular examples of the prominence of ornamental horticulture.

Horticulture is an ancient art, and many of its practices have been empirically derived. However, modern horticulture, as agriculture, has become intimately associated with science, which has served not only to provide the methods and resources to explain the art, but has become the guiding force for its improvement and refinement. Horticulture will never become wholly a science, nor is this particularly desirable. Its curious mixture of science (botany to physics), technology, and esthetics makes horticulture a refreshing discipline that has continually absorbed man's interest and challenged his ingenuity. The science of horticulture nevertheless remains the dynamic influence in the proper use and understanding of the horticultural art. It is with this phase of horticulture that this book is largely concerned.

ECONOMIC POSITION OF HORTICULTURE

It is difficult to ascertain the precise position of any large and diverse industry in our economy. This is particularly true of horticulture, which involves not only the many facets of production, but the added increments of processing, service, and maintenance. For example, ornamentals such as woody perennials are not consumed but become invested in plantings, and increase in value with the passage of time. The value of this wealth is ordinarily not taken into consideration until we become painfully aware of it through the severities of weather or the encroachment of concrete and steel. The replacement of large trees and shrubs is usually economically prohibitive and is often horticulturally impossible.

Commercial horticulture represents a significant portion of American agricultural wealth. Agriculture, the country's biggest industry, has a farm value of over 30 billion dollars, half of which originates directly in agriculture, with the rest representing the contributions of other industries—for example, machinery, fertilizer, chemicals (Fig. 1-4). These production inputs are a reflection of the increased technology inherent in present-day agriculture. Agriculture has increased in production to keep up with a growing population's demand for a high level of nutrition and a high standard of living. Horticulture's percentage share in this expanding industry has been relatively stable over the last 50 years (Fig. 1-5). In 1960, 12% of the annual farm receipts, representing four billion dollars, were attributable to horticulture. The retail value of horticultural products, after being processed,

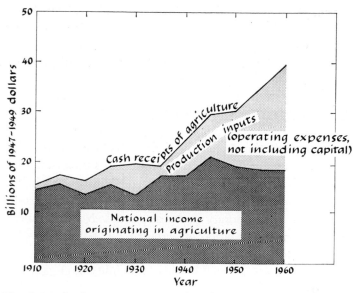

Fig. 1-4. *Cash receipts compared with national income originating in agriculture, 1910–1960.*

[Data from Economic Research Service, USDA.]

transported, and marketed, increased to about ten billion dollars. In the United States about 40% by weight of the food consumed consists of horticultural products. In view of this fact alone, one may expect horticulture to maintain its increasing importance in our lives and economy.

These figures should not imply that each facet of the horticultural industry has or will share equally in this increase. The fortunes of individual crops in the United States over the last five decades reflect the changing habits and preferences of the American people and the technological changes in the food industry. For example, the trend has been toward an increase in the per capita consumption of vegetables used in salads (lettuce, celery) and a decrease in the consumption of potatoes and starchy root crops. Per capita fruit

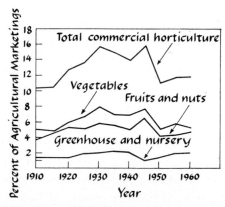

Fig. 1-5. *Horticulture's share of the total agricultural market in the United States, 1910–1960.*

[Data from Economic Research Service, USDA]

consumption has gradually increased, with citrus fruits gaining at the expense of apples. The consumption of processed fruits and vegetables has shown a marked increase over the fresh products, and, on a fresh equivalent basis, now accounts for over half of the total consumed.

A HISTORICAL PERSPECTIVE

Along with the discovery of fire, the "invention" of agriculture represents the most significant achievement in human civilization. In primitive societies based on food gathering or hunting, each individual must be totally involved with the urgencies of securing sustenance. Abundance proved to be temporary and exceptional. Notwithstanding the systematic and efficient organization of certain food gathering societies, each adult is pressed into continued activity. The limiting factor in the development of primitive societies becomes the availability and dependability of a food supply.

Man has been a food collector for the great portion of his existence. Food production by the cultivation of edible plants and the domestication of animals is of relatively recent origin, dating back 7000 to 10,000 years ago to what is known as the Neolithic age. Only through the gradual development of a system of agriculture could a working and regular surplus be depended upon. The immediate reward of a surplus is the release of specialists from food production who, although productive through other skills, do not contribute directly to the food supply. The gradual development of an agriculture, with its increased efficiency and dependability, encouraged the development of new classes of specialists—artisans, clerks, priests. The standard of living of a people increases as the need for specialists becomes necessary. Table 1-1 broadly dates the progress of civilization in terms of advances in agriculture-horticulture.

Selection of Edible Plants

The origin of civilization can be traced to man's discovery that he could assure himself of a plentiful food supply by planting seed. Rapidly growing vegetables and cereals, which produce a crop within a season, must have been the first plants cultivated. The technology involved in cultivating nut or fruit trees, for example, is considerably intricate and time consuming; as a result, these edibles were probably gathered from the wild. Even today in the United States some food is gathered from indigenous

Table 1-1. *Dating the past.*

HISTORICAL EVENT	YEARS AGO	EVENT IN HORTICULTURE AND PLANT AGRICULTURE
Space Exploration		Structure of the gene (DNA)
		Isolation of phytochrome
		Mechanical harvesting
		Plastic films
		Radiation preservation
		Polyploid and mutation breeding
		Organic phosphate pesticides
		Chemical weed control
Controlled Release of		Tissue culture
Atomic Energy		Auxin research
		Respiration cycle
		Plant virus studies
		Hybrid corn
		Photoperiodism discovered
		Gasoline powered tractor
Successful Air Flight		Concept of essential elements
		Bailey's Cyclopedia of Horticulture
		Reaper and combine
		Plant nutrition investigations
		Beginnings of agricultural chemistry
		U. S. Agricultural Experiment Stations
American Civil War	100	Mendel discovers "laws" of heredity
		Morrill Act (established land grant colleges)
		Origins of plant pathology
		Modern plow developed
		Canning of food discovered
American Revolution		
		Gardens of Versailles
		Discovery of microscope
		Importation of plant species
Discovery of America		Rebirth of botanical sciences
Beginnings of Modern Science		
Norman Conquest of England	1000	
		Monastery gardens
"Dark" Ages		Herbals
Roman Civilization		Roman Gardens

Table 1-1. *Continued*

HISTORICAL EVENT	YEARS AGO	EVENT IN HORTICULTURE AND PLANT AGRICULTURE
Birth of Christ		Legume rotation
Golden Age of Greece		Botanical works of Theophrastus of Eresos
'		Fruit varieties
		Hanging gardens of Babylon
		Grafting
Egyptian Civilization		Irrigation
		Domestication of crop plants
Neolithic Age		Discovery of Agriculture
	10,000	

uncultivated plants. For example, Maine's blueberry industry depends upon such a source. The cultivation of cereals and the domestication of animals led to a permanent agriculture, which provided the media for the growth of an advanced civilization. Although it is not known when the cultivation of plants first took place, it is known that the bulk of our present-day food plants were selected by the people of many lands long before recorded history. The way in which wild plants were transformed to their present cultivated forms is often obscure, and the original ancestors of many of our crop plants cannot be traced. The same, of course, is true for animals. Our debt to primitive man is enormous.

Somewhere in the now dry highlands of the Indus, Tigris, Euphrates, or Nile Rivers, the technology we call agriculture was conceived. In about 3000 years, the primitive existence of Stone Age man was transformed to the full-fledged urban cultures of Egypt and Sumeria. By this time the date, fig, olive, onion, and grape, the backbone of ancient horticulture, had been brought under cultivation and the technological base necessary to insure a productive agriculture—land preparation, irrigation, and pruning—had been discovered. By 3000 B.C., field cultivation via the ox replaced cultivation by the hoe; by the time of the flowering of Egyptian culture, *agriculture-horticulture* was an established discipline (Fig. 1-6).

Egypt and the Fertile Crescent

The people living in the Nile valley, which had been inhabited for at least 20,000 years by Stone Age man, developed an agriculture 7000 to

8000 years ago. In Egypt, man's rendezvous with civilization began. By 3500 B.C., Egypt had established a centralized government with Memphis as its capital, and by 2800 B.C., it had developed to a high enough level of civilization to support such monumental engineering projects as the pyramids.

The great accomplishment of Egyptian agriculture was systematic irrigation through hydraulic engineering. Among the notable horticultural achievements of the Egyptians were their formalized gardens complete with pools and full time gardeners, the creation of a spice and perfume industry, and the development of a pharmacopoeia—a collection of drug and medicinal plants (Fig. 1-7).

The Egyptians cultivated a great number of fruits, including date, grape, olive, fig, banana, lemon, and pomegranate, as well as such vegetables as cucumber, artichoke, lentil, garlic, leek, onion, lettuce, mint, endive, chicory, radish, and various melons. In addition, many plants, for example, papyrus, castor bean, and date palm, were cultivated for fiber, oil, and other "industrial" uses. They also created the various technologies associated with the food industry—pottery, baking and fermentation, and drying.

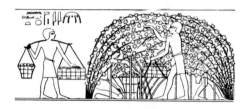

Fig. 1-6. *Egyptian horticulture from a tomb at Beni Hasan (about 1900 B.C.). Top. Picking figs. [From Singer,* History of Technology, *vol. 1, Oxford Univ. Press, 1954.] Middle. A round vine arbor. [Gothein,* History of Garden Art, *vol. 1, Dutton, New York, 1928.] Bottom. Irrigating a vegetable garden. [Gothein,* History of Garden Art, *vol. 1, Dutton, New York, 1928.]*

Egyptian influence lasted an incredible 35 centuries. The periods of stability produced, in addition to their great technology, a magnificent art and a complex, if bewildering, theology. By the time Egypt had become a Roman province (3 B.C.), its influence had already permeated the ancient world—an influence that is still felt today.

East of Egypt, the ancient cultures of Mesopotamia—Babylonia and As-

syria—added to the technology of horticulture the irrigated terraces, gar
dens, and parks (Figs. 1-8 and 1-9). Irrigation canals lined with burnt
brick and asphalt-sealed joints helped keep 10,000 square miles under cultivation which in 1800 B.C. fed over
15,000,000 people. By 700 B.C., an
Assyrian Herbal was compiled containing the names of over 900 plants
including 250 vegetable, drug, and
oil crops. The Old Testament
prophecy ". . . they [all nations]
shall beat their swords into plow-
shares and their spears into pruning hooks" (Isaiah 2, *ca.* 800 B.C.)
attests also to the agriculture and
horticulture of the period.

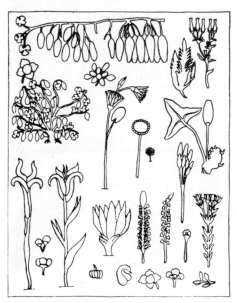

Fig. 1-7. *Plants and seeds brought back
from Syria by Thothmes III and carved
on the temple walls at Karnak, Egypt
(about 1450 B.C.).*

[From Singer, *History of Technology,* Oxford Univ.
Press, London, vol. 1, 1954.]

Greece

The Greeks, while adding only
incidentally to practical agriculture
(Fig. 1-10), did devote their genius
to botany. Although the botanical
writings of Aristotle (384–322 B.C.)
are lost, a portion of the writings of
his most famous student, Theophrastus of Eresos, is extant. These
writings cover various botanical subjects, including taxonomy, physiology,
and natural history. His books, *History of Plants* and *Causes of Plants*, treat
such topics as classification, propagation, geographic botany, forestry and
horticulture, pharmacology, viticulture, diseases (insect), savors and odors.
Theophrastus, now referred to as the Father of Botany, influenced botanical
thinking until the seventeenth century—a reflection both on the Greek mind
and on the stagnation of science that was to come about.

There are some who trace the downfall of Greece, not primarily to wars
or internal decay, but to a gradual erosion brought about by the effects of
increasing population on declining resources. The loss of a sound agricultural base was due to a combination of factors, among which were shallow soil, poor conservation practices, and, perhaps, the reluctance of the
Greek mind to consider the mundane problems of agriculture. With this
loss, the urban centers of Greece, weakened by the intercity struggles and

rivalries that culminated in the 27-
year Peloponnesian Wars, eventually crumbled before the armies of
Macedonia.

Rome

The enigma of the thousand year
history of Rome (roughly 500 B.C.
to A.D. 500) is not that Rome fell
but that it held together as long as
it did, in spite of its conglomera-
tion of diverse peoples and lands.
Unlike the Greeks, the Romans
were extremely interested in practi-

Fig. 1-8. *A royal Assyrian park, watered
by streams from an arched aqueduct.
From a relief in the palace at Nineveh
(seventh century* B.C.*).*

[From Singer, *History of Technology*, Oxford Univ.
Press, London, vol. 1, 1954.]

cal agriculture. It was a vital part of the economy; the largest single group of
producers was agricultural. On this firm foundation, Rome rose to glory,
and, according to some, declined along with its eroded soils.

Roman agriculture had many biographers. The earliest was Cato (234–
149 B.C.), who wrote of farming and useful gardening in his *De Agri
Cultura.* Varro (116–28 B.C.) produced a longer commentary on agriculture,
which was followed by Columella's twelve-book treatise (*ca.* A.D. 50). It is
from these sources, and from the *Georgics* of Virgil (70–19 B.C.), the writings of Pliny the Younger (A.D. 62–116), and especially the *Natural History*
and *Palladius* of Pliny the Elder (A.D. 23–79), that the agrarian history of
Rome has been developed.

Fig. 1-9. *Darius hunting in a grove of palms [fourth
century (?)* B.C.*].*

[From Gothein, *History of Garden Art*, Dutton, New York, vol. 1,
1928.]

The Romans were great borrowers. Although they produced little that was really new, they did make great improvements. The horticultural technology used by the Romans (much of it can be traced to earlier sources, especially Greek and Egyptian) became established, codified, and workable. Their agricultural writings mention grafting and budding, the use of many kinds and varieties of fruits and vegetables, legume rotation, fertility appraisals, and even "cold" storage of fruit. Mention can be found of a prototype greenhouse (*Specularia*) that was constructed of mica and which was used for vegetable forcing.

Fig. 1-10. *Harvesting olives. From a Greek black-figured vase (sixth century* B.C.*).*

[From Singer, *History of Technology*, Oxford Univ. Press, London, vol. 2, 1958.]

In many respects, the well-to-do Roman was a modern type, civilized and urban, yet bound to the land through business. His problems were largely managerial ones: the care and handling of slaves, the management of income properties, the vagaries of profit and loss. The typical Roman—soldier, farmer, voluptuary—is strikingly similar to his recent counterpart; namely, the aristocrat of the antebellum South.

It was in Rome that the portion of horticulture we now call ornamental horticulture was developed to a high level. From the beginnings of Roman history hereditary estates ranging in size from one to four acres were referred to as gardens (*hortus*) rather than farms (*fundus*). (To wish for more was considered to be a sign of a malcontent, if not downright dangerous.) Early Rome has been described as a market place serving a hamlet of truck gardeners. With the conquest of new lands came the development of large slave plantations, which eventually led to free tenancy and estates, and finally to a manorial system. The great fortunes of Rome were invested in farm land. The good life was that of a gentleman farmer; the sign of wealth was the country estate.

The dwelling on an estate reflected the wealth of its owner. The prosperous Roman had a little place in the country, a *suburbanum*. It contained fruit orchards, in which grew apples, pears, figs, olives, pomegranates, and flower gardens, with lilies, roses, violets, pansies, poppies, iris, marigolds, snapdragons, and asters. The mansions of the wealthy became quite splendid. Formal gardens were enclosed by frescoed walls and were amply endowed with statuary and fountains, trellises, flower boxes, shaded walks, terraces, topiary ("bush sculpture"), and even heated swimming pools. The rule was luxury; the desired effect was extravagance.

Rome was largely a parasitic empire based on borrowed culture, slave labor, and stolen goods. This was not destined to last, however, for in the middle of the first millennium A.D. the Roman Empire disintegrated, and Europe took a giant step backward to the village.

Horticulture and Classical Antiquity

Our cultural heritage in art, literature, and ethics is largely traceable to Greek and Roman influences. According to the great historian of science, Charles Singer, this has resulted in an overemphasis on the importance of the technology of these cultures, which tended to be lower than the more ancient cultures of Egypt and Mesopotamia, from which they were derived. The rise of both Greece and Rome was similar in some respects to the rise of the Huns and the Goths—a victory of barbarism over worn-out but advanced cultures. The story of civilization and technology is not the steady upward climb of the past 600 years. The technology of horticulture is a good example of this. One is hard pressed for examples of progress made by the Greeks or Romans that are comparable to those of ancient Egypt. Significant advance was to await the Renaissance.

A specific example of this delay concerns the state of knowledge on

Fig. 1-11. *Winged guardian spirit of the Assyrians pollinating blossoms of the date palm. From the Palace of King Ashur-Nasir-Pal II at Nimrud (Iraq) (ninth century B.C.).*
[Courtesy Boston Museum of Fine Arts.]

the role of sex in plants. The cultivation of the date palm and fig in Mesopotamia clearly shows that the function of the nonbearing staminate plants of the date palm were understood (Fig. 1-11) and that the caprification of the fig (the use of the wild caprifig, which contains a parasitic wasp necessary for pollination) had a sexual significance. Theophrastus was aware of this ancient concept, but this information became virtually lost until the Dutch botanist Camerarius (1694) experimentally proved the sexual nature of plants. Similarly, the ancient arts of graftage and irrigation, part of the basic technology of horticulture, were not improved until very recently. Advances in technology that came about during the early medieval period are largely traceable to Eastern sources—China, Islam, and the Byzantine Empire.

Medieval Horticulture

After the fall of Rome, some of the horticultural art survived in the monastic gardens during the so-called Dark Ages. Gardening became an integral part of monastic life, providing food, decoration, and medicinals. Fruit varieties and vegetable strains were preserved, some of which were even improved. The gardener (*Hortularius* or *Gardinarius*) became a regular officer of the Monastery. The few botanical and horticultural writings of this period are mostly compilations and are traceable largely to Pliny's *Natural History*. Many centuries passed before the horticultural technology of the Romans was equaled.

Revived interest in the art of horticulture began in Italy with the Renaissance. As feudalism gave way to trade, producing a real rise in the standard of living, garden culture again began to be practiced widely. By the thirteenth and fourteenth centuries, orchards and gardens were common outside of the monastery. As the medieval diet increased in meat, gardens became important as a source of spices and condiments. The horticultural revival spread from Italy to France and then to England. The *Maison Rustique*, published by Charles Estienne (1504–1564) and his father-in-law, John Liebault, is a delightful sourcebook of medieval horticulture. The section on the apple illustrates such practices as fertilization, graftage, pruning, breeding behavior, dwarfing, transplanting, insect "control," girdling to promote flowering, proper harvesting technique, processing, and culinary and medicinal utilization.

Maison Rustique, or, The Countrey Farme

Compiled in the French Tongue by
Charles Stevens (Estienne), and John Liebault,
Doctors of Physicke

OF THE APPLE-TREE

The Apple-tree which is most in request, and the most precious of all others, and therefore called of *Homer,* the Tree with the goodly fruit, groweth any where, and in as much as it loveth to have the inward part of his wood moist and sweatie, you must give him his lodging in a fat, blacke, and moist ground; and therefore if it be planted in a gravelly and sandie ground, it must be helped with watering, and batling with dung and smal mould in the time of Autumne. It liveth and continueth in all desireable good estate in the hills and mountaines where it may have fresh moisture, being the thing that it searcheth after, but even there it must stand in the open face of the South. Some make nurceries of the pippins sowne, but and if they be not afterward removed and grafted, they hold not their former excellencie: it thriveth somewhat more when it is set of braunches or shoots: but then also the fruit proveth late and of small value: the best is to graft them upon wild Apple-trees, Plum-trees, Peach-trees, Peare-trees, Peare-plum-trees, Quince-trees, and especially upon Peare-trees, whereupon grow the Apples, called Peare-maines, which is a mixture of two sorts of fruits: as also, when it is grafted upon Quince-trees, it bringeth forth the Apples, called Apples of Paradise, as it were sent from heaven in respect of the delicatenesse of their cote, and great sweetnesse, and they are a kind of dwarffe Apples, because of their stocke the Quince-tree, which is but of a small stature.

The Apple loveth to be digged twice, especially the first yeare, but it needeth no dung, and yet notwithstanding dung and ashes cause it prosper better, especially the dung of Sheepe, or for lesse charges sake, the dust which in Sommer is gathered up in the high waies. You must many times set at libertie the boughes which intangle themselves one within another; for it is nothing else but aboundance of Wood, wherewith it being so replenished and bepestred, it becometh mossie, and bearing lesse fruit. It is verie subject to be eaten and spoyled of Pismires and little wormes, but the remedie is to set neere unto it the Sea-onion: or else if you lay swines dung at the roots, mingled with mans urine, in as much as the Apple-tree doth rejoyce much to be watered with urine. And to the end it may beare fruit aboun-

The Apple-tree

dantly, before it begin to blossome, compasse his stocke about, and tie unto it some peece of lead taken from some spout, but when it beginneth to blossome, take it away. If it seeme to be sicke, water it diligently with urine, and to put to his root Asses dung tempered with water. Likewise, if you will have sweet Apples, lay to the roots Goats dung mingled with mans water. If you desire to have red Apples, graft an Apple-tree upon a blacke Mulberrie-tree. If the Apple-tree will not hold and beare his fruit till it be ripe, compasse the stocke of the Apple-tree a good foot from the roots upward, about with a ring of a lead, before it begin to blossome, and when the apples shall begin to grow great, then take it away.

Apples must be gathered when the moone is at the full, in faire weather, and about the fifteenth of September, and that by hand without any pole or pealing downe: because otherwise the fruit would be much martred, and the young siences broken or bruised, and so the Apple-tree by that meanes should be spoyled of his young wood which would cause the losse of the Tree. See more of the manner of gathering of them in the Chapter next following of the Peare-tree: and as for the manner of keeping of them, it must be in such sort as is delivered hereafter. *Gathering of Apples*

You shall thaw frozen Apples if you dip them in cold water, and so restore them to their naturall goodnesse. There is a kind of wild Apple, called a Choake-apple, because they are verie harsh in eating, and these will serve well for hogges to eat. Of these apples likewise you may make verjuice if you presse them in a Cyder-presse, or if you squeese them under a verjuice milstone.

Vinegar is also made after this manner: You must cut these Apples into gobbets, and leave them in their peeces for the space of three dayes, then afterward cast them into a barrell with sufficient quantitie of raine water, or fountaine water, and after that stop the vessell, and so let it stand thirtie daies without touching of it. And then at the terme of those daies you shall draw out vinegar, and put into them againe as much water as you have drawne out vinegar. There is likewise made with this sort of Apples a kind of drinke, called of the Picardines, Piquette, and this they use in steed of Wine. Of other sorts of Apples, there is likewise drinke made, which is called Cyder, as we shall declare hereafter. *Vinegar*

An Apple cast into a hogshead full of Wine, if it swim, it sheweth that the Wine is neat: but and if it sinke to the bottome, it shewes that there is Water mixt with the Wine. *Neat wine* *Mingled wine*

Infinit are the sorts and so the names of Apples comming as well of natures owne accord without the helpe of man, as of the skill of man, not being of the race of the former: in every one of which there is found some speciall qualitie, which others have not: but the best of all the rest, is the short shanked apple, which is marked with spottings, as tasting and smelling more excellently than any of all the other sorts. And the smell of it is so excellent, as that in the time of the plague there is nothing better to cast upon the coales, and to make sweet perfumes of, than the rinde thereof. The short stalked Apple hath yet furthermore one notable qualitie: for the kernells being taken out of it, and the place fill up with Frankincense, and the hole joyned and fast closed together, and so rosted under hot embers as that it burne not, bringeth an after medicine or remedie to serve when all other fayle, to such as are sicke of a pleurisie, they having it given to eat: sweet apples doe much good against melancholicke affects and diseases, but especially against the pleurisie: for if you roast a sweet apple under the ashes, and season it with the juice of licorice, starch and sugar, and after give it to eat evening and morning two houres before meat unto one sicke of the pleurisie, you shall helpe him exceedingly.

The rise of landscape architecture is one indication of the impact of the Renaissance. Gardening became formalized. The design of gardens became as important as the design of the structures (Fig. 1-12). The peak of Renaissance horticulture is to be found in the magnificent gardens of

Fig. 1-12. *Astronomical observatory (Archis Uraniburgi) of Tycho Brahe (1545–1601) at the Danish Island of Hveen.*
[Courtesy Oliver Dunn, from Joan Blaeu, *Grooten Atlas*, 1664–1665.]

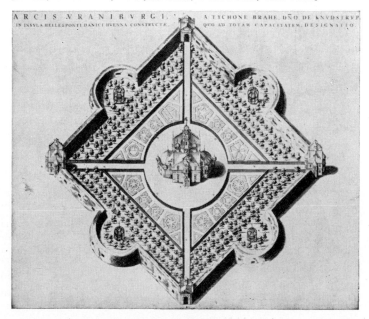

Lenôtre (1613–1700), the most notable being those at the Palace of Versailles, which was built for Louis XIV. This prodigious project lasted over 25 years and employed thousands of workmen. It included tremendous irrigation projects, providing at its peak 1400 jets of water. In one year (1688) 25,000 trees were purchased. Ancient gardens had been more than surpassed; modern gardens have not been its equal.

The New World

The discovery of the New World in 1492—a convenient if inaccurate date to assign to the beginning of the modern age—was inspired by a search for a new route to the spice-rich Orient. The early conquistadores found in the mixture of advanced and Stone Age cultures an agricultural technology that was to make a profound influence on the history of the world. The horticultural contributions of the New World include many new vegetables (maize, potatoes, tomatoes, sweet potatoes, squash, pumpkins, peanuts, kidney and lima beans); fruits and nuts (cranberries, avocados, Brazil nuts, cashews, black walnuts, pecans, pineapple); and other important crops (chocolate, vanilla, wild rice, chili, quinine, cocaine, tobacco). Primitive man in the New World had brought under cultivation practically all of the indigenous plants we now use.

The discovery of America was the most spectacular result of the era of exploration. The broadening of trade routes greatly stimulated horticultural progress. The transplantation of plant species from the old and new worlds marks the beginning of our great horticultural industries. The bulb industry in Holland, the cacao industry of Africa, and the banana and coffee industries of Central and South America can all be traced to those importations of plant species.

The Beginnings of Experimental Science

Science is a method of inquiry whose aim is the organization of information. In the ancient world, technology was the parent of science; only recently has science become the source of technology. The speculative use of information built up through observation and experimentation became a powerful force during the Middle Ages. The discoveries of DaVinci (1452–1519), Galileo (1564–1642), and Newton (1642–1727) in astronomy and the physical sciences represent the flowering of this "new" technique.

As a result of this new method of approach the seventeenth century saw a rebirth of botanical studies. Fundamental studies in plant anatomy and morphology were initiated by Marcello Malpighi (1628–1694) and Nehemiah Grew (1641–1712). The discovery of "cells" in cork by Robert Hooke (1635–1703), initiated the study of cytology, which was destined to reunite botany and zoology. The roots of genetics can be traced to the experimental studies of the Dutch botanist Rudolph Jacob Camerarius' (1665–1721) demonstration of sexuality in plants and to the later hybridization experiments of J. G. Koelreuter (1733–1806). Interest in systematics was revived, and as the number of known plants increased, a series of attempts were made to formulate a system of classification. It remained for Linnaeus (1707–1778) to develop a workable method based on a sexual system. The beginnings of plant physiology were stimulated by Harvey's discovery of blood circulation in 1628. Not until the eighteenth century, however, were fundamental studies in physiology made, such as Stephen Hale's (1677–1761) investigations of the movement of sap and Joseph Priestly's work (1733–1804) on the production of oxygen by plants.

The history of the plant sciences becomes meaningful only when the significance of the fundamental discoveries is understood. The story of botany and experimental horticulture in the last 150 years is in a sense the subject of the following chapters. Similarly, the modern history of the horticultural industry, which represents the accumulated technology and science of many lands, cannot be stated briefly. For the study of this, the reader must investigate particular crops and particular countries. This subject will be discussed briefly, however, in Part III, The Industry of Horticulture.

Influence of Twentieth-century Technology

The most remarkable feature of present-day agriculture in the United States is that the increased production of the last 50 years has taken place in spite of a decreasing acreage and a shrinking farm population. In 1910, each farmer produced for himself and 7 others; in 1960 he "supports" 26 people. This increase in efficiency is the result of improved technology. The magnitude of this increase in efficiency has been such that our recent agricultural problems are overproduction and low prices.

Technological change can be defined as the change in production resulting directly from the use of new knowledge. In general, technological change is measured by the change in output (production) per unit input of land, labor, and capital within a given period of time. The rate of technological change is not constant, because scientific progress does not ordinarily occur as a steady flow.

In agriculture, technological change may produce savings in terms of either labor or capital. The classic agricultural inventions, the plow, the reaper, and the tractor, have reduced labor. They substitute capital for labor, which does not necessarily increase yield *per se*. The technological improvement of labor-saving devices results in capital savings. Technological changes as a result of genetic gain, improved nutrition, or irrigation bring about an increase in yield per unit of land and become capital improvements, saving land and reducing expenses.

The increase in United States agricultural production from 1880–1920 was largely a reflection of the increase in expenditures—more land and more labor. Returns per acre remained relatively constant. The replacement of horse power by the gasoline engine in the 1920's was the first great step in the twentieth-century scientific revolution. Hundreds of thousands of acres formerly used for feed were released. As a result, the heretofore expanding farm acreage, as well as the increasing farm labor force was stabilized during the decade following World War I. The resurgence of genetic investigations in the quarter century following the rediscovery in 1900 of Gregor Mendel's (1822–1884) paper on inheritance began

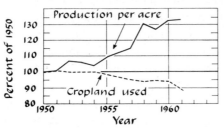

Fig. 1-13. *During the 1950's in the United States, there was a marked increase in the crop production per acre, with less crop land used.*

[Economic Research Service, USDA.]

to yield technological advances in the form of improved plant varieties. The development of hybrid corn was the most spectacular of these achievements. These improved genetic stocks in combination with the increased use of inorganic fertilizers accounted for a large part of the tremendous increase in production necessitated by World War II.

In the late 1940's there was initiated a whole new set of technological advances, made possible by basic research in the preceding decades. Agricultural chemicals in the form of weed killers, organic fungicides and insecticides quickly followed the spectacular commercial success of the broadleaf weed killer 2,4-D. The effects of these improvements were to increase yields per unit area as well as conserve labor (Fig. 1-13). Mechanization increased in the 1950's to include even "chore" jobs, and recently supplemental irrigation in the Eastern United States (it, of course, had long been used in the West) has permitted the use of additional fertilizer. The net

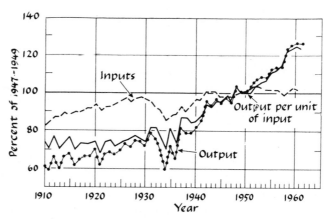

Fig. 1-14. *United States agricultural productivity measured in terms of output per unit of input shows a steady increase from the late 1930's.*
[Agricultural Research Service, USDA.]

result has appeared as a steady increase in agricultural efficiency (Fig. 1-14). This trend does not appear to be changing.

The horticultural industry has followed this trend in agriculture very closely. The average acre yields of the California tomato processing industry provide a striking example of this pattern. Technological improvements in the form of genetic gain in addition to improved fertilization and irrigation practices have tripled the average yield per acre within two decades, as shown in Fig. 1-15.

Fig. 1-15. *Yield per acre of processing tomatoes in California.*
[Data from Agricultural Marketing Service, USDA.]

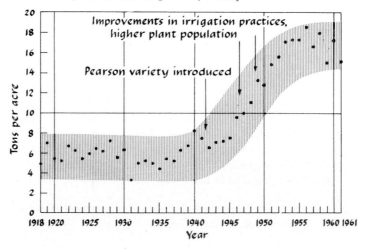

The trend in technological improvements in horticulture is clear. Probably the main increase in efficiency will come from the reduction in the labor force during the harvesting operation. In many crops (beans, sweet corn, and radishes) this has been accomplished by mechanical harvesting. A mechanical "pickle" harvester is in limited operation, and it appears that the mechanical harvesting of tomatoes may soon become a reality as may raspberries, blueberries, and stone fruits. In apples, the reduction in tree size by the use of dwarfing rootstocks or improved pruning methods and the increased mechanization of fruit handling and grading have provided different approaches to labor-saving practices. Large genetic gains in certain seed-propagated horticultural crops (onions, cucurbits, and crucifers) are being obtained with improved breeding methods that incorporate hybrid vigor. In addition, advances in chemical and mechanical weed control point to the complete elimination of hand cultivation. It is difficult to predict the exact course of technological advance. Many necessary discoveries have yet to be made. However, if the increase in technological advance proceeds at the same rate as it has over the last 20 years, this will be sufficient to more than increase production to provide for our increase in population and to compensate for the continuing reduction of farm acreage and farm population. The Malthusian law is not yet in operation!

Many of these improvements have undoubtedly been possible because of the organization of research essential to agriculture. The agricultural experiment stations system, made possible by the Morrill Act of 1862, has provided a ready supply of basic and applied research. The results are evidenced by bountiful supplies of food and fiber.

Selected References

Bailey, L. H. *The Standard Cyclopedia of Horticulture*. Macmillan, New York. 1947. (Probably the best work on horticulture ever assembled. The first edition in 1900 was to compile a "complete record of North American horticulture as it (existed) at the close of the nineteenth century." The work was revised in 1914. Its most valuable use today is for its treatment of plant materials.)

Gothein, M. L. *A History of Garden Art*. Dutton, New York 2 vol. 1928. (The authoritative work on the subject.)

Reed, H. S. *A Short History of the Plant Sciences.* Chronica Botanica Co., Waltham, Mass. 1942. (An excellent review.)

Singer, C., Holmyard, E. J. and Hall, A. R. (editors). *A History of Technology.* Oxford Univ. Press, London. 5 vol. 1954–1958. (A monumental work on science and technology up to 1900. Agriculture and related fields are well documented.)

Wright, R. *The Story of Gardening.* Garden City Publ. Co., Garden City, New York. 1938. (A popular history of horticulture and gardening.)

PART I

The Biology
of Horticulture

CHAPTER 2

The Classification
of Horticultural Plants

By ARTHUR H. WESTING, *Purdue University*

A classification is only a temporary structure, which not only can, but must undergo changes in accordance with the growth of factual knowledge.

K. D. GLINKA

Since ancient times man has named and categorized the many plants that surround him and upon which he is dependent for his very existence. One can readily surmise that his earliest classifications simply divided plants into the harmful ones and the useful ones (a division of value to this day!). Additionally he probably divided the plants according to their uses. Such classifications thus met the need of arranging what must have been an otherwise bewildering array of objects. Practical systems are, of course, perfectly valid provided they are logically conceived, consistent, and therefore capable of predictive use.

Often superimposed on the practical systems of classification are those based upon growth habit or other gross physiological characteristics. Thus plants can be characterized as being *succulent* (*herbaceous*) or *woody*. Succulent seed plants possessing self-supporting stems are known as *herbs*. A plant whose stem requires support for upright growth may be a climbing or trailing plant; if nonwoody it is known as a *vine*, whereas a woody plant of such habit is correctly called a *liana*, although often included with the vines. The self-supporting woody plants are either *shrubs* or *trees*, the trees being characterized by a single central axis and the shrubs by several more

27

or less upright stems. Trees are frequently taller than shrubs. Occasionally the distinction between trees and shrubs may be obscured by environmental conditions or by horticultural "training."

Plants that are leafless during a portion of the year (usually the winter) are referred to as *deciduous;* those whose leaves persist the year round are known as *evergreens.* Evergreens actually may lose their leaves annually, but not until a new set of leaves has developed. The deciduous habit is often associated with temperate regions; the persistent, with tropical regions.

Another classification of obvious importance to the horticulturist is based on life span, and divides plants into annuals, biennials, and perennials. The *annual* plant is one that normally completes its entire life cycle during a single growing season. Spinach, lettuce, and petunia are examples of annuals. When a subtropical perennial such as tomato, eggplant, or coleus is grown in a temperate region, it cannot survive the relatively cold winters, and under such conditions becomes an annual. Certain biennials such as carrots or beets are grown for their overwintering storage organs and are thus harvested as annuals at the end of the first growing season.

The *biennial* plant normally completes its life cycle during a period of two growing seasons. During the first summer its growth is entirely vegetative, the plant often being low in form—a so-called rosette. The winter following the first growing season provides the low temperatures necessary for this type of plant to "bolt" or send up a seed stalk during the second growing season, and then to flower and set fruit. Celery, parsnip, and evening primrose are among the biennials. If the climate is mild enough, an annual such as spinach can be planted in the fall and harvested the following spring, and thus, although not requiring a period of low temperature, it can be grown in much the same way that biennials are grown.

The *perennial* plant grows year after year, often taking many years to mature. Unlike annuals and biennials, the perennial does not necessarily die after flowering. Although herbaceous plants are found in all three categories, woody plants are usually perennial. The many fruit trees, as well as the ornamental shrubs and trees, are examples known to all (Fig. 2-1). Asparagus, rhubarb, and our various bulb crops are among the herbaceous perennials in which the above-ground parts are killed each year in a temperate region, but where the roots remain alive to send up new shoots each spring. An interesting situation exists with respect to the genus *Rubus* (the raspberries and other brambles) in which the roots are perennial and the shoots biennial (Fig. 2-2).

Plants can also be variously classified according to their temperature tolerances. Thus the horticulturist refers to *tender* plants and *hardy* plants with

Fig. 2-1. *Blue spruce* (Picea pungens *Engelm.; Family Pinaceae, Order Coniferales, Class Gymnospermae). This majestic tree is found scattered primarily on the middle and upper slopes of the Rocky Mountains. Mature trees are often 100 ft tall and live for more than 500 years. The several available cultivars are prized highly as ornamentals, owing not only to their beautiful habit and foliage but also to their ability to withstand drought and extremes of temperature.*
[Photograph by J. C. Allen & Son.]

reference to their ability to withstand low winter temperatures. For woody plants the additional distinction is sometimes made between so-called *wood hardiness* and *flower-bud hardiness*. The former refers to the winter cold-resistance of the plant as a whole; the latter, to the ability of the flower buds

Fig. 2-2. *Black raspberry* (Rubus occidentalis *L.; Family Rosaceae, Subclass Dicotyledoneae). Raspberries are noted for their fruits, equally delicious raw or as preserves. There are numerous cultivars of this native North American shrub and its various related species. Although the roots of the raspberry are perennial, its shoots are biennial. Members of this genus are often referred to as brambles, particularly in England.*
[Photograph by J. C. Allen & Son.]

to survive low winter temperatures. For example, even though apricot trees could survive in many parts of the United States, their culture is restricted to California because of their limited flower-bud hardiness. Similarly, the ginkgo can be grown as an ornamental in central Canada but cannot flower and set fruit there. It must be remembered that temperate-zone plants "harden off" in the fall to become far more cold-resistant in winter than in summer.

Plants are sometimes also classified according to their temperature requirements during the growing season. For example, peas are a typical cool-season crop, whereas tomatoes are a typical warm-season crop. This characteristic is sometimes related to seed-germination requirements.

The landscape architect may wish to classify plants according to their habitat or site preferences. In addition to recognizing the obvious desert and aquatic types, it is very important for him to know whether an ornamental plant is best suited to moist or dry sites, to sunny or shady conditions, to acid or alkaline soils.

A HORTICULTURAL PLANT CLASSIFICATION

Elaborations of the ancient plant classifications, which were based upon use, are still the most important ones to the horticulturist. Plants are conveniently separated into those which are edible, those which serve as a source of drugs or spices, those that are of ornamental value, and so forth. Although almost any intensively cultured plant rightly comes under the domain of horticulture, primary effort is centered about the various traditional "garden" plants. The grains, for example, are excluded from horticultural consideration because they are extensively managed field crops.

The horticulturist divides the *edible* garden plants into *vegetables* and *fruits*. Generally considered as *vegetables* are those herbaceous plants of which some portion is eaten, either cooked or raw, during the principal part of the meal (Figs. 2-3 and 2-4). Common examples are spinach (edible leaf), asparagus (edible stem), beet (edible root), cauliflower (edible flower), eggplant (edible fruit), and pea (edible seed). *Fruits*, on the other hand, are the plants from which a more or less succulent fruit or closely related structure is commonly eaten as a dessert or snack. Fruit plants are most often perennial and are usually woody. Whereas those of the temperate zones are primarily deciduous, the tropical and subtropical plants are usually evergreen. Fruits borne on trees are termed *tree fruits*, among which

Fig. 2-3. *Artichoke* (Cynara scolymus *L.; Family* Compositae, *Subclass Dicotyledoneae*). *The fleshy flower head of the artichoke is cooked as a vegetable and is considered a delicacy by many. This perennial herb is native to the Mediterranean region and is grown as a field crop in parts of Europe and the United States. The artichoke illustrated is not to be confused with the Jerusalem artichoke (*Helianthus tuberosus *L.*), *another vegetable plant in the same family grown for its edible tuber.*

[Photograph by J. C. Allen & Son.]

Fig. 2-4. *Sweet potato* (Ipomoea batatas *Poir.; Family* Convolvulaceae, *Subclass Dicotyledoneae*). *The edible portion of this vine is the tuberlike root, which is cooked and eaten as a vegetable. Sweet potatoes originated in tropical America but are now a common starchy food throughout the warmer regions of the world and are a truck crop of some importance in the southern United States. The many cultivars fall into two general types, those having dry mealy flesh, and those having soft, moist flesh. Sweet potatoes are known as yams in the southern United States but are not to be confused with the true yam (*Dioscorea *spp., Family* Dioscoreaceae, *Subclass Monocotyledoneae*), *another very important starchy, tuberlike vegetable grown in the tropics.*

[Photograph by J. C. Allen & Son.]

Fig. 2-5. *Sour cherry* (Prunus cerasus *L.; Family Rosaceae, Subclass Dicoty- ledoneae). Cherries have been an im- portant fruit crop in Europe and in Asia since the beginnings of agricul- ture. Hundreds of cultivars of this species and the closely related sweet cherry* (P. avium L.) *are cultivated throughout the temperate portions of the world. Because of their blossoms, cherry trees also rank among our most valued ornamentals. Some species of cherry provide an important cabinet wood that is known for its high silky luster and great beauty.*
[Photograph by J. C. Allen & Son.]

are the pear, cherry (Fig. 2-5), orange, papaya (Fig. 2-6), and date (Fig. 2-7). Fruits borne on low-growing plants, such as shrubs, lianas, and some herbs, are known as the *small fruits.* Examples are the raspberry, cranberry, grape, and strawberry. *Nuts,* which may be considered as a special sub-

Fig. 2-6. *Papaya* (Carica papaya *L.; Family Caricaceae, Subclass Di- cotyledoneae). The tree-like semiherb that bears this delicious fruit is a na- tive of tropical America but is now cultivated pantropically. Papayas have become exceedingly popular in Hawaii and elsewhere. They are mostly eaten raw but are also either boiled as vege- tables or pickled. The seeds are a com- mercial source of the enzyme papain.*
[Photograph by J. C. Allen & Son.]

Fig. 2-7. *Date palm* (Phoenix dactylifera *L.; Family* Palmae, *Subclass* Monocotyledoneae). *Date palms have been cultivated for their fruits along the Tigris and Euphrates Rivers for more than 4000 years. Apparently originally native to the Near East, date palms are now widely cultivated throughout the warmer regions of the world, including parts of California and Arizona. Dates are the principal food crop from Iran to Arabia and all throughout North Africa. The trees, often 100 ft tall, are also locally important for their wood as well as for their sugary sap.*
[Photograph by J. C. Allen & Son.]

category of the fruits, are characterized by a hard shell that is separable from a firm inner kernel—the meat. Familiar examples are the pecan, walnut, and cashew.

It must be stressed that no precise distinction can be made between the terms fruit and vegetable. Although the definitions given above hold true for most edible plants, especially those grown in the north temperate regions, the ancient and popular origins of these terms have resulted in certain anomalies. Thus, when the edible portion of a plant is stem, leaf, or root, there is seldom any question that one is dealing with a vegetable. However, rhubarb, with its edible petiole, is considered a fruit in some parts of the world because of its use as a dessert. If the fruit (botanically speaking) consists of the edible portion of an herbaceous plant, the situation is often more confusing. Thus, the banana and the pineapple are considered as fruits, whereas the melon, tomato, cucumber, squash, pepper, and plantain are variously regarded as vegetables or fruits, depending upon national or even local tradition. It might be mentioned that as a result of a question of import duties the status of the tomato was legally established in this country as a vegetable by a U.S. Supreme Court decision of 1893.

Plants used for their *ornamental* value are commonly separated into *nursery plants* and floricultural plants, or *flowers*. The flowers (often herbaceous) are primarily grown for their blossoms (Fig. 2-8), but are occa-

Fig. 2-8. *Lady slipper* (Calceolaria herbeohybrida Voss; *Family Scrophulariaceae, Subclass Dicotyledoneae). Lady slippers or calceolarias are admired for their showy pouch-shaped flowers, which come in a variety of colors. These herbaceous flowers are native to tropical America. The lady slipper illustrated is not to be confused with the orchids of the same name* (Cypripedium spp.; *Family Orchidaceae, Subclass Monocotyledoneae*).

[Photograph by J. C. Allen & Son.]

sionally grown for their showy leaves (Fig. 2-9). They are often separated according to their annual, biennial, or perennial nature. The petunia, evening primrose, and tulip are examples of each. The nursery plants (primarily woody and perennial) are most often raised for landscaping purposes. They are thus often classified according to their form or growth habit. The horticulturist recognizes *lawn* or *turf plants* (herbaceous perennials), *ground cover* (either herbaceous or woody perennials), *vines* (herbaceous or woody, and most often perennial), *shrubs* (usually restricted by the nurseryman to deciduous shrubs), *evergreens* (woody, evergreen shrubs or trees), and *trees* (commonly limited by the nurseryman to deciduous trees).

Fig. 2-9 *Caladium* (Caladium bicolor Vent.; *Family Araceae, Subclass Monocotyledoneae). Caladium is a deciduous herbaceous perennial native to tropical America. It is grown as a foliage plant because of its beautifully and variously patterned leaves.*

[Photograph by J. C. Allen & Son.]

Fig. 2-10. *Periwinkle* (Vinca minor L.; *Family Apocynaceae, Subclass Dicotyledoneae*). *Periwinkle, also known as myrtle, is an often cultivated, trailing, evergreen herb. It makes a hardy ground cover that is especially suited to moist shady areas. The plant illustrated is a particularly attractive variegated cultivar that has solitary blue flowers.*
[Photograph by J. C. Allen & Son.]

Common examples of each of these categories are blue grass, periwinkle (Fig. 2-10), English ivy, viburnum (Fig. 2-11), juniper (Fig. 2-12), and birch (Fig. 2-13), respectively.

The discerning student will recognize that the various categories being described are not all mutually exclusive. Thus a grape vine when cultured for its edible berry is considered to be a small fruit, but when grown in a garden to cover a trellis or arbor it is considered to be an ornamental. A walnut tree can be grown for its nuts or as an ornamental or for its highly prized wood. A hazel shrub may be considered to be a crop plant (filberts) by the commercial grower, may be considered an ornamental by the gardener, or may be considered an undesirable or weed species by the forester.

Fig. 2-11. *Arrowwood viburnum* (Viburnum dentatum L.; *Family Caprifoliaceae, Subclass Dicotyledoneae*). *These handsome woody perennials are among our most important ornamental shrubs. They are noted for their attractive clusters of flowers and fruits, as well as for their foliage. There are about two dozen viburnum species of horticultural importance. The arrowwood illustrated here is a native of the United States and prefers moist sites. The tough, pliant shoots were once used to make arrows.*
[Photograph by J. C. Allen & Son.]

Fig. 2-12. *Pfitzer juniper* (*Juniperus media var.* pfitzeriana [*Beissn.*] *Van Melle* [= J. chinensis f. pfitzeriana (*Späth*) *Rehd.*]; *Family Cupressaceae, Order Coniferales, Class Gymnospermae*). *This beautiful evergreen shrub from China forms a broad pyramid with its spreading branches and nodding branchlets. The grayish-green leaves are needle-shaped on juvenile plants and scale-like on mature ones, a widespread phenomenon in this family. This shrub, perhaps a staminate clone and perhaps the hybrid* J. sabina *L.* × J. sphaerica *Lindley, is one of the rare gymnospermous polyploids. The blue berry-like cones of a related juniper are used to give gin its characteristic flavor. Seen climbing the wall in the background is Japanese (or Boston) ivy* (Parthenocissus tricuspidata [*Sieb. et Zucc.*] *Planch.*), *a deciduous liana.* [Photograph by J. C. Allen & Son.]

The horticultural plant classification just described (outlined below) is an operational one, since it is based upon the use to which we put the plants. As such it is not only an overlapping classification but may often be an empirical and arbitrary one as well. Moreover, it is a classification that is subject to change over the years as we discover new uses for plants and

Fig. 2-13. *Weeping birch* (Betula pendula *Roth; Family Betulaceae, Subclass Dicotyledoneae*). *The slender, gracefully drooping branches and the white papery bark explain the extensive use of the weeping birch as a lawn tree. Numerous cultivars are available. Tannins for the leather industry have been extracted from the bark in Europe, where it is native.* [Photograph by J. C. Allen & Son.]

discard old ones. The fundamental value of this classification, of course, is that it groups economic plants according to the similarities of their cultural requirements as well as according to the similarities of their utilization and marketing problems.

A HORTICULTURAL CLASSIFICATION OF PLANTS

Edible plants

VEGETABLES

Plants grown for aerial portions
Cole crops (cabbage, cauliflower, broccoli)
Legumes or pulse crops (pea, bean, soybean)
Solanaceous fruit crops (tomato, eggplant, pepper)
Cucurbits or vine crops (cucumber, squash, melon)
Greens or pot herbs (spinach, chard, dandelion)
Salad crops (lettuce, celery, parsley, endive)
Miscellaneous (corn, asparagus, okra, mushroom)

Plants grown for underground portions
Root crops (beet, carrot, radish, turnip)
Tubers and rootstocks (white potato, Jerusalem artichoke, taro, cassava, yam)
Bulb (and corm) crops (onion, garlic, shallot)

FRUITS

Temperate (deciduous) fruits
Small fruits (cranberry, grape, raspberry, strawberry)
Tree fruits
Pomes (apple, pear, quince)
Stone fruits or drupes (cherry, peach, plum, apricot)
Nuts (pecan, filbert, walnut)

Tropical and subtropical (evergreen) fruits
Herbaceous perennials (pineapple, banana)
Tree fruits
Citrus fruits (orange, lemon, grapefruit)
Miscellaneous (fig, date, mango, papaya, avocado)
Nuts (cashew, Brazil nut, macadamia)

Ornamental plants

FLOWERS AND FOLIAGE PLANTS

Annuals (petunia, zinnia, snapdragon)
Biennials (evening primrose, hollyhock, sweet william)
Perennials (tulip, peony, chrysanthemum, philodendron)

NURSERY PLANTS

Lawn (turf) plants (blue grass, Bermuda grass)
Ground cover (periwinkle, sedum)
Vines, both herbaceous and woody (Virginia creeper, grape, English ivy)
Shrubs, commonly restricted to deciduous shrubs (forsythia, lilac)
Evergreens, both shrubs and trees (spreading juniper, rhododendron, white pine)
Trees, commonly restricted to deciduous trees (pin oak, sugar maple, larch)

Miscellaneous plants

Herbs, spices, drugs (dill, nutmeg, castor bean, quinine, digitalis)
Beverage plants, nonalcoholic (coffee, tea, cacao, maté)
Oil-yielding plants (tung, spearmint)
Rubber plants (pará rubber tree)
Plants yielding gums or resins (sweet gum, slash pine)
Christmas trees (balsam fir, Scotch pine)

A SCIENTIFIC PLANT CLASSIFICATION

Man is by nature a methodical creature and has always attempted to discover natural order in the universe. His physical environment he early classified into its "elements"—air, earth, water, and fire. All living things were classed as either animal or vegetable. The vegetable or plant kingdom he has attempted to divide in many ways. As long ago as three centuries before Christ the Greek philosopher Theophrastus classified all plants into annuals, biennials, and perennials according to their life spans, and into herbs, shrubs, and trees according to their growth habits; he further divided the trees according to their deciduous or evergreen natures and their various branching habits.

During the twenty centuries following the time of Theophrastus a multitude of classifications and an endless number of lists of useful plants ("herbals") were accepted and discarded (Fig. 2-14). It was not until the middle of the eighteenth century that a Swedish physician named Carl von Linné revolutionized the fields of plant and animal classification, or taxonomy. His labors earned Linnaeus (the Latinization by which Linné is most commonly known) the title of the father of taxonomy. He established groups, large and small, that depended upon structural or morphological similarities and differences. He recognized the value of basing the taxonomic criteria for plants on the morphology of their sexual or reproductive parts—the plant organs least likely to be influenced by environmental conditions.

Linnaeus singlehandedly described and assigned names to over 1300 different plants from the four corners of the earth (and to as many or more animals!). It was he who brought order out of chaos by standardizing a worldwide system of nomenclature. Linnaeus has been described rightfully as the greatest cataloguer and classifier of all time.

The next important advance in plant classification, or taxonomy, came in the middle of the nineteenth century, with the publication of Charles Darwin's *Origin of Species*. The principles of evolution propounded in this tome had perhaps nowhere a more profound impact than on the fundamentals of taxonomy. Darwin's concept of evolution finally provided a natural framework upon which to hang a scheme of classification. According to this concept all plants on earth today are more or less closely related taxonomically according to their proximity on the family tree of plant evolution. Thus the classification is based upon the hypothesis that genetic relationships exist between all plants and that present-day plants are through successive generations the offspring of ancestral plants. Of course, the pos-

Fig. 2-14. *An illustration of the cowpea* (Vigna sinensis *Endl.; Family Leguminosae, Subclass Dicotyledoneae) taken from a famous early herbal written by the Physician Pedanius Dioscorides in the first century* A.D. *It remained the standard materia medica for centuries. Actually Dioscorides appears to have taken his illustrations from an even earlier Greek text written in the first century* B.C. *by Krateuas, physician to Mithridates Eupator.* [Courtesy Austrian National Library.]

sibility exists that the plant kingdom owes its origin to more than one primordial organism. It is further assumed that there has occurred throughout the history of the earth, and is still occurring, an evolution of plant characteristics that has brought about an increasingly complex structure and genetic organization.

To the taxonomist or systematist falls the task of reconstructing these evolutionary connections—a task that is simple in theory, but which is formidable, and in large part impossible, in actual practice. The job is such an immense one owing to the countless numbers of now extinct and largely unknown plants. Paradoxically, however, it is the very discontinuities result-ing from these extinctions that really make it possible for the taxonomist to establish and delimit his various categories. Without them there would be an essentially unclassifiable continuum stretching from the lowest plant to the highest. The job is further complicated by the occasional hybridizations which reticulate the family tree. The approach the systematist takes when he attempts to determine evolutionary lines and group relationships can perhaps best be described as scientific sleuthing. He bases much of his case on morphological and anatomical comparisons and gleans as much informa-tion as possible from distributional or geographic evidence. Of fundamental importance, however, is fossil, or paleobotanical evidence; each new fossil found fills another small gap in the family tree. The recently developed methods of determining the age of rock strata and the plants preserved in them also have been of inestimable help.

Particularly among the more closely allied groups the modern taxonomist also leans heavily on cytological, genetic, ecological, and even physiological and biochemical evidence. For example, some decades ago the German botanist Karl Mez demonstrated the feasibility of determining plant-group affinities by the similarities of their protein contents. Borrowing standard serological techniques, he would sensitize a rabbit by injecting into its blood-stream the proteins from one plant. He then based the relationship of this plant to another on the degree to which the newly developed antibodies in the rabbit's blood reacted to the proteins of the second plant. The less severe the reaction, the more distantly related the plants were assumed to be. More recently the taxonomy of the pines has been verified, and to some degree clarified, on the basis of their oleoresin chemistry. Chromatography, a powerful chemical technique, has become an indispensable adjunct to biochemical taxonomy. Imaginative research in a variety of related fields and a subsequent correlation of the information constitute the difficult task that confronts the modern taxonomist.

One important attempt at a natural classification (although it was based primarily on floral morphology) was made toward the close of the nine-teenth century by the German botanist August Eichler. This was elaborated by Adolph Engler, who with his collaborator Karl Prantl, published a twenty-volume classification of all plants then known to man. Although much of the information that has since come to light indicates that Engler's arrangement of the plants is phylogenetically incorrect in many respects, it still is used by most botanists in the United States and elsewhere in the world. A widespread conversion to more recent systems is unlikely at this time, since none of them is sufficiently better to warrant such a major effort.

The classification of the plant kingdom that follows, however, has been revised to conform to the latest information available.

THE PLANT KINGDOM

The plant *kingdom* is, first of all, separated into about a dozen major phyla or *divisions*. It is the most advanced (that is, most recently evolved) division with which the horticulturist is directly concerned. This is the division that contains the so-called higher plants—those with roots, stems, leaves, and a vascular or tracheary system (the source of the name Tracheophyta). The remaining divisions contain almost no horticultural crop plants as such (edible mushrooms are an exception) and are therefore primarily of indirect interest to us. They are responsible, however, for many of our crop diseases. Included among these lower divisions are such diverse plants as the algae, fungi, bacteria, slime molds, and mosses.

A synopsis of the traditional plant categories, or taxa, is given below. Each taxon is subdivided by the one below it. All categories need not be used, but the sequence must not be altered. Intermediate subdivisions are frequently made and designated by the prefix "sub." The categories from Kingdom to Family are called the major taxa; and those below, the minor taxa.

Kingdom
  Division
    Class
      Order
        Family
          Genus (plural genera)
            Species (abbreviated sp. or, for plural, spp.)
              Variety (Latin *varietas;* abbreviated var.)
                Form (Latin *forma;* abbreviated f.)
                  Individual (Latin *individuum*)

The tracheophyte division is divided by many into about a dozen *classes,* including the horticulturally important Filicinae (or ferns), Gymnospermae (or cycads, ginkgoes, and conifers), and Angiospermae (the many flowering plants). Figure 2-15, constructed from current information, represents a possible family tree of the living vascular plants.

The evolutionary lines or phylogenetic histories within the Filicinae and Gymnospermae have been defined comparatively well, primarily because

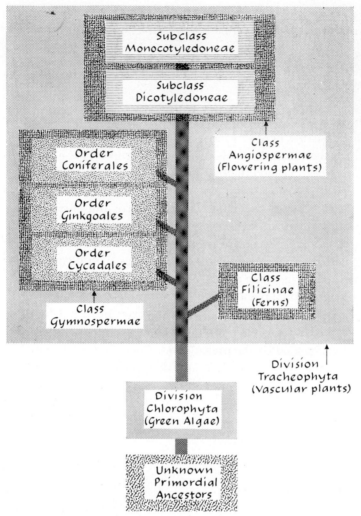

Fig. 2-15. *An abridged family tree of the living vascular plants. The solid lines indicate direct lines of descent. The higher the relative position of a group on the family tree, the more recent its emergence in the evolution of plants.*

a relatively complete fossil record exists for these classes. The phylogeny of the Angiospermae, on the other hand, is unfortunately still much more of a mystery, partially owing to the great scarcity of paleobotanical information. Since the seed plants (the gymnosperms and angiosperms) all may have evolved from a common ancestor, the many different plants with which the horticulturist deals are probably the result of descent with modification.

The gymnosperms, represented by less than 700 living species, are primarily evergreen trees of the temperate zones of the world. They characteristically have naked seeds, which are usually borne on cones, and often have narrow or needle-like leaves. The gymnosperms provide us with lumber, pulp, turpentine and rosin (the so-called naval stores), and some edible seeds, and are often highly prized as ornamental plants.

The angiosperms, numbering some 250,000 species, are worldwide in their distribution and are found in almost all conceivable habitats. Economically, they are the most important class of plants. They are man's primary source of food and beverage, shelter and clothing, paper and rubber, oils and spices. The angiosperms characteristically have seeds that are fully enclosed in a fruit, and often have broad leaves.

Although most classes are divided directly into *orders* (the Cycadales, Ginkgoales, and Coniferales previously mentioned are each an order of gymnosperms), the angiosperm class is first divided into two major subclasses, the Dicotyledoneae (or dicots) and the Monocotyledoneae (or monocots). The dicots are characterized by two cotyledons in their seedling stage, usually by flower parts in fours or fives or multiples of these numbers, and often by reticulate leaf venation; the monocots are characterized by one cotyledon, by flower parts in threes or multiples thereof, and often by parallel leaf venation. The dicots number about 200,000, and are represented by most of our broadleafed herbs, shrubs, and trees; the 50,000 or so monocots are grouped into such orders as the Liliales (or lilies), the Palmales (or palms) and the Graminales (or grasses and sedges). The grasses and palms together provide the main source of food and shelter for most peoples on earth.

The order is split in turn into groups known as *families.* The family is frequently encountered in taxonomic studies because it is often small enough to permit study of the natural relationships among its members. The horticulturist will often note structural and cultural similarities among the genera within a family. Well-known families among the monocots are the Orchidaceae (or orchids) and the Graminae (or grasses); among the dicots are the Leguminosae (or legumes), the Cucurbitaceae (gourds, melons), the Umbelliferae (carrot, celery), and the Rosaceae (roses, pome fruits and stone fruits).

The Minor Plant Categories

The categories mentioned thus far—the divisions, classes, orders, and families—are known as the major taxa. They are of great evolutionary or phylogenetic importance, but it is with the somewhat less arbitrary, minor categories—those below the family—with which the horticulturist is most concerned. They are, in decreasing order of magnitude (or genetic diversity), the *genus, species, variety, form,* and *individual.* Each of these categories will now be discussed in turn.

The *genus* (the subdivision for a family) is a group, or taxon, in which the member plants have much in common morphologically. It is usually a small enough group such that all of its members can be brought together, and their genetic, cytological, and other relationships studied. It is for this reason the most intensively studied taxon. The generic concept is an old one. Even the ancients were familiar with the oaks (*Quercus*), the roses (*Rosa*), the tulips (*Tulipa*), the pines (*Pinus*), and the maples (*Acer*). Since many of our genera were established long before the time of Darwin, they were based primarily on readily apparent morphological characteristics. As a result of their diverse and frequently popular (that is, nonscientific) origins, these genera are often most annoyingly of different levels of genetic complexity. Modern taxonomists strive to base their systematic studies, not merely on the traditional morphological criteria, but on genetic and other experimental evidence as well. As a matter of fact, when possible their main criterion for including or not including a population of plants within a particular genus is a genetic one that can be experimentally verified. The members of such a genus are, by their definition, at least somewhat capable of crossing among themselves, but are absolutely incapable of crossing with the plants of any other genus. A genus of this sort, bounded by total genetic incompatibility, is referred to as a *comparium.* The white and red oak subgenera of *Quercus* (a traditional genus) could each be considered a comparium. A synopsis of the modern taxonomic categories, such as the comparium, is presented below, each category being subdivided by the one underneath it.

Comparium: Integrity maintained entirely by genetic barriers (Often equivalent to a traditional genus)

  Cenospecies: Integrity maintained by genetic barriers reinforced by ecological barriers (Often equivalent to a traditional genus or species)

    Ecospecies: Integrity maintained by ecological barriers reinforced by genetic barriers (Often equivalent to a traditional species)

      Ecotype: Integrity maintained entirely by ecological barriers (Often equivalent to a traditional subspecies, variety, or form)

The *species* (the subdivision for a genus) comprises a group of plants that often exhibit many more morphological similarities than do the members of the genus. The members of a species have been referred to as coming from like parents and throwing like progeny. They often constitute an exclusive interbreeding population. It was long held that all species had been created originally just as they look today.

The species has always been the basic unit of all taxonomic work. It is the fundamental category upon which Linnaeus based his system of nomenclature. With his students, he established that each species be identified by two names, the generic and the specific. Examples of this binomial system of nomenclature are *Quercus alba,* the scientific name for white oak, and *Cornus florida,* that of flowering dogwood. It should be emphasized that a specific epithet is invariably preceded by a generic name. Throughout the world the genus and species are given in Latin using the Roman alphabet (the genus is capitalized; the species should not be; and both are italicized). The name (or abbreviation of a name) often found to follow such a binomial designation is of the person who first named and described that species, for example, *Spinacia oleracea* Linnaeus (spinach). Many details of the international code of botanical nomenclature, now strictly adhered to by every nation, were worked out in Vienna at the turn of the century by botanists from all over the world. Further international congresses have been held from time to time to resolve minor conflicts and to revise the code where necessary. Here is an example of worldwide cooperation to be envied by our statesmen!

The modern taxonomist, basing his classification of the minor taxa on genetics and ecology to a far greater extent than did his traditional counterpart, has sometimes found it necessary to consider both a *cenospecies* and its subdivision, the *ecospecies.* He thus divides the genetically isolated comparium into one or more cenospecies. Each cenospecies encompasses a group of similar plants separated from other cenospecies almost entirely by genetic barriers. Cenospecies do not cross under natural conditions, but can be made to cross. The offspring of such a cross will be sterile, and often are unable to survive.

The ecospecies (the subdivision for a cenospecies) maintains its integrity through a combination of ecological and genetic mechanisms. The genetic barriers between ecospecies are somewhat less effective than those found between cenospecies, but are reinforced by spatial separation, owing to differing ecological requirements.

Upon investigation, some traditional species and some traditional genera turn out to be the parallel of a cenospecies. The one or more ecospecies making up a cenospecies is often found to be the equivalent of the traditional species.

A *variety* (or *varietas*) is a subclassification of the traditional species.

(This botanical variety is not to be confused with the horticultural variety, or cultivar, which will be discussed below.) When one or more of the populations of plants making up a species is sufficiently different in appearance from the remaining members of the species, it is often given varietal status. A variety is designated by a trinomial, for example, *Juniperus communis* var. *depressa* (or prostrate common juniper). As soon as a variety is established, the remaining typical element of that species is designated by a trinomial formed by repeating the specific name, *Juniperus communis* var. *communis* for the example just given. A population deviating not quite enough to be called a variety is sometimes called a race or more properly a *form* (or *forma*). Two forms of the attractive ornamental *Taxus cuspidata* (or Japanese yew) are *Taxus cuspidata* f. *densa* (an erect form) and *Taxus cuspidata* f. *nana* (a spreading form) (Fig. 2-16). On the other hand, a group deviating perhaps somewhat more from the species norm than a variety may be ranked as a *subspecies*.

Two varieties of a single species, through isolation and subsequent divergent evolution, may eventually differ enough to be considered as two species. If, however, during this time the barrier between the two groups breaks down, they may again converge. The taxonomist is often hard pressed to decide whether to combine or split two such groups.

The modern systematist who prefers to experimentally revise the classification of plant populations with particular emphasis on genetic and eco-

Fig. 2-16. *Japanese Yew* (Taxus cuspidata *Sieb. et Zucc.; Family Taxaceae, Order Coniferales, Class Gymnospermae). The dark green foliage and small scarlet fruits make this hardy evergreen shrub from the Orient a favorite ornamental. (Left) An erect form (*T. c. f.* densa *Rehd.). (Right) A spreading form (*T. c. f.* nana *Rehd. ex Wilson). There are numerous other yews, some attaining tree proportions. Yew wood makes fine archery bows.*
[Photographs by J. C. Allen & Son.]

logical considerations finds it necessary, as we have learned, to introduce such new concepts as the comparium, cenospecies, and ecospecies (see the table on p. 44). The ecospecies is further divided into one or more *ecotypes*. The ecotype is thus his substitute for the traditional subspecies, variety, or form. It is fully capable of crossing with other ecotypes within its ecospecies but is separated from them by differing habitat preferences and therefore by geographic distributions. Ecotypic variation can often be expected to occur in species of wide latitudinal extent. Scotch pine, a desirable Christmas tree, provides a good example. If, on the other hand, the ecospecies exhibits a continuous gradient of characters from one end of its range to the other, this is referred to as clinal or *ecoclinal* variation.

Normally self-pollinating plants such as tomatoes or peas maintain inbred lines that become stabilized after several generations and thenceforth breed true. Such populations of plants, even more genetically homogeneous than ecotypes, are referred to as *biotypes*.

A special situation exists in *Citrus, Mangifera* (mango), some species of *Rubus* (brambles), *Poa* (blue grass), and several other plants. These plants outwardly seem to depend upon sexual propagation. In reality, although pollination may occur and trigger fruit production, fertilization occurs only occasionally. Most new plants develop from diploid ovular tissue, thereby bypassing the usual meiotic division. Genetically similar lines are thus also maintained in these plants, and are referred to as *apomicts* (abbreviated ap.).

The horticulturist is continually on the lookout for an individual horticultural plant (technically, *individuum*) which by some quirk of genetic recombination or chance mutation is especially desirable. To perpetuate this valuable selection, or "sport," he may propagate it vegetatively; that is, he creates a *clone*. If left to its own sexual devices the selection or "sport" might not breed true. Thus the clone is a group of plants all of which arose from a single individual (the *ortet*) through some means of vegetative or asexual propagation.

Each member of a clone is technically known as a *ramet* and, of course, has a genetic makeup identical with the ortet or clonal progenitor. The Redhaven peach, the Delicious apple, the Russet Burbank potato, and the Thompson seedless grape are all examples of clones.

It should perhaps be re-emphasized that of the traditional taxa in general use today most are based strictly on floral morphology; some on profound ignorance; and only a handful on sound principles and experimental evidence. *Prunus* (cherry, plum), *Rubus* (raspberries and other brambles), *Vitis* (grape), *Rosa* (rose), and *Crataegus* (hawthorn) are, for example, just a few of the horticulturally important genera requiring extensive revision on the basis of modern taxonomic experimentation. The field is wide open for those with imagination and broad scientific interests.

The Horticultural Variety

The horticulturist is often particularly interested in the botanical variety, form, biotype, and clone. When these are intentionally maintained he refers to them all as "varieties." In fact, such varieties can in a sense be considered the very keystone of horticulture. Horticultural varieties have been known since the beginning of history. Some present-day clonal varieties, such as the Bartlett pear and the Yellow Newtown apple, have been known for centuries.

The use of the term "variety" in its horticultural sense considerably ante-dates the taxonomic usage previously defined (see p. 45). It is perhaps best to avoid ambiguity by referring to the variety in its taxonomic sense as a "botanical variety," or "*varietas*," and in its horticultural sense as a "horticultural variety," or "*cultivar*" (abbreviated cv.). The term cultivar, in fact, is rapidly gaining international acceptance by both horticulturists and foresters. It has been suggested that the names of cultivars be set off by single quotation marks.

Some of our horticultural plants are known only in cultivation. They have been bred and selected by man for so many centuries that their wild origins have become obscure. Such plants are referred to as *cultigens*. Cabbage and corn are two examples.

THE IDENTIFICATION OF PLANTS

When one is confronted with a plant unknown to him he often must turn in his dilemma to an appropriate book of plant descriptions. Horticulturists living in the continental United States are fortunate in having at their disposal several regional manuals, as well as two that span the continent. These latter two manuals (see Selected References at the end of this chapter) describe virtually all of the horticultural species capable of surviving under our conditions. The one was compiled by the renowned American horticulturist Liberty Hyde Bailey, the other, by the well-known dendrologist Alfred Rehder.

Should the unknown plant in question be an exotic incapable of growing in the continental United States, it will not be covered by either Bailey or

Rehder. One can then often learn to which manual to turn by consulting the list compiled by Sidney F. Blake and Alice C. Atwood (see Selected References).

The use of manuals will prove successful for the identification of most plants likely to be encountered by the horticulturist. The possibility always exists, however, that the unknown plant may have been considered to be too rare or too unimportant horticulturally for inclusion, or even that it is a plant new to science. The safest recourse under such circumstances is to send the plant to some botanical institute for identification (or naming!) by a professional taxonomist.

The actual identification of the unknown plant is usually accomplished by the use of the *analytical keys* that are a part of most manuals. A key contains the diagnostic features of all plants listed in the manual, arranged in such a manner that all but the correct plant can be rejected. The dichotomous key, the most commonly used, is constructed as a series of couplets, each containing a pair of contrasting statements. One examines the first couplet and chooses the statement that fits the unknown plant; this leads to the next correct couplet to use, that, to the next, and so on until the plant is "keyed out." The following is an example of such an analytical key.

AN ANALYTICAL KEY TO THE WALNUTS (*Juglans*)

1A Leaf scars with a hairy upper fringe;
      pith not light brown 2
1B Leaf scars with a glabrous upper edge;
      pith light brown 3
2A Pith dark brown; fruits solitary or in clusters of 2 to 5;
                                  Butternut or white walnut (*J. cinerea*)
2B Pith violet-brown; fruits in clusters of 12 to 20;
                                  Japanese walnut (*J. sieboldiana*)
3A Leaves glabrous; bark smooth and silvery gray;
                                  Persian or English walnut (*J. regia*)
3B Leaves pubescent; bark rough and dark brown;   Black walnut (*J. nigra*)

A key is occasionally ambiguous with respect to species, because an attempt has been made to separate the species by their vegetative characters, when actually these taxa originally were established on the basis of their sexual structures. If desired, final verification can be made by comparison with a known example of that species. Such examples can be found as dried and pressed specimens (known as herbarium specimens) in many botanical institutes. Finally, it must be pointed out that, in order to get full information on varieties, one frequently must consult monographs dealing with the particular plant group in question.

CONCLUSION

It has been shown that the subject of plant classification, although perhaps the most elementary branch of horticulture, is also its most inclusive portion. Whereas nothing can be discussed in a scientific way without some taxonomic knowledge, a classification serves also to integrate and to summarize all that we know about our plants, whether morphological, genetic, ecological, or physiological. A knowledge of classification often permits the horticulturist to predict the cultural requirements of a plant. It will also help him predict its graft compatibilities and the other plants with which it will hybridize. Finally, it will aid him in his search for and development of new plants of horticultural importance.

Selected References

Lawrence, G. H. M. *Taxonomy of Vascular Plants.* Macmillan, New York. 1951. (This is a standard text in systematic botany. Part I covers both the theoretical and practical aspects of classification, nomenclature, and identification. Part II describes all tracheophyte families known to be native or introduced to the United States. The appendix contains a detailed glossary of botanical terms.)

Bailey, L. H. *Manual of Cultivated Plants Most Commonly Grown in the Continental United States and Canada.* Rev. ed. Macmillan, New York. 1949. (This manual provides a means for the identification of 5347, or almost all, cultured tracheophyte species covered by the title. Varieties are not described. Identification is done by means of keys, descriptions, and some illustrations. There is a glossary.)

Rehder, A. *Manual of Cultivated Trees and Shrubs Hardy in North America Exclusive of the Subtropical and Warmer Temperate Regions.* 2nd ed. Macmillan, New York. 1940. (This manual includes 2550 species with about 2900 varieties and about 580 hybrids, or almost all the cultured trees, shrubs, lianas, and partially woody plants covered by the title. There are keys to the species, a glossary, and species descriptions that include indications of hardiness.)

Blake, S. F. and Atwood, A. C. *Geographical Guide to Floras of the World; Annotated List with Special Reference to Useful Plants and Common*

Plant Names. I. Africa, Australia, North America, South America, and Islands of the Atlantic, Pacific, and Indian Oceans. II. Western Europe: Finland, Sweden, Norway, Denmark, Iceland, Great Britain with Ireland, Netherlands, Belgium, Luxembourg, France, Spain, Portugal, Andorra, Monaco, Italy, San Marino, and Switzerland. USDA, Wash., D.C., Miscellaneous Publications 401 and 797. 1942, 1961. (This is an exhaustive bibliography containing 9866 titles, and the only one of its kind. It covers over half the world, but does not include Germany, central and eastern Europe, or Asia and associated islands.)

CHAPTER 3

The Structure
of Horticultural Plants

THE PLANT BODY

Flowering plants, which make up almost the entire range of horticultural interest, show extreme diversity in size and structure. Nevertheless, there are essential similarities, for many structures (for example, the air borne root of the orchid and the swollen root of the sweet potato), although superficially very different, can be shown to be functionally and morphologically related. The flowering plant consists of two basic parts—the *root*, the portion that is normally underground, and the *shoot*, the portion that is normally above ground. The shoot is made up of stems and leaves. The leaves grow from enlarged portions of the stem called *nodes*. The shoot shows several significant modifications. The *flower* may be thought of as a specialized stem with leaves adapted for reproductive functions. *Buds* are miniature leafy or flowering stems. Figure 3-1 illustrates the fundamental plant parts.

The plant body is made up ultimately of microscopic components called *cells*, which, although they are essentially similar, may be structurally and functionally very different. Masses of cells in various combinations and arrangements build up the various morphological structures of the plant.

THE CELL AND ITS COMPONENTS

The structural unit of plants, as well as of animals, is the cell. Although the notion that the cell is the basic unit of all living things has been somewhat challenged by recent studies of viruses, horticultural plants are indeed cellular. The complex organism is an integrated collection of cells, but it is equally true that the cell is merely a component part of the organism. This contradiction in terms is a result of the fantastic synchronization and co-ordination achieved in multicellular organisms. *Cytology*, the study of cells, is concerned with the organization, structure, and function of cell life.

Plant cells vary greatly in shape from spheres, polyhedrons, amoeboids, to long thin tubes. They are usually 0.025–0.25 mm (0.001–0.01 in.) long; some fibers, however, are as much as two feet long, as in hemp. The typical or generalized plant cell, although nonexistent, is a useful concept (Fig. 3-2). The basic components involve a *cytoplasm* that contains a nucleus and

Fig. 3-1. *The fundamental plant parts.*

[Adapted from Holman and Robbins, *A Textbook of General Botany*, Wiley, New York, 1939; after Sachs.]

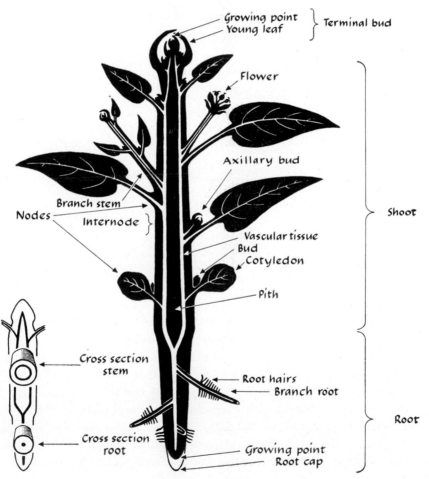

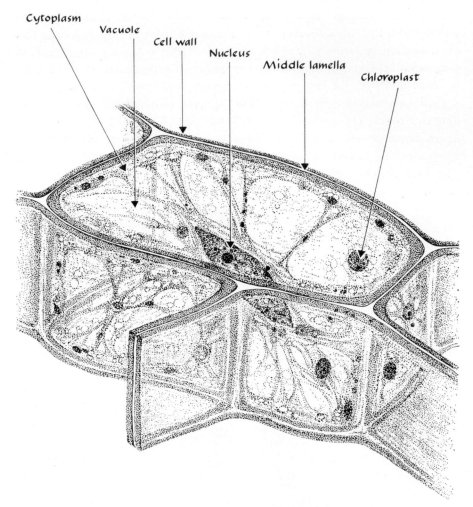

Fig. 3-2. *A cell from the petiole of a sugar beet leaf and its component parts.*
[Adapted from Esau, *Plant Anatomy*, Wiley, New York, 1953.]

which is surrounded by a *plasma membrane* within a more or less rigid
cell wall. The living organism is composed of living and nonliving cells.

The cytoplasm (synonymous with the term protoplasm) is an inordinately
complex substance, physically and chemically. It is composed of 85–90%
water (by fresh weight); the remaining 10–15% consists of organic and inorganic substances that are either dissolved (salts and carbohydrates) or in
the colloidal state (proteins and fats). The cytoplasm contains a number
of structural bodies, such as *plastids, mitochondria,* and *vacuoles,* as well as
various "nonliving" entities. It is the seat of the physiological activity of the

cell. It is organized in that biological state we refer to as "living," although this state appears to be dependent on its being within the structural confines of a "cell" and in contact with the nucleus.

Surrounding the cytoplasm is the plasma membrane, which lies against the cell wall. The plasma membrane is composed of lipoproteins, which explains its elasticity and its high permeability to fatty substances. Although it is ultramicroscopic in thickness, the plasma membrane can be defined in plasmolyzed cells.

The nucleus, usually a spheroidal body, is enclosed within the cytoplasm and separated only by a nuclear membrane. Even though the nucleus is denser than the cytoplasm, it is not easily distinguished in unstained cells. Yet the close affinity of the nuclear material for many dyes makes it the most conspicuous feature of the cell in stained material. The nucleus is, in effect, the control center of the cell, since it contains the *chromosomes*. These "colored" (*chromo*) "threads" (*soma*) contain genetic information, somewhat analogous to the punch cards in a large electronic computer. This information, or code, is not only the basis of the physiological functioning of the cell but is a major part of the hereditary bridge between generations.

The *cell wall*, one of the distinguishing features of the plant cell, is usually thought of as a deposit, or secretion, of the cytoplasm. It is laid down in distinct layers, and its thickness varies greatly with the type of cell (Fig. 3-3). Three regions of the cell wall are generally distinguished:

1. The *middle lamella*, a pectinaceous material associated with the intercellular substance. The slimy nature of rotted fruit is due to the dissolving of the middle lamella by fungal organisms.

2. The *primary cell wall*, the first wall formed in the developing cell, is composed largely of cellulose and pectic compounds, but closely related

Fig. 3-3. *Diagrammatic cross section of a tracheid, showing the structure of the cell wall. The secondary cell wall deposited inside the primary wall may be composed of three layers.*

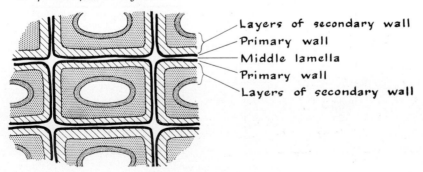

Layers of secondary wall
Primary wall
Middle lamella
Primary wall
Layers of secondary wall

substances and noncellulose compounds may also be present. It may become lignified. It is the wall of dividing and growing cells; in many cells it is the only wall.

3. The *secondary cell wall* is laid down inside the primary cell wall after the cell has ceased to enlarge. It appears to have a mechanical function, and is similar in structure to the primary wall, although higher in cellulose.

The cell wall in plants is not continuous. It appears to be pierced by cytoplasmic strands (*plasmodesmata*) that provide a living connection between cells. Furthermore, thin areas known as *pits* occur as cavities or depressions in the cell wall (Fig. 3-4).

Plastids are specialized bodies contained in the cytoplasm that are peculiar to plant cells. They are classified on the basis of pigment into leucoplasts (colorless) or chromoplasts (colored). Some types of leucoplasts are involved in the storage of starch (amyloplasts). Of the colored plastids, those containing chlorophyll (*chloroplasts*) are the most significant.

Mitochondria appear as small, dense granules, and are lipoprotein. All of the known functions of mitochondria are related to enzymatic activity connected with oxidative metabolism.

Vacuoles are membrane-lined cavities located within the cytoplasm and filled with a watery substance known as the *cell sap*, which is considered to be nonliving. In actively dividing cells the numerous vacuoles are small, whereas in mature cells the vacuoles coalesce into one large vacuole that occupies the center of the cell, pushing the cytoplasm and the nucleus next to the cell wall.

Fig. 3-4. *Pits are thin areas in the cell wall:* left, *bordered pit;* right, *simple pit.*
[Adapted from Eames and MacDaniels, *An Introduction to Plant Anatomy*, McGraw-Hill, New York, 1947.]

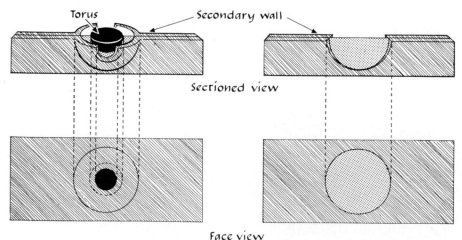

A number of obviously nonliving materials are found contained in the cytoplasm; among these are crystals, starch grains, oil droplets, silica, resins, gums, alkaloids and many organic substances. These compounds may be products of metabolism, such as reserve products or waste products of the cell.

TISSUES AND TISSUE SYSTEMS

Although the plant ultimately originates from a single cell (the fertilized egg), the marvels of cell division and differentiation produce an organism composed of many different kinds of cells—different structurally and physiologically. It is this difference in cell morphology and cell arrangement that results in the complex variation between plants and within an individual plant.

Plants can be shown to be made up of groups of similar types of cells in a definite, organized pattern. Continuous, organized masses of similar cells are known as *tissues.* Tissues have been classified in several ways. No universally accepted system exists. The following system is a logical one that retains the customary botanical terms.

Meristematic tissue—actively dividing, undifferentiated cells
Permanent tissues—nondividing differentiated cells
   Simple tissues: composed of one type of cell
      parenchyma: simple thin-walled cells
      collenchyma: thicker-walled "parenchyma"
      sclerenchyma: thick-walled supporting cells
   Complex tissue: composed of more than one type of cell
      xylem: water-conducting tissue
      phloem: food-conducting tissue

Meristems

Meristematic tissue is composed of cells actively or potentially involved in cell division and growth. The meristem not only perpetuates the formation of new tissue but perpetuates itself. Since many so-called permanent tissues may, under proper stimulation, assume meristematic activity no strict line of demarcation exists between meristematic and permanent tissue.

Meristems are located in various portions of the plant (Fig. 3-5). Those at the tips of shoots and roots are known as *apical meristems.* The shoot

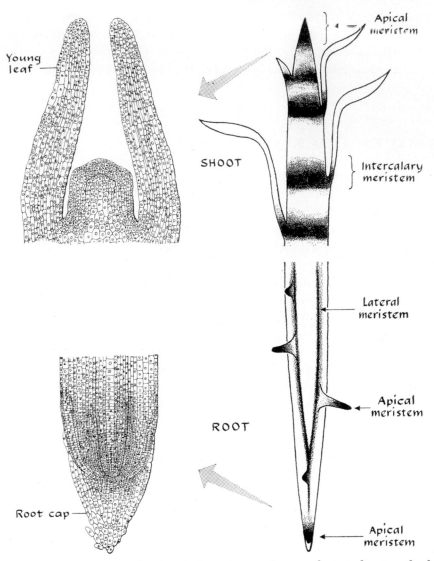

Fig. 3-5. *Diagrammatic longitudinal section of a grass plant, indicating the location of the meristems. These shaded areas are the youngest parts of the plant.*

[Adapted from Eames and MacDaniels, *An Introduction to Plant Anatomy*, Wiley, New York, 1947.]

apical meristem is known horticulturally as the growing point. The increase in girth of woody stems results from the growth of lateral meristems, specifically referred to as the *cambium*. The meristematic regions of grasses become "isolated" near the nodes, and are called *intercalary meristems*.

Thus, the mowing of lawns does not interfere with the growing portion of the grass plant. Tissues differentiated from apical meristems are referred to as *primary tissues*. Others, especially tissues formed from the cambium, are *secondary tissues.*

Although there are many exceptions, meristematic cells are usually small, may be roughly spherical to brick-shaped, and have thin walls with inconspicuous vacuoles. In preparations they appear darkly stained, owing to the small amount of cytoplasm in relation to the nucleus.

Simple Tissue

Permanent tissues are derived directly from meristems. These are referred to as simple tissues when they are composed of one type of cell (Fig. 3-6).

Parenchyma is unspecialized vegetative tissue. It makes up a large portion of many plants, such as the fleshy portion of fruits, roots, and tubers. It is thought of as relatively undifferentiated tissue.

Collenchyma tissue is characterized by elongated cells with thickened primary walls composed of cellulose and pectic compounds. (It may be thought of as thick-walled parenchyma.) This tissue functions largely as mechanical support in early growth. The strands of the outer edge of celery petioles are collenchyma (Fig. 3-7).

Sclerenchyma tissue is composed of especially thick-walled cells that are often lignified. When these cells are long and tapered they are usually referred to as fibers. Others are referred to as sclereids. Clusters of these sclereids, or "stone cells," are responsible for the gritty quality in pears. In masses, sclereids produce the hard quality of walnut shells and of peach and cherry pits. Unlike parenchyma and collenchyma, sclerenchyma cells are nonliving when mature.

Complex Tissue

Complex tissue is composed of combinations of simple and specialized tissue. The two major types of complex tissue are xylem and phloem.

Xylem

Xylem, the principal water-conducting tissue, is an enduring tissue that consists of living and nonliving cells. Wood is largely xylem. Herbaceous plants also contain xylem, although the amount is very much less than that contained in "woody" plants. The water-conducting function in xylem is accomplished through specialized nonliving cells called tracheids. These

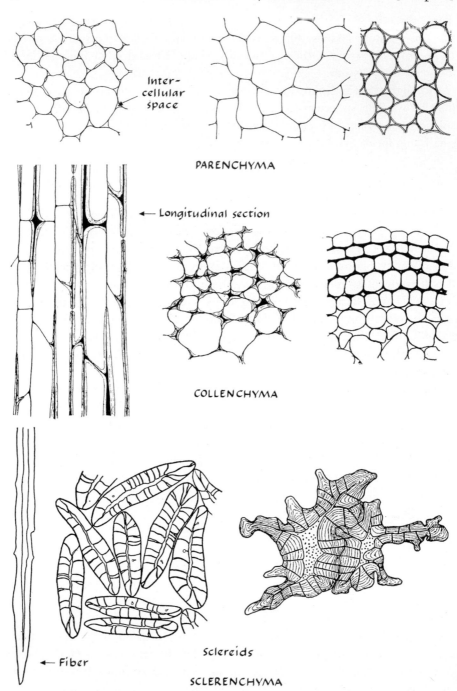

Fig. 3-6.   *Simple tissue.*

[Adapted from Eames and MacDaniels, *An Introduction to Plant Anatomy*, McGraw-Hill, New York, 1947.]

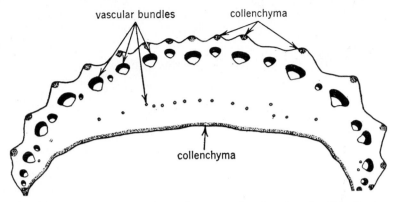

Fig. 3-7. *Cross section of a celery petiole, showing the distribution of collenchyma and vascular bundles.*
[Adapted from Esau, *Plant Anatomy*, Wiley, New York, 1953.]

are elongated, tapered cells having walls that are hard and usually lignified, although not especially thick. The water, in the form of cell sap, moves readily through the empty tracheid, flowing from cell to cell through the

numerous pits. The cell walls of tracheids are often unevenly thickened or sculptured, which makes these cells easy to distinguish in longitudinal section.

In addition to tracheids, a specialized series of cell members called vessels also functions in water conduction. These are formed from meristematic cells lined up end to end from which the cell contents and end walls have been dissolved. The series may be many feet long. Xylem typically includes fibers and parenchyma cells Fig. 3-8).

Xylem is formed by differentiation of the apical meristems of root and shoot. In perennial woody plants, secondary xylem is also formed from the cambium. The differential seasonal growth of xylem produces the familiar annual rings.

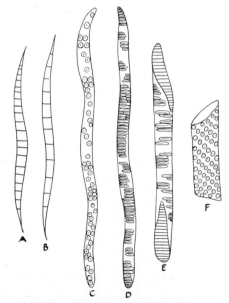

Fig. 3-8. *Fibers, tracheids, and vessels of the xylem.*
[Adapted from Esau, *Plant Anatomy*, Wiley, New York, 1953.]

The spring wood consists of larger cells with thinner walls and appears lighter, or less dense, than the summer wood

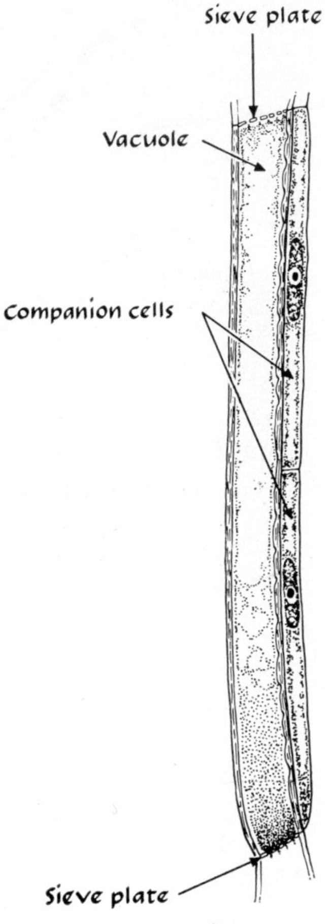

Phloem

The basic components of the phloem are series of specialized cells called *sieve elements*. It is through these elongated living cells with thin cellulose walls that the food-conducting function of the phloem is carried out. Upon maturity the nucleus of the sieve disappears. However, specialized cells called *companion cells* are in intimate association with the sieve cells (Fig. 33-9). In addition to these, fibers and sclereids may be present. The fibers of hemp and flax are derived from the phloem tissue.

The phloem is formed, as is the xylem, both by the apical meristem and by the cambium. The phloem, however, is not enduring, and the old phloem disintegrates in woody stems. It is protected by special meristematic tissues (cork cambium) that produce parenchymatous tissue. The phloem, the corky tissue, and the other incidental tissues constitute *bark*.

Sieve plate

Vacuole

Companion cells

Sieve plate

Fig. 3-9. *The sieve element of the phloem.*
[Adapted from Esau, *Plant Anatomy*, Wiley, New York, 1953.]

ANATOMICAL REGIONS

The tissues that form the various regions of the plant can be classified in terms of structure and function. In much the same way, the bricks, boards, pipe, and wire used in the construction of a house (figuratively speaking, its cells and tissues) can be classified on the basis of structure and function as

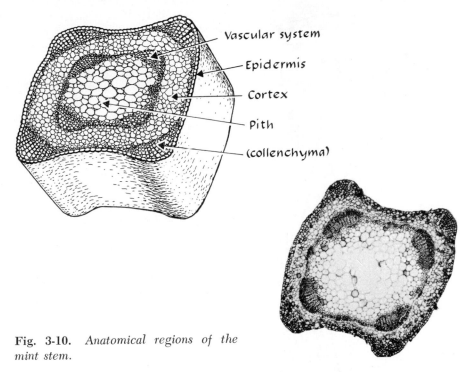

Vascular system

Epidermis

Cortex

Pith

(collenchyma)

Fig. 3-10. *Anatomical regions of the mint stem.*

masonry, frame, plumbing system, and wiring system. Since these are inter-related, it is sometimes hard to decide where one "region" ends and the other begins. (Is an electric hot water heater part of the electrical or the plumbing system?)

Horticultural plants are grossly divided into the vascular system (plumbing), the cortex (frame and insulation), and the epidermis (siding, floor, and roof) (Fig. 3-10). The pith, pericycle, endodermis, and secretory glands, however, are components of one or more of these regions.

The Vascular System

The vascular system consists principally of the xylem and phloem tissues. The vascular system serves as the conduction system of the plant, but because it also serves in support it may be compared to both the circulatory and skeletal systems of animals. There are differences between the structural relationship of xylem and of phloem. Typically, the vascular system forms a continuous ring in the stem, in which the inner portion is xylem, and surrounds an area of parenchymatous tissue known as the *pith*. The vascular system, however, may be discontinuous, and may appear as a series of

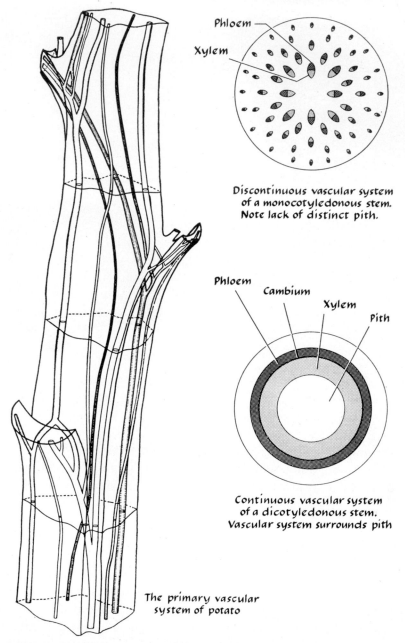

Phloem

Xylem

Discontinuous vascular system
of a monocotyledonous stem.
Note lack of distinct pith.

Phloem

Cambium

Xylem

Pith

Continuous vascular system
of a dicotyledonous stem.
Vascular system surrounds pith

The primary vascular
system of potato

Fig. 3-11. *Discontinuous and continuous arrangements of the vascular system. The primary vascular system of the potato stem initially appears as separate bundles but becomes embedded in secondary tissue as the stem matures. The vascular system of the mature stem is continuous.*

[Adapted from Eames and MacDaniels, *An Introduction to Plant Anatomy*, McGraw-Hill, New York, 1947.]

strands in longitudinal section, and as bundles in cross section (Fig. 3-11). This is the usual case in monocotyledonous plants. The vascular system makes up the core of roots, and the pith is absent.

In roots the vascular system is separated from the cortex by specialized tissues called the *pericycle* and the *endodermis*. The pericycle encircles the vascular system. It is composed of parenchymatous tissue and is the source of the branch roots and stems that arise from the root. The endodermis is commonly a single sheet of cells separating the vascular system from the cortex, and it is not absolutely clear whether it is part of the vascular system or of the cortex. It appears to have a protective function. The pericycle and endodermis are usually absent in the stem.

Cortex

The cortex is the region between the vascular system and the epidermis. It is made up of primary tissues, predominantly parenchyma. In older woody stems, the formation of cork in the cortex, with the subsequent disintegration of the outer areas, tends to obliterate the cortex as a distinct area. Cork is formed when mature tissue becomes meristematic and forms cells having suberized walls. This corky protective sheath is known as the *periderm*. Callus tissue that is formed in response to wounding may also become corky. The cork industry is based on the large amounts of this tissue produced by wounding of the cork oak (*Quercus suber*).

Differentiated portions of the cortex that form ruptured, rough areas are referred to as *lenticels*. These are conspicuous in woody stems and in bark. The "dots" on apple skin are lenticels. This loose arrangement of cells tends to tear the epidermis, thus fruit lenticels become subject to the entrance of decay organisms and act as a point of water loss.

Epidermis

The epidermis is a continuous cell layer that envelops the plant. Except in older stems and roots, where the epidermis may be obliterated, it sheaths the entire plant. The structure of the epidermis varies, and may be composed of different primary tissue. Slightly above the root tips, the epidermal cells form tube-like extensions called root hairs, which function in the absorption of water and inorganic nutrients. Hairs are also found in epidermal cells of the shoot and may be of complex multicellular structure. The velvety feel of rose petals is due to the uneven surface of their upper epidermal

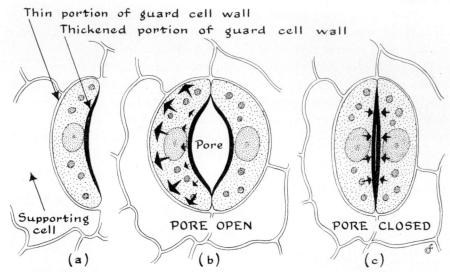

Fig. 3-12. *The stomata is an epidermal structure composed of two guard cells that form a pore. The guard cell wall abutting the pore is thicker than the other surfaces. This causes the pore to open when the guard cells become turgid.*

[Adapted from Bonner and Galston, *Principles of Plant Physiology*, Freeman, San Francisco, 1952.]

cells. The guard cells forming *stomata* are modified epidermal cells (Fig. 3-12).

A significant feature of epidermal cell structure is the *cuticle*, a waxy layer that appears on the exposed surface of the cell. The waxy material, *cutin*, acts as a protective covering that prevents the desiccation of inner tissues (Fig. 3-13). It is particularly noticeable in many fruits, for example, the apple, nectarine, and cherry, where its accumulation results in a blush that polishes to a high gloss. The cuticle is responsible for the difficulty found in wetting leaves and fruit, an important objective in disease control.

MORPHOLOGICAL STRUCTURES

The Root

The root, although visibly inconspicuous, is a major component of the plant both in terms of function and absolute bulk. It may consist of over half of the dry weight of the entire plant body. The root is structurally adapted for its major function of absorption of water and nutrients. Owing

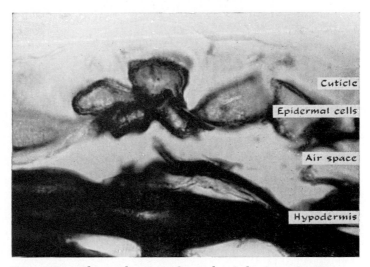

Cuticle

Epidermal cells

Air space

Hypodermis

Fig. 3-13. *The epidermis and cuticle of the Stayman Winesap apple fruit. The skin of an apple is several cells thick and consists of epidermis and hypodermis. The latter is composed of compressed layers of cortical cells. The cause of the separation of the epidermis and hypodermis shown in the photograph is unknown. It produces a white patch on the fruit, sometimes referred to as "scarfskin."*

[Photograph courtesy D. F. Dayton.]

to its complex branching, which occurs irregularly rather than by nodes as in stems, and its tip area of root hairs, the root presents a very large surface in intimate contact with the soil. The process of absorption in most plants is carried out mainly in the root hairs, which are constantly renewed by new growth. The growth of the plant is largely limited by the extent of its underground expansion. This vast network of roots anchors the plant and supports the superstructure of food-producing leaves. The older roots also serve as a storage organ for elaborated foodstuffs, as in the sweet potato and carrot.

The original seedling root, or *primary root*, generates the root system of the plant by forming various branching patterns. When the primary root becomes the main root of the plant the network is referred to as a *taproot* system, as in the walnut, carrot, beet, and turnip. In many plants, however, the primary root ceases growth when the plant is still young, and the root system is taken over by new roots that grow adventitiously out of the stem, forming a *fibrous* root system, as is typical of grasses. In addition many taprooted plants (for example, apple) form an upper network of fibrous-like feeder roots. This permits deep anchorage and a more reliable water

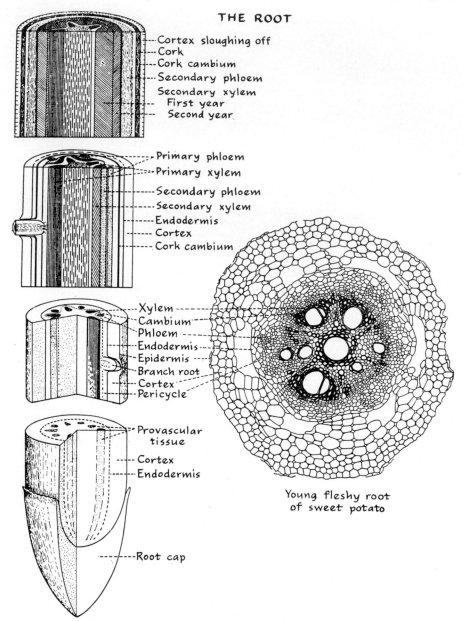

THE ROOT

Cortex sloughing off
Cork
Cork cambium
Secondary phloem
Secondary xylem
First year
Second year

Primary phloem
Primary xylem
Secondary phloem
Secondary xylem
Endodermis
Cortex
Cork cambium

Xylem
Cambium
Phloem
Endodermis
Epidermis
Branch root
Cortex
Pericycle

Provascular tissue
Cortex
Endodermis

Root cap

Young fleshy root of sweet potato

Fig. 3-14.   *Diagrammatic sections through a root.*
[Adapted from Weatherwax, *Plant Biology*, Saunders, Philadelphia, 1947.]

supply while providing absorptive capacity at the more fertile upper layers of soil. A fibrous-like root system may be formed artificially by destroying the taproot. This is accomplished by transplanting or undercutting and is a standard horticultural practice with shrubs and trees. Nurserymen build up a fibrous root system concentrated in a "ball" below the plant. This permits even relatively large plants to be successfully transplanted.

In general, plants having a fibrous root system are shallow-rooted in comparison with taprooted plants. Shallow-rooted plants will, of course, be more subject to drought and will show quicker response to variations in fertility treatments.

The morphological structure of the root is shown in Fig. 3-14. The arrangement of its vascular system is different from that of the stem. Note the lack of pith and the predominant pericycle and endodermis. A cambium serves to increase the girth of perennial roots, as in the stem.

The major root modifications of horticultural interest are those affecting the storage function. Roots of certain species become swollen and fleshy

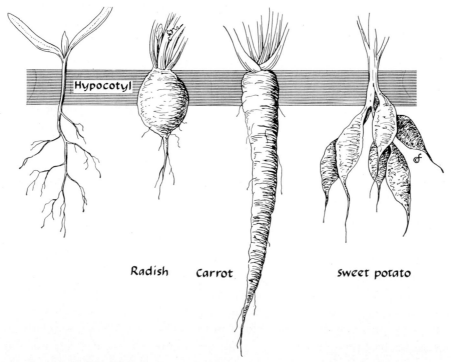

Fig. 3-15. *Root modifications. The swollen roots of the radish and carrot include the hypocotyl, a transition zone between the rudimentary seedling root and shoot.*

(Fig. 3-15). The stored food is in the form of starches and sugars. Some of these storage roots, such as the carrot, sweet potato, and turnip, are edible. The stored food, coupled with the ability of some of these roots, for example, the sweet potato and the *Dahlia,* to form adventitious shoot buds, renders them important in propagation.

The Shoot

The shoot has been described as a "central axis with appendages." The "central axis," that is, the stem, connects and supports the food-producing leaves with the nutrient-gathering roots. The stem is also a storage organ, and in many plants its structure is greatly modified for this function. Young green stems also have a small role in food production. Plants assume extremely varied forms, ranging from a single upright shoot, as in the date palm, to the prostrate branched "creepers." It is the structure and growth pattern of the stem that determine the form of the plant. Basic structural and anatomical features of herbaceous and woody stems are shown in Fig. 3-16.

The upright growth of plants having one active growing point and a rigid stem is considered the normal, and our descriptive terms are used to differentiate other growth patterns. Typical shrubby or bushy growth is brought about by the absence of a main trunk or *central leader.* Growth is characterized by a number of erect or semierect stems, none of which dominates. The distinguishing feature is form rather than size. Similarly, slender and flexible stems that cannot support themselves in an erect position are known as *vines.* Vines will trail unless mechanical support is used to make them grow upright. They may be either herbaceous (morning glory, pea) or woody (grape).

Buds

The stem is divided into mature and actively growing regions in which growth and differentiation take place. The "embryonic stem" is referred to as a bud. All buds do not grow actively; many assume an arrested development or dormancy but are nevertheless potential sources of further growth. Although buds may be so embedded in the stem tissues as to be relatively inconspicuous, they may become quite structured. The form, structure, and arrangement of buds prove to be a useful guide in describing woody plants even when the leaves are absent, as in winter. Typical buds are shown in Fig. 3-17. Growth may originate from a single *terminal* bud or from *lateral* buds which occur in the leaf axis. In addition, buds may be formed in

THE STEM

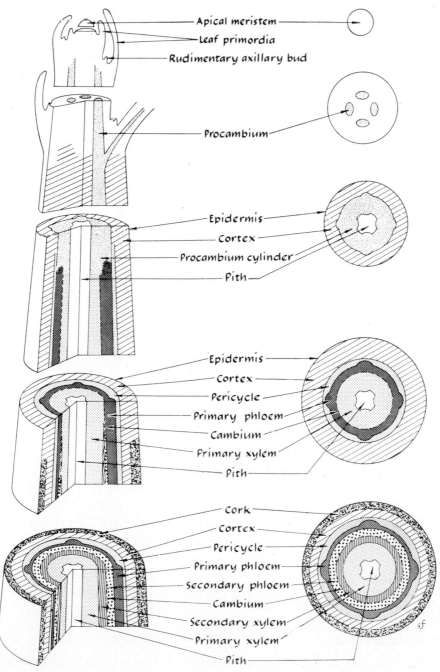

Fig. 3-16.   *Diagrammatic sections through a stem.*

[Adapted from Holman and Robbins, *A Textbook of General Botany*, Wiley, New York, 1939.]

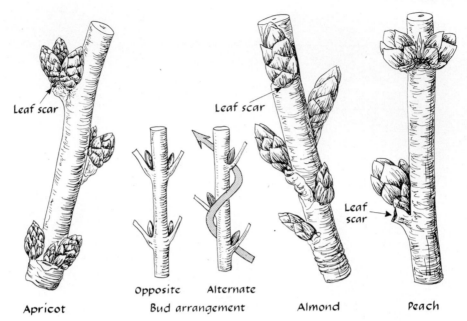

Fig. 3-17. *Dormant fruit and leaf buds of apricot, almond, and peach. The arrangement in each is alternate.*

[Adapted from Zielinski, *Modern Systematic Pomology*, Brown, Dubuque, 1955.]

internodal regions of the stems, leaves, or roots, often as a result of injury. These are called *adventitious* buds.

Buds may produce leaves, flowers, or both, and are referred to as *leaf, flower,* or *mixed* buds, respectively. When more than one bud is present at a leaf axis all but the central or basal bud are called *accessory* buds. The arrangement or topology of buds on a stem is based on the leaf arrangement. If two or more leaves are opposed to each other at the same level, the leaf (and bud) arrangement is said to be *opposite* or *whorled*. When they are at different levels they are arranged in a spiral and are said to be *alternate* (Fig. 3-17). The spiral pattern of leaf arrangement (*phyllotaxy*) is varied and is expressed as a fraction ($\frac{1}{2}$, $\frac{1}{3}$, $\frac{2}{5}$, $\frac{3}{8}$), where the numerator is the number of turns to get to a leaf directly above another and the denominator is the number of buds passed. Phyllotaxy has taxonomic significance, since it is often the same throughout a genus and often even applies to a whole family.

Stem Modifications

The stem may be greatly modified from a basically cylindrical structure (Fig. 3-18). Some of these alterations may appear quite bizarre; yet upon

ABOVE GROUND MODIFICATIONS

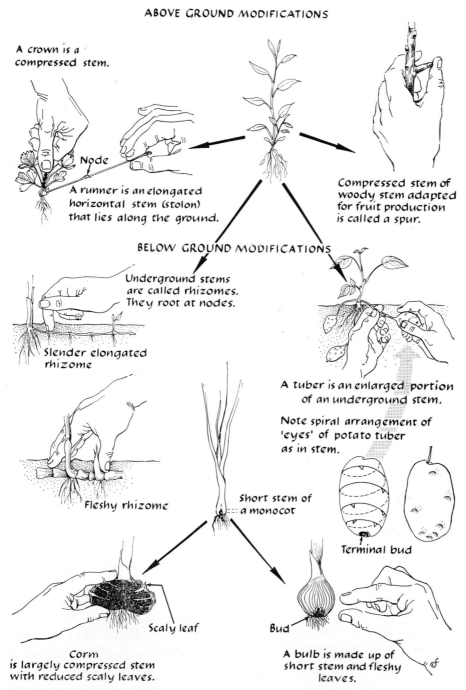

A crown is a compressed stem.

Node

A runner is an elongated horizontal stem (stolon) that lies along the ground.

Compressed stem of woody stem adapted for fruit production is called a spur.

BELOW GROUND MODIFICATIONS

Underground stems are called rhizomes. They root at nodes.

Slender elongated rhizome

Fleshy rhizome

Short stem of a monocot

A tuber is an enlarged portion of an underground stem.

Note spiral arrangement of 'eyes' of potato tuber as in stem.

Terminal bud

Scaly leaf

Bud

Corm is largely compressed stem with reduced scaly leaves.

A bulb is made up of short stem and fleshy leaves.

Fig. 3-18. *Stem modifications. Note that all have nodes and leaf-like structures.*

close analysis these modifications can be shown to be basically stem-like in structure; that is, they have nodes, leaves, or similar scale-like structures, and they function in transport or storage. Stem modification can be divided into above-ground forms (crowns, stolons, spurs) and below-ground forms (bulbs, corms, rhizomes, tubers). Since many stem modifications contain large amounts of stored food, they are especially significant in propagation, and, in white potatoes, are important as a source of food.

ABOVE-GROUND STEM MODIFICATIONS. The *crown** of a plant refers generally to that portion just above and just below ground level. This portion of the plant may be greatly enlarged as in Bald cypress (*Taxodium distichum*). Crowns may be thought of as "compressed" stems. The structure of the strawberry crown can be clearly seen by artificially elongating it through treatment with gibberellic acid, as shown in Fig. 3-19. Leaves and flowers arise from the crown by buds, as they do in stems. In addition, fleshy buds from crowns may produce a whole new plant, referred to as *crown divisions*. The crown may be modified into a food storage organ, as it is in asparagus.

Fig. 3-19. *The crown of a strawberry is a compressed stem. This can be clearly seen by elongating the stem with gibberellic acid (lower photograph). Note that the runners are formed from the leaf axils.*

[Courtesy J. Hull, Jr.]

Short, many-noded, horizontal branches growing out of the crown, bearing fleshy buds or leafy rosettes, are referred to variously as offsets, slips, suckers, pips, and so on. These stem modifications, which can be collectively termed *offshoots*, are important in that they provide both natural and artificial means of propagation.

Stolons refer to stems that grow horizontally along the ground. A *runner* is a stolon with long inter-

---

* The forester's term crown refers to the branched top of a tree.

nodes originating at the base or crown of the plant. At some of the nodes, roots and shoots develop. A well-known example of runners is found in the cultivated strawberry.

Spurs are stems of woody plants whose growth is restricted. They are characterized by greatly shortened internodes, and appear laterally on branches. In mature fruit trees, such as apple, pear, and quince, flowering is largely confined to spurs. Spurs are not irrevocably static, and may revert to normal stem growth even after many years of fruiting.

BELOW-GROUND STEM MODIFICATIONS. *Bulbs* appear as compressed modifications of the shoot, and consist of a short, flattened, or disk-shaped, stem surrounded by fleshy, leaf-like structures called scales. They may enclose shoot or flower buds. Bulbs and corms are found only in some monocotyledonous plants. The scales, filled with stored food, may be continuous, and form a series of concentric layers surrounding a growing point, as in the onion or tulip (*tunicate bulbs*) or may form a more or less random attachment to a small portion of stem, as in the Easter lily (*scaly bulbs*). Bulbs commonly grow under the ground or at ground level, although bulblike structures (*bulbils*) may be formed on aerial stems, as they do in some lily species, or even in association with flower parts, as in the onion.

Corms are short, fleshy, underground stems having few nodes. The corm is stem; the few rudimentary leaves are nonfleshy. The gladiolus and crocus are propagated by corms.

Rhizomes are horizontal, underground stems. They may be compressed and fleshy, as in *Iris*, or slender with elongated internodes, as in turf grasses (for example, Bermuda, bent). Normally, roots and shoots develop from the nodal regions. Such weeds as quack grass and Canadian thistle are particularly insidious because they spread so rapidly, owing to their natural propagation by rhizomes.

Tubers are greatly enlarged, fleshy portions of underground stems. They are typically noncylindrical. (The word "tuber" is derived from a Latin word meaning lump.) The edible portion of the white potato is a tuber. The "eyes" arranged in a spiral around the tuber are the buds. Each eye consists of a rudimentary leaf scar and a cluster of buds.

The Leaf

Leaves are the photosynthetic organs upon which higher plants depend for the formation of carbon-linked compounds. The leaf is basically a flat appendage of the stem, arranged in such a pattern as to present a large surface for the efficient absorption of light energy. The leaf *blade* is usually attached to the stem by a stalk or *petiole.* Leaf-like outgrowths of the petioles, known as *stipules,* are commonly present.

The anatomical structure of the leaf is shown in Fig. 3-20. Note that the vascular system in leaves forms a branching network called veins. The veining is typically net-like in dicots and parallel in monocots. The leaf blade, although commonly bilaterally symmetrical, is not radially symmetrical, since it has a distinct upper and lower side. Beneath the upper epidermal layer, which is characterized by heavy deposits of cutin, lie series of elongated, closely packed "palisade" cells that are particularly rich in chloroplasts. The irregularly arranged cells beneath the palisade cells produce a sponge-like region (*spongy mesophyll*) that provides an area necessary for gaseous exchange in photosynthesis and transpiration. The lower epidermis is interspersed with *stomata*—openings in the leaf that permit the exchange of carbon dioxide and water vapor with the environment.

Leaves of plants vary from the flat, thin disks described to the stem-like fleshy structures found in *Sansevieria.* The tendrils of peas are modifications

Fig. 3-20.   *Structure of an apple leaf.*

[From Eames and MacDaniels, *An Introduction to Plant Anatomy,* McGraw-Hill, New York, 1947.]

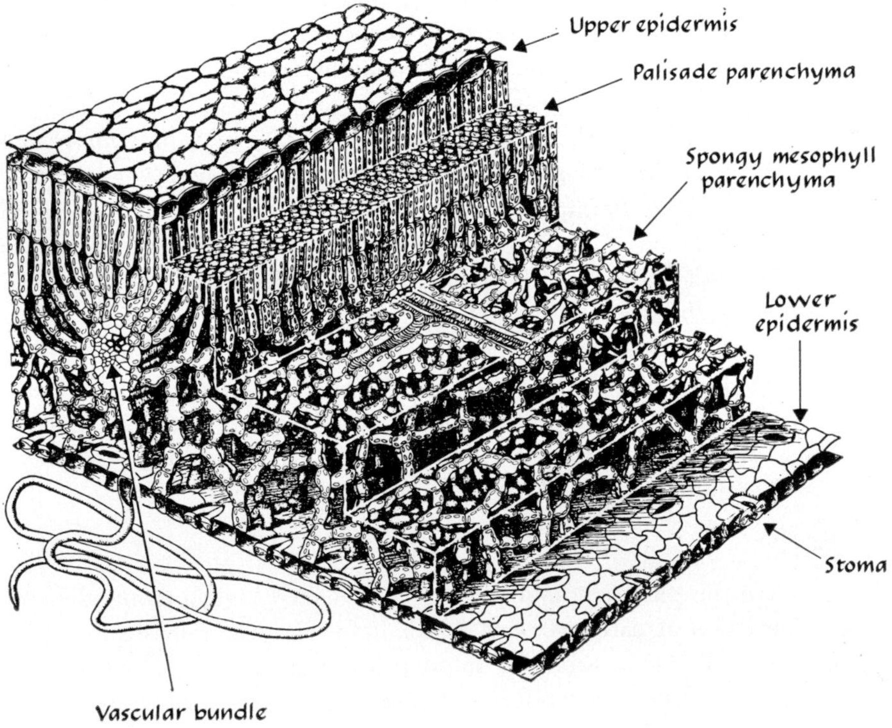

of the leaf. Leaves are the edible portion of many plants, such as lettuce, cabbage (Fig. 3-21), spinach, and are often the chief features of many ornamentals (poinsettia, foliage plants), especially when they are rich in red and yellow pigments.

The Flower

The flower shows great variety in structure, composition, and size. The principal flower parts (Fig. 3-22) are as follows:

Sepals (collectively, the calyx) enclose the flower in bud. They are usually small, green, leaf-like structures below the petals.

Fig. 3-21. *The cabbage head consists of large fleshy leaves attached to a compressed stem.*
[Photograph by J. C. Allen & Son.]

Petals (collectively, the corolla) are the conspicuous portion of most flowers. They are often highly colored, with the usual exception of green pigments, and may contain perfume, as well as nectar glands that produce a viscous, sugary substance. The extremely large, showy flowers of many

Fig. 3-22. *The structure of the flower.*

[From Porter, *Taxonomy of Flowering Plants*, Freeman, San Francisco, 1959.]

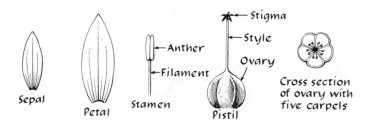

cultivated ornamentals are the result of rigorous selection for this character.

Stamens are composed of pollen-bearing *anthers* supported by a *filament*. When the pollen is mature it is discharged through the ruptured anther wall.

Pistils consist of an *ovule*-bearing base (or *ovary*) supporting an elongated region (or *style*) whose expanded tip (or surface) is called the *stigma*. The ovule gives rise to the seed. The mature ovary (with or without seeds) becomes the fruit.

The petals and sepals of the flower, as well as the reproductive parts— that is, the stamens and pistils—are essentially modified leaves. The leafy origin of the stamens can be clearly shown in the stamenoids or "extra" petals of the cultivated rose (Fig. 3-23). These flower parts are borne on an enlarged portion of the flower-supporting stem, called the *receptacle*.

Flowers composed of sepals, petals, stamens, and pistils are referred to as *complete* (Fig. 3-24). *Incomplete* flowers lack one or more of these parts. For example they may lack stamens (*pistillate* or "female" flowers) or pistils (*staminate* or "male" flowers). Those that contain both stamens and pistils (*perfect, bisexual,* or *hermaphroditic* flowers) may lack calyx or corolla.

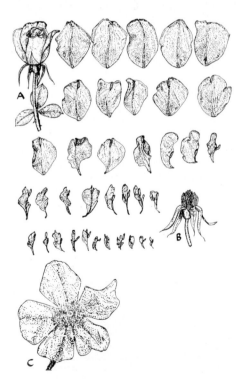

Fig. 3-23.   *Roses have five sepals, five petals, numerous stamens or petaloids, and several pistils. A petaloid is a petal-like structure developed from a stamen, forming what is termed semi-double or double flowers. (A) Double flowering rose with all five petals intact. From this specimen the five petals and 31 petaloids have been removed progressively inward. Each petaloid shows a rudimentary anther. (B) The same specimen after removing all the petals and petaloids to expose the numerous stamens. The number of petaloids depends largely on genetic factors. Compare with (C), a single rose with five petals and no petaloids.*

[From Honeywell, *Roses,* Extension Circular 427, Purdue Univ.]

Fig. 3-24. *The flower of the lily has all parts and is therefore perfect and complete. When grown commercially, the anthers are removed because the pollen stains the petals.*
[Photograph by J. C. Allen & Son.]

Similarly, plants are referred to as *staminate, pistillate,* or *perfect* on the basis of the type of flowers they bear. When both staminate and pistillate flowers occur on the same plant, as in corn, the sex type is *monoecious.* Species in which the sexes are separated into staminate and pistillate plants are *dioecious* (date palm, papaya, spinach, asparagus, hemp). Other combinations of flower types also occur. For example, muskmelons have perfect and staminate flowers on the same plant; this sex type is referred to as andromonoecious.

The Fruit

The botanical term "fruit" refers to the mature ovary and other flower parts associated with it. Thus, it may include the receptacle as well as withered remnants of the petals, sepals, stamens, and stylar portions of the pistil. It would also include any seeds contained in the ovary.

The structure of the fruit is related to the structure of the flower. Fruits are classified by the number of ovaries incorporated in the structure (for example, as *simple, aggregate,* or *multiple* fruits); the nature and structure of the ovary wall; their ability to and the method by which they split apart when ripe (*dehiscence*); and the way in which the seed is attached to the ovary.

SIMPLE FRUITS. The majority of flowering plants have fruits composed of a single ovary, and are referred to as simple fruits. In the mature fruit (when

Fig. 3-25. *The muskmelon is a berry-type fruit called a pepo. The rind is exocarp; the edible flesh is mesocarp.*
[Photograph by J. C. Allen & Son.]

the enclosed seed is fully developed), the ovary wall may be *fleshy* (composed of large portions of living succulent parenchyma) or *dry* (made up of nonliving sclerenchyma cells with lignified or suberized walls).

The ovary wall or *pericarp* is composed of three distinct layers. From outer to inner layer, these are the *exocarp, mesocarp,* and *endocarp.* When the entire pericarp of simple fruits is fleshy, the fruit is referred to as a *berry* (not to be confused with the horticultural term used in reference to the edible portion of some "small fruits"). The tomato, grape, and pepper are berry fruits. The muskmelon is a berry (specifically, a *pepo*) with a hard rind made up of exocarp and receptacle tissue (Fig. 3-25). Citrus fruits are also berries, called *hesperidium,* in which the rind is made up of exocarp and mesocarp; the "edible" juicy portion is endocarp.

Simple fleshy fruits having a stony endocarp are known as *drupe* (or *stone*) fruits (peach, cherry, plum, olive). The skin of these fruits is the exocarp; the fleshy, edible portion is the mesocarp. Simple fleshy fruits in which the inner portion of the pericarp forms a dry, paper-like "core" are known as *pomes* (apple, pear, quince).

The dry, dehiscent, simple fruits include such types as pods (pea), follicles (milk weed), capsules (jimson weed), or siliques (crucifers). The dry, simple fruits that do not dehisce when ripe include achenes (sunflower), caryopsis (corn), samara (maple), schizocarp (carrot), and nuts (walnut). These are diagrammed in Fig. 3-26.

AGGREGATE FRUITS. Aggregate fruits are derived from a flower having many pistils on a common receptacle. The individual fruits of the aggregate

TYPES OF FRUIT

FLESHY

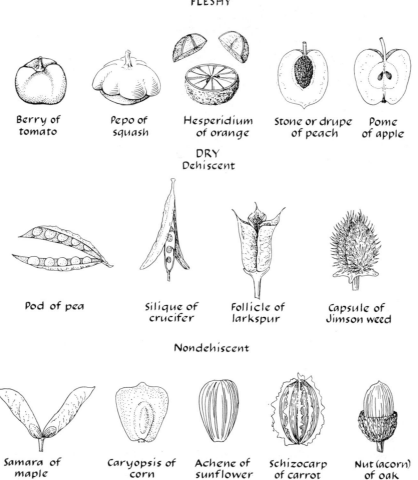

Berry of tomato	Pepo of squash	Hesperidium of orange	Stone or drupe of peach	Pome of apple

DRY
Dehiscent

Pod of pea	Silique of crucifer	Follicle of larkspur	Capsule of Jimson weed

Nondehiscent

Samara of maple	Caryopsis of corn	Achene of sunflower	Schizocarp of carrot	Nut (acorn) of oak

Fig. 3-26. *Various types of simple fruits.*

[Adapted from Holman and Robbins, *A Textbook of General Botany*, Wiley, New York, 1939.]

may be drupes (stony), as in blackberries, or achenes—that is, one-seeded, dry fruits attached to the receptacle at a single point, as in strawberries. In the strawberry the fleshy edible portion is the receptacle (Fig. 3-27).

MULTIPLE FRUITS. The multiple fruit is derived from many separate but closely clustered flowers. Familiar examples of multiple fruits are the pineapple, fig, and mulberry. The beet "seed" is a multiple fruit.

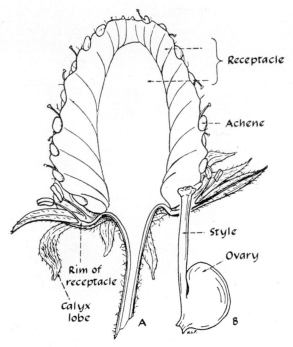

Fig. 3-27. *The strawberry is an aggregate fruit. The seed-like structures are achenes, which are small, dry, indehiscent, one-seeded fruits.*

[From Holman and Robbins, A *Textbook of General Botany*, Wiley, New York, 1939.]

The Seed

A seed is a miniature plant in an arrested state of development. Most seeds contain a "built-in" food supply (the orchid seed is an exception). Structurally, the seed is a matured ovule, although various parts of the ovary may be incorporated in the *seed coat*. The miniature plant, or embryo, develops from the union of gametes, or sex cells. The details of the fertilization process will be discussed in Chapter 9, *Mechanisms of Propagation*. By the time the seed is *mature,* the *embryo* is differentiated into a rudimentary shoot (*plumule*), a root (*radicle*), and one or two specialized seed leaves (*cotyledons*). A transition zone between the rudimentary root and shoot is known as the *hypocotyl*. Diagrams of various seeds are shown in Fig. 3-28.

The stored food is present in seeds as carbohydrates, fats, and proteins. Seeds are thus a rich source of food as well as of fats and oils for industrial purposes. This stored food may be derived from a tissue called the *endosperm*, which is formed as a result of the fertilization process. The endo-

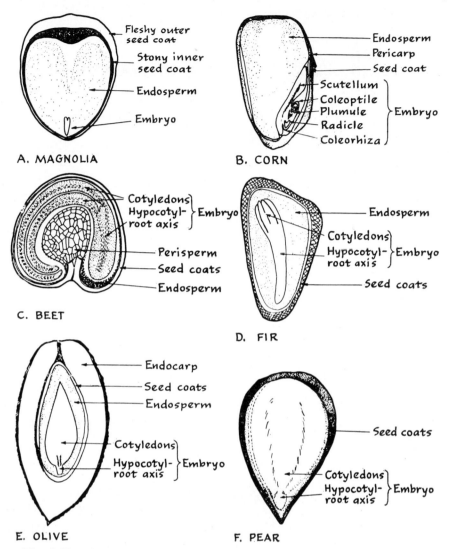

Fig. 3-28. *Structure of seeds and one-seeded fruits.*

[Adapted from Hartmann and Kester, *Plant Propagation*, Prentice-Hall, Englewood Cliffs, 1959.]

sperm may produce a specialized region of the mature seed, as in corn, or may be absorbed by the developing embryo. In the latter case, the cotyledons serve as the food-storage organ (for example, beans and walnuts).

Seeds vary greatly in size, form, and shape. Most plants can be identified by their seeds alone. In addition, great variation exists within seeds of a

ONION GERMINATION

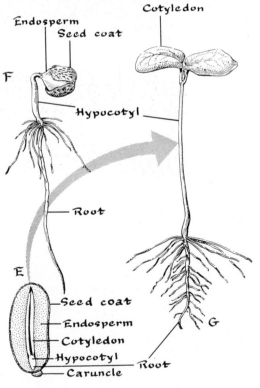

Seed coat

Endosperm

Embryo

A

Haustorial tip of cotyledon

Cotyledon

Shoot apex

Root

B

Cotyledon

Leaf primordium

Shoot apex

Cotyledonary sheath

Root

C

Root

D

CASTOR BEAN GERMINATION

Endosperm

Seed coat

Cotyledon

F

Hypocotyl

Root

E

Seed coat

Endosperm

Cotyledon

Hypocotyl

Caruncle

Root

G

Fig. 3-29. *Seed germination and seedling morphology in onion (a monocot) and castor bean (a dicot). In some dicotyledonous plants the expansion of the hypocotyl elevates the cotyledon above ground (epigeous germination), whereas in others the hypocotyl fails to expand, and the cotyledons remains below ground (hypogeous germination).*

[Adapted from Foster and Gifford, *Comparative Morphology of Vascular Plants*, Freeman, San Francisco, 1959.]

species. This includes such things as the presence or absence of spines (spinach), color variation (beans), and differences in the chemical composition of stored food (sugary versus starchy corn).

Seed germination refers to the change from the status of arrested development to active growth. The subsequent seedling stage, the interval during which the young, foraging plant becomes dependent on its own food manufacturing structures, is diagrammed in Fig. 3-29.

Selected References

Eames, A. J. and MacDaniels, L. H. *An Introduction to Plant Anatomy.* McGraw-Hill, New York. 1947. (An elementary but authoritative text on vascular plant anatomy.)

Esau, K. *Plant Anatomy.* Wiley, New York. 1953. (A comprehensive, advanced treatise on the anatomy of seed plants.)

Heyward, H. E. *The Structure of Economic Plants.* Macmillan, New York. 1938. (This book is especially noted for its treatment of particular species of plants, including corn, onion, beet, radish, pea, celery, sweet potato, tomato, squash, and lettuce.)

Holman, R. M. and Robbins, W. W. *A Textbook of General Botany.* Wiley, New York. 1939. (An excellent text, particularly valuable for the vocabulary of botany.)

CHAPTER 4

Plant Growth

In all ages the growth of plants has interested thoughtful men.
SIR JOHN RUSSELL

THE CELLULAR BASIS OF PLANT GROWTH

Plant growth refers to an irreversible increase in size. The increase in size and dry weight of an organism reflects an increase in protoplasm. This may occur through increases both in cell size and in the number of cells. The increase in the size of the cell has some limitations imposed on it by the relationship between its volume and its surface area. (The volume of a sphere increases faster than its surface area.) The process of *cell division* provides the basis for growth. Cell division is a biochemically regulated process, however, and is not necessarily directly controlled by any relationship between the volume of a cell and its membranal area.

The increase in protoplasm is brought about through a series of events in which water, carbon dioxide, and inorganic salts are transformed into living material. With respect to plant cells, this process involves the production of carbohydrates (*photosynthesis*), the uptake of water and nutrients, and the elaboration of complex proteins and fats from carbon fragments and inorganic compounds (*metabolism*). The required chemical energy is provided by *respiration*. These physiological processes are functions of individual cells and of multicellular organisms. They are not unrelated to each other any more than the ignition system is unrelated to the compression stroke of the cylinders in the gasoline engine. Nevertheless, their classification into separate processes is a useful concept.

Photosynthesis

Photosynthesis is the process in which carbon dioxide and water in the presence of light are transformed to carbon-containing, energy-rich, organic compounds. This conversion of light energy into chemical energy is the most significant of the life processes. With few exceptions all of the organic matter in living things is ultimately provided through this sequence of biochemical reactions.

Photosynthesis takes place primarily in the presence of two pigments, chlorophyll *a* and chlorophyll *b*, and as far as is known, it takes place only in the chloroplasts of the living cell. Photosynthesis is a complex series of integrated processes that can be stated in abbreviated form by the following chemical reaction.

$$12H_2O + 6CO_2 + \begin{array}{c} \text{light energy} \\ \text{in the presence} \\ \text{of chlorophyll} \end{array} \longrightarrow \underset{\text{sugar}}{C_6H_{12}O_6} + \underset{\text{oxygen}}{6O_2} + \underset{\text{water}}{6H_2O}.$$

The first process in this series of reactions is temperature independent and involves the trapping of light energy. This step appears to involve the formation of certain compounds that affect the decomposition or cleavage of the water molecules into hydrogen and oxygen. The second phase of the reaction is greatly affected by temperature. Essentially the hydrogen atoms from water are "stored" in the chloroplasts and are accepted by carbon dioxide to form CH_2O units, the bases of the sugars. This reduction of carbon dioxide is an energy-storing reaction. Radioactive isotope techniques have shown that all the oxygen released in photosynthesis is derived from the water molecule.

Respiration and Metabolism

Respiration, the process of obtaining energy from organic materials, is in a sense the reverse process of photosynthesis.

$$C_6H_{12}O_6 + 6O_2 \longrightarrow 6H_2O + 6CO_2 + \text{energy}.$$

The captured energy of light is released from the low-temperature oxidation (burning) of sugars and fats. While part of the released energy appears as heat, useful energy is channeled into chemical work. This chemical energy accommodates the synthesis of organic materials, which is manifested in growth. Respiration is a feature of all living plants. The measurement of carbon dioxide given off in respiration is often utilized as a test for life.

The biologic combustion of sugar is an extremely complicated series of biochemical reactions involving many specific enzyme systems and energy carriers. The steps from 6-carbon sugar to carbon dioxide involves the transformation of phosphate derivatives of sugar to 3-carbon pyruvic acid

(CH₃COCOOH). This step is common to many organisms. Organisms that do not require oxygen (*anaerobes*) transform pyruvic acid to alcohol or lactic acid. Those organisms, such as the higher plants, that require oxygen (*aerobes*) transform pyruvic acid to water and carbon dioxide. This involves the participation of a number of plant acids in a cyclic series of steps known as the Krebs, or citric acid, cycle. The relationship between respiration and photosynthesis is shown diagrammatically in Fig. 4-1.

The rate of respiration depends on many factors. It is highest in rapidly growing tissues and is lowest in dormant tissues. The rate of respiration is greatly influenced by temperature, and approximately doubles for each 18°F rise over a range of 40–97° (Fig. 4-2). Among other environmental factors that influence the respiration rate are the availability of oxygen and nitrogen, the availability of sugar and fat, and the age and condition of the cells and tissues.

Fig. 4-1. *Metabolic pathways in green plants.*

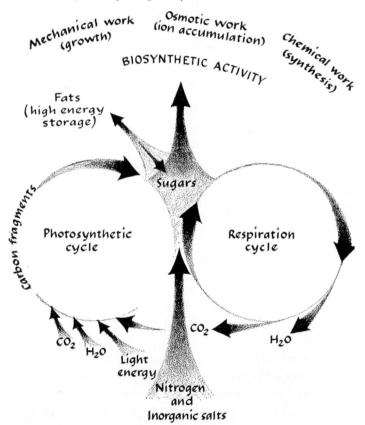

All of the various materials produced in plants (carbohydrates, proteins, sterols, essential oils, alkaloids, pigments, and so forth) are derived from the carbon fragments produced by photosynthesis and from the inorganic nutrients absorbed from the soil. The synthesis (*anabolism*) and degradation (*catabolism*) of these materials is referred to as *metabolism*. The degradation of sugar and fats, with their release of energy in respiration, can be considered as a specialized portion of metabolism. The elucidation of this metabolic action represents some of the brightest chapters in biochemistry.

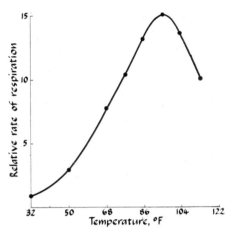

Fig. 4-2.   *The relationship between the respiration rate of germinating pea seedlings and temperature.*

[Adapted from Bonner and Galston, *Principles of Plant Physiology, Freeman,* San Francisco, 1952; after data of Fernandes.]

Nutrient Absorption

With respect to absorption, the cell can be considered as a mass of protoplasm surrounded by a differentially permeable membrane that permits passage of water and inorganic salts but restrains the passage of large complex molecules. The movement of molecules through a selectively permeable membrane is known as *diffusion*. The diffusion of water molecules through such a membrane is *osmosis*.

The movement of molecules in the process of diffusion can be demonstrated in nonliving systems by immersing a differentially permeable membrane that contains sugar water into a solution of pure water, as shown in Fig. 4-3. The water moves from the solution of high concentration (pure water) to the solution of low concentration (sugar solution). Living cells, however, are able to accumulate certain ions unaccounted for by the straightforward process of diffusion. The cell appears to act as a metabolic pump. This process, known as active uptake, requires energy, which is supplied ultimately from respiration. This is demonstrated by the fact that metabolic inhibitors or poisons such as carbon monoxide prevent active uptake.

The ability of molecules to move in and out of plant cells is related to the size of the molecules, their oil (lipid) solubility, and their membrane permeability. Thus, large complex molecules produced in the cell tend to

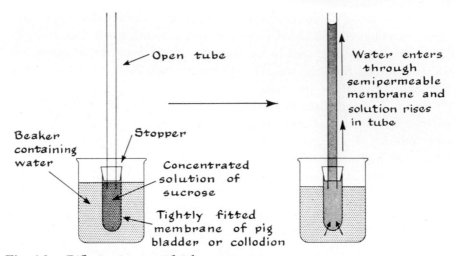

Fig. 4-3. *Diffusion in an artificial osmotic system.*

[Adapted from Bonner and Galston, *Principles of Plant Physiology*, Freeman, San Francisco, 1952.]

remain in the cell. The fact that the rate of movement of solutes through cell membranes is roughly proportional to their fat solubility suggests that the membranes are largely composed of fatty material. Membrane permeability is affected by the ionic concentration of the nutrient medium. Monovalent ions (K^+, Na^+, Cl^-) appear to increase the permeability of membranes, whereas polyvalent cations (Ca^{++} and Mg^{++}) decrease membrane permeability. Furthermore, different ions interact in their effect on membrane permeability (*ion antagonism*).

Although chemical analysis of plant cells may indicate the presence of many different elements, only 15 have been shown to be essential. The most abundant elements, carbon, hydrogen, and oxygen, are derived from carbon dioxide and water. The other 12 are ultimately derived from the soil in the form of inorganic salts (Table 4-1). The growth of a cell is dependent on the quantity and availability of the essential nutrients. Since nutrients and water are ultimately supplied to the plant from the soil, the study of plant nutrition is largely involved with the biology and chemistry of the soil.

Translocation

Translocation may be defined as the movement of inorganic and organic solutes from one part of the plant to another. The transport of water and solutes in and out of single cells and simple multicellular plants is largely

Table 4-1. *The twelve essential elements derived from the soil.*
[From Bonner and Galston, *Principles of Plant Physiology*, Freeman, San Francisco, 1952; after Leeper.]

ESSENTIAL ELEMENT	PERCENTAGE IN REPRESENTATIVE AGRICULTURAL SOILS	AMOUNT (LB/ACRE)
Fe	3.5	70,000
K	1.5	30,000
Ca	0.5	10,000
Mg	0.4	8000
N	0.1	2000
P	0.06	1000
S	0.05	1000
Mn	0.05	1000
B	0.002	40
Zn	0.001	20
Cu	0.0005	5
Mo	0.0001	2

accomplished by diffusion. In higher plants, however, this conduction of solutes is carried out largely in distinct tissue systems. Physiological specialization in multicellular plants is made possible because of the rapid, large-scale transport of substances within the plant. This movement is largely a two way stream, in which water and its dissolved contents move up from the roots through the xylem, and synthesized sugars move out from the leaves through the phloem.

The upward movement of water and solutes in higher plants is not fully understood. It is thought to be related to transpiration, the evaporative loss of water vapor from the leaves through the numerous stomatal openings. As water is lost by the cells, a diffusion-pressure deficit draws the water from the xylem elements. Because the xylem elements form a continuous tube from roots to leaves, the tension is transmitted through the entire column. This reduced pressure deficit transmitted to the root cells results in increased water absorption (Fig. 4-4).

The rate of transpiration is affected by the position of the stomatal openings and by environmental factors, such as temperature and humidity, that affect the rate of evaporation of water. The opening of the stomata is a mechanical process regulated by the turgidity of the guard cells. The turgidity of the guard cells is proportional to the carbon dioxide content

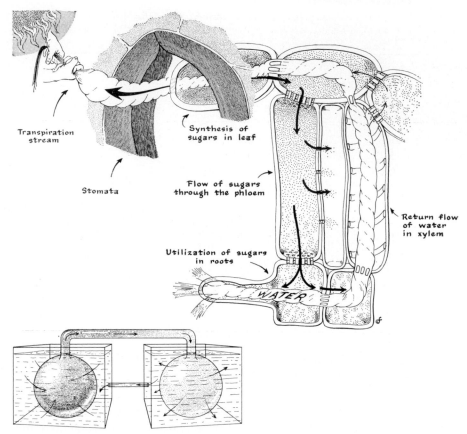

Transpiration
stream

Synthesis of
sugars in leaf

Stomata

Flow of sugars
through the phloem

Return flow
of water
in xylem

Utilization of sugars
in roots

WATER

Fig. 4-4. *Diagram of the translocation of water and elaborated sugars in the plant. The upward movement of water through the xylem can be explained on the basis of a tension on the continuous water column in the plant. This tension, produced by the evaporation of water from the leaf (transpiration), is transmitted to the absorbing cells of the root. Sugars synthesized in the leaves move through the sieve tubes of the phloem. Phloem transport is a pressure flow brought about by a high osmotic concentration in the leaf cells and a low concentration in the receiving cells. A model of this system, called the osmometer, is shown at lower left.*

[Adapted from Bonner and Galston, *Principles of Plant Physiology*, Freeman, San Francisco, 1952.]

of the substomatal capacity, although the mechanism involved is unknown. The cessation of photosynthesis at night raises the CO_2 content of the substomatal cavity. The subsequent decrease in the turgidity of the guard cells closes the stomatal cavity. Light during the day initiates photosynthesis, which lowers the carbon dioxide content (from about .03–.01%) and reverses the process. The turgidity of the guard cells is also lowered by an excessive water loss. Thus, the stomatal movements are controlled by a biological governor that regulates the water economy of the plant.

The movement of sugars occurs principally in the phloem. Phloem transport appears to be accomplished by increased osmotic concentration in the leaf meophyll cells brought about by the high concentrations of dissolved photosynthates elaborated there. These sugars then move into the anucleated sieve tubes of the phloem by a process that is not clearly understood. The resultant sugar gradient results in a pressure flow, and other substances appear to be swept along the sieve tube stream. The sugars are utilized in the receiving cells through respiration, growth, or storage processes. There is also evidence of lateral transport from xylem to phloem, and consequently there is some movement of minerals in the phloem. In addition, the xylem of woody stems appears to function in the upward movement of organic nitrogen.

DIFFERENTIATION

Growth and development are interrelated phenomenon. Growth has been defined as an irreversible increase in size (and usually in dry weight); *development* involves differentiation, and refers to a higher order of change involving anatomical and physiological specialization. The mechanisms of development and differentiation are one of the great problems of biology. The transformation from the single cell to the complex multicelled organism is imperfectly known; only a very few of the pathways involved in these changes are understood.

Differentiation is also a characteristic of individual cells. Unicellular organisms are capable of complex differentiation, with no other apparent stimulus than their own genetic make up. Development of the multicellular plant is the summation of individual cell differentiation. However, the cells of multicellular organisms have exchanged versatility for specialization.

The mitotic process in cell division (see Chapter 9) insures genetic continuity of all cells in an organism. How can multicellular organisms made up of genetically identical cells differentiate? The general answer lies in the interaction of the genetically controlled processes with their immediate external environment. The immediate environment of all parts of a cell, or cells, in a multicellular organism may be quite different. In multicellular organisms, particular cells take over the control of differentiation. This control takes place through the media of "chemical messengers," referred to by such names as growth regulators, hormones, auxin, antiauxin, growth promoters, and inhibitors, and so on (Fig. 4-5). On a cellular basis it is probably an enzyme that carries the message. Thus the environment of any cell in a complex organism includes the interaction of its own genetic endowment with substances produced from other cells.

The family of substances that affect growth and development may be conveniently termed *growth regulators*. These are organic substances whose activity appears far out of proportion to their concentration. Minute amounts (as little as one part per billion), exert measurable physiological effects. The term growth regulators includes both naturally occurring and synthetically copied, or created, substances. They may be either inhibitors or promoters of growth.

The term *hormone,* widely used in animal physiology, refers to organic substances that are produced by the organism and whose action may be involved in sites removed from their origin. Plant differentiation is also controlled by hormones (that is, *phytohormones*). The class of growth regulators known as *auxins* has received considerable attention in plant physiology and horticulture. *Auxins* are hormone-like growth-promoting substances. *Cell elongation,* the simplest example of anatomical differentiation, is directly affected by auxin concentration. The mode of action appears to involve alternations in the plasticity of the cell wall.

This fundamental property of auxin to affect simple elongation has been exploited as an assay of auxin activity. The most basic assay consists in measuring the rate of elongation of oat coleoptile sections floating in the solution, as compared with a control. Similar tests involve rates of stem curvatures in response to auxin application, as in the split pea test (Fig. 4-6). Phototropism, the bending towards light of a growing seedling, can be explained on the basis of differential cell elongation as a result of auxin redistribution and inhibition of auxin synthesis in the growing point by light. The auxins accumulating on the darkened side of the meristem elongate the cells on that side. The result is that the stem bends toward the light, as shown in Fig. 4-7. The term auxin is now reserved for compounds that, when assayed by a specific test involving oat coleoptiles, effect enlargement of the sections. Thus, gibberellic acid, a naturally occurring growth-regulating substance that effects stem elongation, is not considered auxin because of the negative results obtained by this assay. The most common natural auxin is *indoleacetic acid* (IAA), which, with its chemically related active compounds, is, in fact, often referred to as auxin. This usage, however, is unprecise and confusing.

Auxin, the most studied of the phytohormones, is at present the best understood of the many substances affecting plant development. It is formed

Fig. 4-5. *Plant growth and development is directed by organic substances produced in various parts of the plant and translocated to others. One group of such substances, called auxins, are produced in the plant extremities. Auxins are associated with various growth functions as indicated by the shaded portions of the diagram.*

[Adapted from Bonner and Galston, *Principles of Plant Physiology*, Freeman, San Francisco, 1952; and Leopold, *Auxins and Plant Growth*, University of California Press, Berkeley, 1955.]

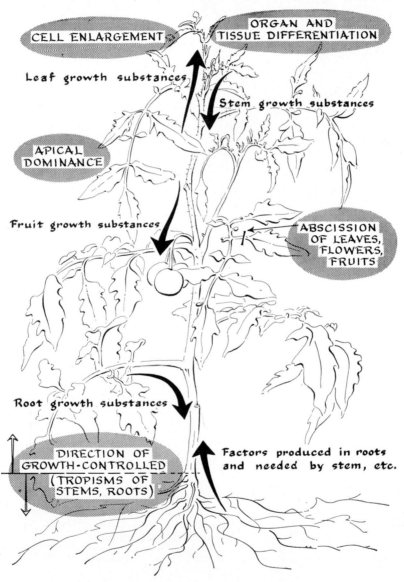

CELL ENLARGEMENT

ORGAN AND TISSUE DIFFERENTIATION

Leaf growth substances

Stem growth substances

APICAL DOMINANCE

Fruit growth substances

ABSCISSION OF LEAVES, FLOWERS, FRUITS

Root growth substances

DIRECTION OF GROWTH-CONTROLLED (TROPISMS OF STEMS, ROOTS)

Factors produced in roots and needed by stem, etc.

Fig. 4-6. *The split pea test measures the biological activity of auxins. Sections of stems are split with a razor blade and placed in the solution to be tested. The amount of inward curvature is proportional to the auxin concentration. The petri dish on the left contains auxin; the dish on the right is the control and shows no activity.*
[Courtesy Purdue Univ.]

Fig. 4-7. *Phototropism results from the redistribution and inhibition of auxin in the growing point by light. The subsequent accumulation of auxin on the darkened portion elongates cells on that side and bends the seedling toward the light.*

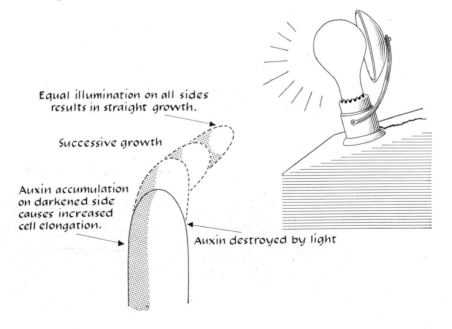

Equal illumination on all sides results in straight growth.

Successive growth

Auxin accumulation on darkened side causes increased cell elongation.

Auxin destroyed by light

in the stem and root apices, from where it moves to the rest of the plant. The subsequent distribution, however, is not uniform. The resultant concentration of auxin has been correlated with inhibition and stimulation of growth (Fig. 4-8), as well as organ and tissue differentiation. Such processes as cell enlargement, leaf and organ abscission, apical dominance, and fruit set and growth have been shown to be auxin mediated. These will be discussed more fully in subsequent chapters.

The precise mechanism for complex cell differentiation, as from elongated cell to sieve tube, is not clear. However, some of the grosser factors influencing tissue and organ differentiation have been investigated. It can be shown that many of these changes involve the interaction of "growth" substances produced from differentiated portions of the organism. In some plants these growth substances have been isolated. Thus, the artificial culture of roots can only be accomplished if enough root meristem is provided and if certain substances normally provided by the leaves are made available. In the tomato, these growth substances have been shown to be thiamine and pyridoxine, which are produced in the leaves. Similarly, the growth and development of fruit, embryo, and bud are related to specific growth substances produced by the plant. The role of auxin is intimately

Fig. 4-8. *The effect of auxin concentration on the growth of roots, buds, and stems.*

[Adapted from Machlis and Torrey, *Plants in Action*, Freeman, San Francisco, 1956; after Thimann.]

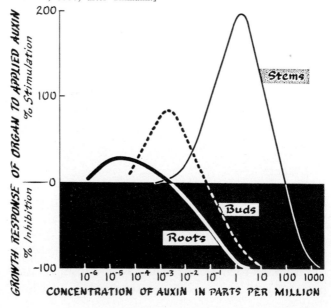

involved in many of these systems, and it has been suggested that IAA behaves as a "master" hormone, affecting differentiation and growth in plants.

ENVIRONMENTAL FACTORS IN PLANT GROWTH

The primary environmental factors involved in plant growth are (1) *soil*, which provides nutrients and moisture in addition to mechanical support, (2) *radiant energy* in the form of heat and light, and (3) *air*, which provides both carbon dioxide and oxygen. Soil and radiant energy vary greatly over the surface of the earth. Although the composition of air over the earth is fairly uniform above the ground, the percentage of air in the soil varies greatly.

Certain areas in the temperate and tropical regions of the earth are capable of supporting luxuriant plant growth. In these favored locations the plant becomes adjusted to its environment and becomes an integral part of it. When these plants are cultivated the delicate balance of nature is often disturbed. Any factor of the plant's environment that becomes less than optimum will limit its growth.

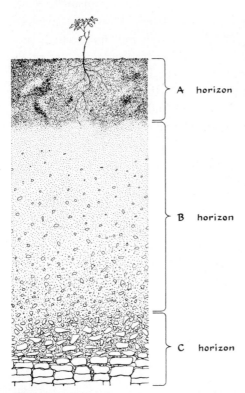

A   horizon

B   horizon

C   horizon

Fig. 4-9.   *A soil profile.*

[From Bonner and Galston, *Principles of Plant Physiology*, Freeman, San Francisco, 1952; after Lyon and Buckman.]

The Soil

Soil—the reservoir of nutrients and moisture—and the plant are in intimate association. The soil, far more than an inorganic mass of debris, is a biological system in a state of dynamic equilibrium. The genesis of soil from the earth's crust begins with a disintegration process whereby the parental rock becomes finely subdivided. Leaching and the subsequent action of leached materials on the original mineral substances form entirely new substances. It is the biological action of plant and microorganism, however, that transforms the subdivided minerals to the complex known as soil.

Soil genesis is a continuing process. It can be seen from a vertical slice through shallow soil, where bedrock is just slightly beneath the soil surface. The three rather distinct gradations from bedrock to "topsoil" are referred to as horizons (Fig. 4-9). The morphology of these horizons makes it possible to classify soil into types, in order that its structure and potential fertility may be predicted.

The Physical Properties of Soil

ORGANIC MATTER. A fertile soil is literally alive. Although the insects and earthworms are the most obvious of the soil fauna, the largest bulk of the organisms in terms of weight are microorganisms, bacteria and fungi (Fig. 4-10), which must be considered as the primary feeders of the soil. The organic matter of the soil is derived not only from the decomposed plant and animal tissue but from the microorganisms themselves.

Fig. 4-10. *The weight of soil organisms per acre-foot of fertile agricultural land is equivalent to 20–30 marketable (200 lb) hogs. This is about $\frac{1}{1000}$ of the weight of an acre-foot of soil. The microorganisms of the soil are the primary feeders and get first call on nutrients; the plant gets what is left over.*
[Data of Allen, *Experiments in Soil Bacteriology*. Burgess, Minneapolis, 1957.]

Average weight (lb/acre-ft of fertile soil)

ORGANISM	LOW	HIGH
Bacteria	500	1000
Fungi	1500	2000
Actinomycetes	800	1500
Protozoa	200	400
Algae	200	300
Nematodes	25	50
Other worms and insects	800	1000
Total weights	4025	6250

The decomposition of plant and animal material is accomplished by enzymatic digestion carried out by soil microorganisms. The decomposition of simple carbohydrates (starches and sugars) is a fairly rapid process and results in the release of carbon dioxide in the soil. Water-soluble proteins are decomposed readily to amino acids and then to available ammonium compounds. Ammonium compounds, under the action of certain "nitrifying" bacteria, are transformed to nitrates, in which form they are again available to plants. The decomposition of organic materials, however, is not complete. Certain substances, such as lignins, waxes, fats, and some proteinaceous materials resist decomposition, but, through complex biochemical processes, form a dark noncrystalline, colloidal substance called *humus.* Humus has absorptive properties for nutrients and moisture that are even higher than those of clay. Yet, unlike clay, it has extremely low plasticity and cohesive properties. Thus, small amounts of humus greatly affect the structural and nutritive properties of soil.

SOIL TYPES. There are two basic types of soil—mineral and organic. Mineral soils are composed of inorganic substances and varying amounts of decaying organic matter (from a trace to 20%). Organic soils (for example, muck and peat) are formed from partly decayed plant materials under marshy or swampy conditions. When such soils contain over 65% organic matter, they are referred to as peat; those containing 20–65% organic matter are called muck. Organic soils are dark brown to nearly black in color. These soils cannot be cultivated unless they are drained and soil fertility problems are corrected. Properly managed organic soils are highly productive (Fig. 4-11). These soils are porous, are well aerated, and have a high water-absorption capacity.

The mineral substances of the soil consist of particles of different size; in decreasing order, these are stone, gravel, sand, silt, and clay. The proportion of these substances determines the soil *texture* (Fig. 4-12). Such names as clay, loam, or silty clay are textural classifications of soils.

Although the physical properties of the coarser materials do not differ greatly from those of the rocks from which they are derived, materials composed of particles of submicroscopic size, known as *clays,* show distinct physical properties. The clays, the most chemically and physically active portion of the soil, are of colloidal size and are crystalline in structure. They are formed from the parent minerals by a crystallization process and are not merely finely subdivided rock. The clay particles are made up of "flakes," or sheet-like units, held together by O—H linkages or by ions between the plates. Their significant structural characteristic is their tre-

Fig. 4-11. *Properly managed muck soils are among our most productive agricultural lands. Almost 1800 bushels/acre of hand-crated onions is an impressive sight seldom seen in the age of automatic harvesters.*
[Photograph by J. C. Allen & Son.]

mendous surface area relative to their volume. The clay particle carries a negative charge. Thus, clay particles are electrically active, attracting positively charged ions (H^+, Na^{++}, K^+, Ca^{++}, Mg^{++}, and others). The adsorbed water on clays acts both as a lubricant and as a binding force. The clay platelets act in this regard as a stack of wet poker chips. This, to a large

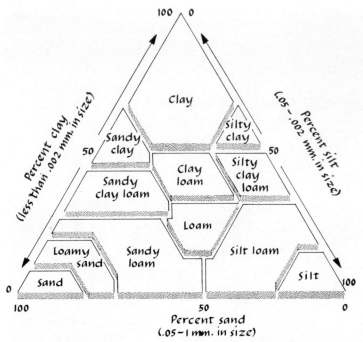

Figure 4-12. *Soil texture triangle. To find the textural name of a soil, locate the points corresponding to the percentage of clay and silt on each side of the triangle. The silt line is projected inward parallel to the clay side; the clay line is projected inward parallel to the sand side. The lines will meet in the class name of the soil.*

[Adapted with permission of the publisher from *The Nature and Properties of Soils* by Lyon, Buckman, and Brady, 5th ed., copyright 1952 by the Macmillan Company.]

degree, explains the plasticity of clay. Wet clay soils low in organic matter and low in weakly hydrated cations, such as calcium, become *sticky* or *puddled*.

SOIL STRUCTURE. The structure of soil refers to the arrangement of the soil particles into aggregates. The factors determining good structure are the size and arrangement into granules of the soil particles. Soil granules are masses of mineral particles of various sizes interspersed with organic material or some cementing compound. *Granulation* is largely brought about by the aggregation of soil particles by exudates of microorganisms. In addition, environmental factors such as freezing and thawing or wetting and drying help break up larger aggregates into granular size. The granulation of soils is particularly important to proper plant growth because of the effect on interstitial spaces, known as *pores*.

The pore space of soil is occupied by water and air in varying proportions, the soil acting as a huge sponge. The total pore space of soil, about 50% of the total volume, is not as important as the characteristic size of the pore spaces. Clay soils have more total pore space than sandy soils, yet their small size allows only slow gas and water movement. When the small pores of clay soils become filled with water, the lack of aeration so essential to root growth becomes limiting. The larger pore spaces of soils, when filled with water, will soon drain out by gravity, whereas the small pore spaces hold the water by capillary action. This *capillary* water is of the utmost importance to the plant; it is the soil solution.

The main factors contributed by good soil structure are proper aeration and water-holding capacity. The crumbly nature of good agricultural soils depends directly on soil texture and the percentage of organic matter. Under field conditions only organic matter is amenable to variation. In potting soils both the texture and percentage of organic matter may be modified.

The Chemical Properties of Soil

CATION EXCHANGE. As regards plant nutrition, the most significant features of the colloidal particles, clay and humus, are their ability to attract cations and to undergo the subsequent exchange of one ion for another—a process known as *cation exchange*. Thus, nutrients that otherwise would be lost by leaching are held in reserve by the clay particles. When exchanged, these ions become available to the plant.

The process of base exchange is not a random process. The cations differ in their replacement process such that if present in equal amounts:

$$H^+ \text{ replaces } Ca^{++} \text{ replaces } Mg^{++} \text{ replaces } K^+ \text{ replaces } Na^+.$$

The addition of large amounts of one cation may replace another by "sheer force of number" (*mass action*). This is largely what occurs with the addition of inorganic fertilizer.

Hydrogen ions are made continually available by the dissociation of carbonic acid formed from the dissolved CO_2 released by living roots in respiration and from the biological decay of carbohydrates.

$$CO_2 + H_2O \rightleftharpoons H_2CO_3 \rightleftharpoons H^+ + HCO_3^-.$$

The steady release of H^+ tends to promote the exchange of cations making them available for plant growth. The cations are replenished by the decomposition of rocks, the degradation of organic materials, and artificial application of "fertilizers." The cations in a productive soil exhibit an equilibria between soil particle, soil solution, and the plant.

The *cation-exchange capacity* of a soil is expressed in milliequivalents (meq) per 100 grams and is equivalent to the milligrams of H^+ that will combine with 100 g of dry soil. The exchange capacity of soil differs with the percentage of humus and with the percentage and composition of clay. The clays differ markedly in their ability to exchange cations. Montmorillonite clays have an exchange capacity of about 100 meq/100 g, whereas the kaolinite clays have a low exchange capacity of about 10 meq/100 g. In contrast, the exchange capacity of humus ranges from 150–300 meq/100 g. The ranges of exchange capacity for various soils is presented in Table 4-2.

Table 4-2. *Cation exchange capacity ranges for various soil types.*

[Adapted from Lyon, Buckman, and Brady, *Nature and Properties of Soils*, Macmillan, New York. 1952.]

SOIL TYPE	CATION EXCHANGE CAPACITY (MILLIEQUIVALENTS/100G)
Sands	2–4
Sandy loams	2–17
Loams	7–16
Silt loams	9–30
Clay and clay loams	4–60
Organic soils	50–300

SOIL REACTION. *Soil reaction* refers to the acidity or alkalinity of the soil. It is expressed in terms of pH, the logarithm of the reciprocal of the hydrogen ion concentration, and is usually expressed in units from 0 to 14.

$$pH = \log \frac{1}{[H^+]}.$$

Table 4-3 gives the concentration in moles of H^+ and OH^- for pH values of 0 to 14. Note that the molar concentration of $H^+ \times$ the molar concentration of OH^- equals a constant of 10^{-14}. The pH of the soil is regulated by the extent of the colloid fraction charged with hydrogen ions. For example, a clay particle charged with abundant H^+ acts as a weak acid and imparts an acid reaction or low pH. Similarly, a clay particle charged with mineral cations imparts an alkaline reaction, or high pH (Fig. 4-13).

The proper soil pH (6–7) is vitally important in plant growth. Abnormally high soil pH (above 9) or low pH (below 4) are, in themselves, toxic

Table 4-3. *The concentration of H^+ and OH^- with varying pH.*

pH	SOIL REACTION		H^+ CONCENTRATION (MOLES/LITER)*	OH^- CONCENTRATION (MOLES/LITER)†	REACTION OF COMMON SUBSTANCES
0			10^{-0}	10^{-14}	
1			10^{-1}	10^{-13}	
2			10^{-2}	10^{-12}	
3		very strong	10^{-3}	10^{-11}	lemon juice
4		strong	10^{-4}	10^{-10}	orange juice
5	Acidity	moderate	10^{-5}	10^{-9}	
6		slight	10^{-6}	10^{-8}	milk
7		neutral	10^{-7}	10^{-7}	pure water
8		slight	10^{-8}	10^{-6}	sea water
9	Alkalinity	moderate	10^{-9}	10^{-5}	soap solution
10		strong	10^{-10}	10^{-4}	
11		very strong	10^{-11}	10^{-3}	
12			10^{-12}	10^{-2}	
13			10^{-13}	10^{-1}	
14			10^{-14}	10^{-0}	

(soil range brackets pH 3–11)

* 1 mole of H = 1 g

† 1 mole of OH = 17 g

to plant roots. Within this range the pH determines the behavior of certain nutrients, precipitating them or making them unavailable (Fig. 4-14). For example, the chlorotic condition (chlorosis) found in some plants grown in high pH is a result of iron deficiency resulting from the precipitation of iron compounds. Soil organisms, especially bacteria, are also affected by pH. Vigorous nitrification and nitrogen fixation require pH above 5.5.

Soil Fertility

The fertility of the soil is only indirectly related to the chemical composition of the primary inorganic minerals. The most important factor is the level of the forms of the nutrients available to the plant. Such levels are related to many factors, among which are solubility of the nutrients, soil pH, the cation-exchange capacity of the soil, soil texture, and the amount of organic matter present.

Nitrogen tends to be the most limiting element to plant growth. The main available forms of nitrogen in the soil are nitrate (NO_3^-) and ammonium

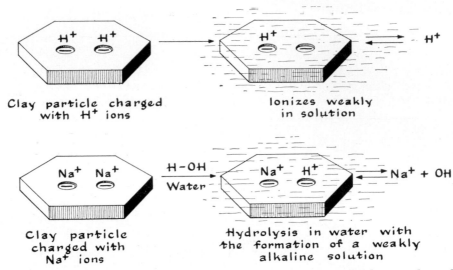

Fig. 4-13. *The soil reaction depends on whether the clay particles are charged with hydrogen ions or mineral cations.*

[From Bonner and Galston, *Principles of Plant Physiology*, Freeman, San Francisco, 1952.]

(NH_4^+) ions. The nitrite ion (NO_2^-) can be utilized by the plant, but it tends to be unstable and toxic in high amounts. The transformation of nitrogen-containing compounds to available forms is referred to as the "*nitrogen cycle.*" This circuitous route of nitrogen from element to protein and back is largely biological, as shown in Fig. 4-15.

Fig. 4-14. *The relation between soil reaction and the availability of plant nutrients to crops.*

[Courtesy of Virginia Polytechnic Inst.]

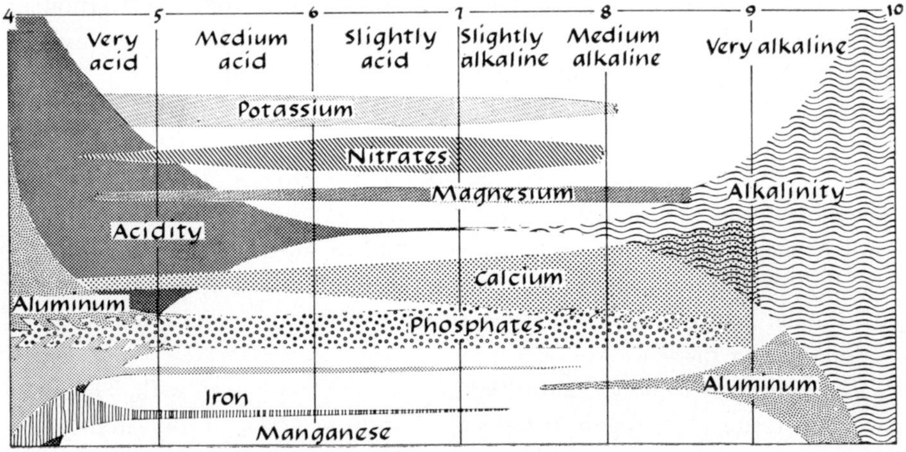

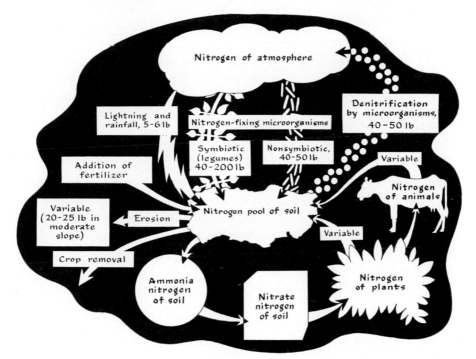

Fig. 4-15 *The nitrogen cycle. Nitrogen removal by crops must be compensated for by nitrogen addition.*

[Adapted from Bonner and Galston, *Principles of Plant Physiology*, Freeman, San Francisco, 1952.]

NITROGEN ADDED		NITROGEN REMOVED	
METHOD	LB/ACRE	METHOD	LB/ACRE
plant and animal residues	variable	crop harvested	variable
nitrogen fixation		leaching	
symbiotic	40–200	crop rotation	5–10
nonsymbiotic	40–50	bare soil	60–70
lightning and rainfall	5–6	erosion (moderate slope)	20–25
		denitrification	40–50

The transformation of atmospheric nitrogen into forms available to plants, *nitrogen fixation,* is accomplished by certain species of bacteria (Table 4-4). The most efficient of these bacteria are symbiotic; that is, they convert atmospheric nitrogen to combined forms only in association with the roots of legumes. The breakdown of the complex proteins of organic material into

Table 4-4. *Nitrogen-fixing bacteria.*

TYPE	GROUP	REQUIREMENTS
Symbiotic	*Rhizobium*	Carbohydrates, inhibited by nitrates and ammonium
Nonsymbiotic		
Anaerobic	*Clostridium*	Carbohydrates, inhibited by nitrates
Aerobic	*Azotobacter*	Calcium, traces of molybdenum

amino acids is also accomplished largely by bacterial action. But the nitrogen from this process is only available after the death and disintegration of the bacteria involved in this decaying process. Soil organisms have the first call on nutrients. This is especially true for material with a carbon to nitrogen ratio by weight greater than 10:1. The breakdown of amino acids to forms of nitrogen available to plants takes place by transformations referred to as *ammonification* and *nitrification*.

AMMONIFICATION

Amino Acids $\longrightarrow$ NH_4^+ (Ammonium ion)

from protein degredation (many bacteria)

NITRIFICATION

NH_4^+ $\longrightarrow$ NO_2^- (nitrite ion) $\longrightarrow$ NO_3^- (nitrate ion)

Nitrosococcus   *Nitrobacter*

Nitrosomonas

The bacteria involved in nitrification are autotrophic and aerobic; that is, they do not require organic nutrition, but they do require oxygen. Thus, they are greatly affected by soil aeration, temperature, and moisture.

The removal of nitrogen from the soil is partly biological. In addition to its removal by plants (which is permanent when a crop is harvested), certain bacteria convert nitrates back to atmospheric nitrogen. This process of denitrification is an anaerobic process. Thus, loss of proper aeration results in the loss of available nitrogen! Furthermore, nitrates are readily soluble in water and, if they are not utilized by microorganisms or higher plants, are lost by leaching. In summary, the level of available nitrogen is dependent upon the content of organic matter and the microbiological activity of the soil. Consequently the amount of nitrogen available is related to cropping practice. The available soil nitrogen is, of course, greatly affected by the application of fertilizer. Quickly available forms of inorganic nitrogen probably account for most of the nitrogen in intensively cropped soils today.

Phosphorus, unlike nitrogen, is relatively stable in the soil (Fig. 4-16). Phosphorus is "tied up" or fixed in compounds associated with calcium, magnesium, iron, or aluminum. The availability of phosphorus to the plant is low and is primarily related to *p*H.

At very low *p*H (2–5), applied phosphorous is precipitated out of the soil solution as complex aluminum and iron compounds. At high *p*H (7–10) phosphorus becomes fixed in complex calcium compounds. At *p*H 5–7 it is in the form of mono- or dicalcium phosphates and is most available for plant use. The concentration of phosphorus in the soil solution at best is low. In fertile agricultural soils only $\frac{1}{2}$–1 part per million of phosphorus is in solution as compared to 25 parts per million of nitrogen. However, the movement of phosphorus in the soil is low, and leaching is slight.

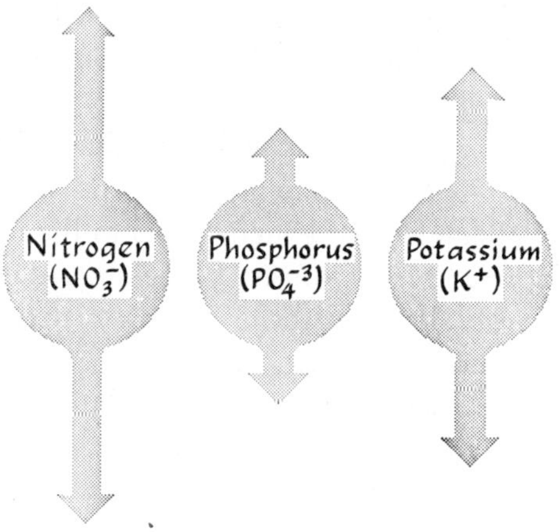

Potassium is available largely as exchangeable ions on the soil colloid. Although potassium is high in mineral soils the low solubility of the primary mineral results in low availability from theis source. There is, however, a continual renewal from the primary mineral to exchangeable form. Potassium tends to be low in organic soil. The leaching of potassium varies greatly, depending upon the type of clay and the amount of organic matter in the soil.

Fig. 4-16. *The relative mobility of nitrogen, phosphorus, and potassium in the soil. The high movement of nitrogen is due to the complete solubility of nitrates in the soil. The movement of phosphorus is regulated by the low solubility of the phosphorus compounds formed. Although the potassium compounds in the soil are soluble, the movement of potassium is controlled by its exchange properties with the colloidal fraction.*

Calcium is seldom deficient as a nutrient. However, its many effects on soil microbial activity, *p*H, and the subsequent absorption of other ions make it a common soil amendment. It is present in the soil both in water-soluble form as an exchangeable cation and in combination with organic compounds.

Magnesium, like calcium, is absorbed as an ion. It occurs in the soil solution in soluble form and as an exchangeable cation. Like calcium, it is sometimes deficient in acid, sandy soils in humid regions.

Sulfur is not present in large amounts in the soil. It is continually leached, but there appears to be a continuous turnover in the soil. It is added by rainfall near industrial regions, where rain absorbs sulfur dioxide from the air. The chief source, however, lies in organic material, thus deficiencies occur in soils that are either low in organic matter or removed from industrial areas. Actual sulfur deficiencies in horticultural crops are rare under present practices. Sulfur is commonly added in association with such compounds as superphosphate.

Manganese is available in the soil in ionic form. However, in alkaline soils high in organic matter and under aerobic conditions, manganese is oxidized from the manganous to the manganic form ($MnO \longrightarrow MnO_2$; that is, from Mn^{++} to Mn^{4+}), rendering it unavailable. On the other hand, soil acidity, low content of organic matter, and anaerobic conditions may result in manganese toxicity.

Boron, zinc, copper, and *molybdenum* are definitely trace elements, since they are required by the plant only in minute amounts. In areas under intensive production, deficiencies are not common or extensive.

Moisture

Water is a constituent of all cells, the amount varying with the tissue involved. It may be as low as 3% in shelled peanut seed, 40% in dormant wood, and up to 95% in succulent fruits, such as the watermelon. Water is the solvent system of the cell and provides a medium for transfer within the plant. It maintains the turgor necessary for the intricacies of transpiration and plant growth. In addition, water is itself required as a nutrient for the production of new compounds. One third of the weight of carbohydrates and proteins is derived from chemically combined water.

The water in a plant is in a continual state of flux. A net loss of water causes growth to stop, and a continued water deficiency causes irreversible alterations of the plant that result in death. This may occur quite rapidly under hot, dry conditions in plants that are not structurally adapted to prevent water loss.

The high percentage of water in plants and its capacity as a nutrient carrier and solvent do not explain the high rate of water utilization by plants. The water requirements of plants, expressed as the number of units of water absorbed per unit of dry matter produced, varies from about 50 in conifers to 2500 in leafy vegetables! Most crop plants range from 300 to 1000. While growing, the plant continuously absorbs water from the soil and gives it off in transpiration. This loss of water is a by-product of carbon fixation. Carbon dioxide, which provides the carbon necessary for growth, enters the plant through the water films surrounding the spongy mesophyll of the leaf. As this film evaporates, it is replenished from the tissues of the plant, which in turn draw water from the vascular system.

The transpirational loss of water by the plant can be considered as an exchange for carbon, and in this sense transpiration is necessary for plant growth. Rapidly growing plants thus require great amounts of water, greatly in excess of the amount found in the plant itself. The rate of water loss depends largely on the temperature, relative humidity, and air movement. Radiation from the sun provides the energy required to change the state of the water from film to vapor. This "boiling off" of water is responsible for the dissipation of a large part of the total energy received by the plant from the sun.

Soil Moisture

The amount of soil moisture that is of benefit to plants has definite limits. Too much water may be as troublesome as not enough. The excess water is not in itself toxic, but rather it is the lack of aeration in waterlogged soils that causes damage. Plants can be grown satisfactorily in water solutions when aeration is provided (Fig. 4-17).

The amount of water in a soil may be expressed in a number of ways. The expression of soil moisture in inches of water per foot of soil is useful for some purposes (1 acre-in. is equivalent to approximately 27,000 gallons). Expressing soil moisture in terms of the *field capacity* of a soil takes into account the physical condition of the soil and has great agricultural significance. The field capacity of a soil is the maximum amount of moisture that

Fig. 4-17. *Effect of aeration on asparagus plants grown in a nutrient solution containing all the essential elements.*

[Adapted from Hoagland and Arnon, Circular 347, California Agr. Exp. Sta., 1950.]

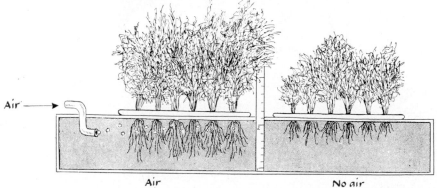

Air ⟶

Air   No air

is retained after surface water is drained and after the water that passes out of the soil by gravity (free water) is removed.

The water content of soils can also be expressed in terms of availability to the plant. The moisture content under which irreversible wilting occurs is known as the *permanent wilting point*. The percentage of water present depends upon the soil but is relatively independent of the test plant. The moisture left in the soil, but which is unavailable to the plant, is known as *hygroscopic water* and *chemically combined water*. The hygroscopic water is held tenaciously by the soil in "atomically" thin films. The amount of hygroscopic water varies with the amount of interfaces present and is therefore highest in clay and organic soils.

The total amount of soil moisture present is not as important as its availability. The *available moisture* is the level present between the permanent wilting point and the field capacity. This water is often referred to as *capillary water*. It is retained in the smaller soil pores, where the capillary forces prevent water drainage, and as films around the soil particles (Fig. 4-18).

Fig. 4-18.   *The classes of soil moisture. All the capillary water is not equally available to plants. As the capillary water is depleted, the tension by which this water is held in the soil increases from 1 atmosphere of pressure at field capacity to about 15 atmospheres at the permanent wilting point. The amount of capillary water present increases with the fineness of the soil pore space.*
[Adapted from Bonner and Galston, *Principles of Plant Physiology*, Freeman, San Francisco, 1952.]

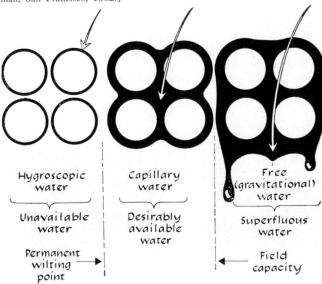

Soils differ in their ability to hold moisture; this ability depends upon their texture (Table 4-5). Although sandy soils afford better drainage and aera-

Table 4-5. *General range of available moisture-holding capacities for normal soil conditions.*

[From Shockley, in *Sprinkler Irrigation Manual*, Wright Rain, Ringwood, England, 1956.]

| | AVAILABLE MOISTURE | |
| | --- | --- |
SOIL TEXTURE	RANGE (IN./FT)	AVERAGE (IN./FT)
Very coarse-textured sands	0.4–0.7	0.5
Coarse-textured sands, fine sands and loamy sands	0.7–1.0	0.8
Moderately coarse-textured sandy loams and fine sandy loams	1.0–1.5	1.2
Medium-textured very fine sandy loams, loam, sandy clay loams, and silt loams	1.5–2.3	1.9
Moderately fine-textured clay loams and silty clay loams	1.7–2.5	2.1
Fine-textured sandy clays, silty clays and clay	1.6–2.5	2.0

tion, they have a lower water-holding capacity than clay soils. The total amount of capillary water can be increased in sandy soils by increasing its content of organic matter. The total amount available to a crop will depend on many factors, among which are the type and depth of soil, the depth of rooting of the crop, the rate of water loss by evaporation and transpiration, temperature, and the rate at which supplemental water is added. In addition, the level of available water itself is a factor. The less the water in a soil, the greater is the tenacity with which the water is held. This tenacity is measured in atmospheres of pressure required to drive off the water. At field capacity, water is held with a force of one atmosphere. At the permanent wilting point water is held with a force of about 15 atmospheres.

The rate of water extraction of soil is a function of root concentration, and therefore decreases with the depth of the root zone. About 40% of the total water is extracted from the upper quarter of the root zone, 30% from the second quarter, 20% from the third quarter, and 10% from the bottom quarter. Under maximum transpiration sufficient water for maximum growth cannot be obtained when the upper quarter of the root zone is depleted.

Water Movement

The movement of water through a soil is related to the amount present. Water applied to a soil moves through the soil only as fast as field capacity is attained (Fig. 4-19). The rate of water movement depends to a great extent on soil texture. Because the pore size is smaller and more tortuous, water moves much slower through heavy clay soils than through loamy or sandy soils.

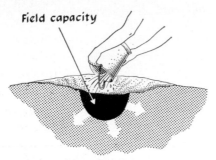

Field capacity

Fig. 4-19. *The rate of movement of water added to the soil is related to the speed at which field capacity is attained.*

The movement of water up through the soil takes place by capillary action. Since this is a surface-tension phenomena, the height that the water will reach is inversely related to the diameter of the tube. Thus, the finer the soil spaces, the greater the distance of capillary movement. The upward rise of capillary water from the water table (the depth at which all the soil is at field capacity) is a factor in the replenishment of water lost to the plant and evaporated from the soil. This evaporative loss of water is restricted to the upper portion of the soil, since it takes more and more pressure to pull the water, depending on the height of the water column. During a period of extended drought, it becomes easy to recognize the shallow-rooted plants.

Radiant Energy

The sun is the primary source of energy available to the earth and its atmosphere. This energy is transferred across 93 million miles of space in the form of radiation. Solar radiation reaches the earth in the form of electromagnetic waves travelling at the speed of 186,000 miles/sec. The energy is described in terms of its wavelength just as sound is described in terms of its pitch. The radiant energy occurring as visible light is but a small fraction of the frequency range of the electromagnetic spectrum (Fig. 4-20).

The amount and quality of the solar energy that any portion of the earth's surface receives is dependent upon its duration and intensity. The seasonal difference in duration of the intercepted radiation is a consequence of the variation in day length and cloud cover. The intensity of the intercepted radiation is related to the angle at which the solar rays penetrate the earth's atmosphere. The water vapor, and to a smaller extent the air and dust of the atmosphere, diffuse, reflect, and absorb this radiant energy. The damaging ultraviolet radiation at the short wavelength end is absorbed by the ozone layer. Because the earth is spherical the rays of the sun falling on the poles are oblique as compared to those falling on the equator. These rays are spread over a larger surface of the earth and pass through a thicker layer of atmosphere. When the sun is directly over the equator its rays must penetrate an air mass at the poles equivalent to 45 air masses at the equator.

Absorption of Solar Radiation

The quantity and quality of radiation depend on the temperature of the radiating body. The higher the temperature, the greater the rate of radiation and the richer the proportion of short wavelength (high frequency) radiations. Thus, the high-temperature solar radiation consists mostly of shortwave radiation in the visible or near visible frequency. This shortwave solar energy is absorbed at the earth's surface, where it is transformed into heat. The earth then becomes a radiating body at a lower temperature (average, 57°F). The earth's radiation is in the form of long waves (low frequency) radiation.

Water vapor, the most significant of the atmosphere's absorbing gases, absorbs only about 14% of the incoming shortwave radiation, but absorbs 85% of the earth's long-wave radiation. This tends to maintain surface temperatures much higher than they otherwise would be. The atmosphere thus

Fig. 4-20. *The electromagnetic spectrum and action spectra of certain plant processes.*

[Adapted from Machlis and Torrey, *Plants in Action*, Freeman, San Francisco, 1959.]

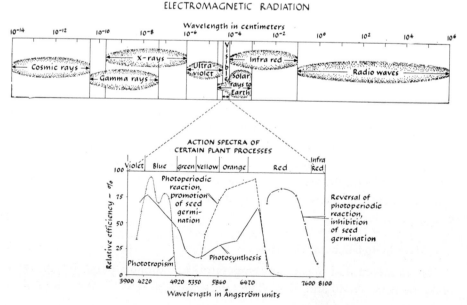

acts as a pane of glass, transparent to the sun's short waves, but opaque to the earth's long waves; hence, the name *greenhouse effect* for this phenomenon (Fig. 4-21). The earth thus receives most of its heat only indirectly from the sun.

Heat Transfer

The transfer of heat energy is accomplished by *radiation, conduction, convection,* and *reflection. Radiation* as described refers to an organized flow of energy through space. It does not travel in the form of heat, for heat involves molecular motion, but in the form of electromagnetic waves. When radiation is absorbed on a surface it usually produces a rise in temperature. In this case, radiation is transformed into heat energy. In *conduction,* the energy flows through the conducting surface from the warmer to the cooler body. The transfer of heat through the soil takes place by conduction. The ability of a substance to conduct heat (*conductivity*) varies with the material, as shown in Table 4-6. The movement of heat by *convection* or circula-

Table 4-6. *Heat conductivity of various substances.*

SUBSTANCE	VALUE (CAL/CM-SEC-°C)
Silver	1.0
Iron	0.1
Water	0.0013
Dry Soil	0.0003
Sawdust	0.0001
Air	0.00005

tion of warmed air or water is related to its change in density as a result of heat. Air near a stone radiating heat warms and becomes less dense than the cooler air farther away and is pushed upwards. Similarly, cool water sinks. Heat, as well as light, is *reflected* from a surface. A sheet of polished metal will reflect both heat and light and will reflect both in the same way. The persistence of snow in mild weather is a result of its high reflective property.

The Plant in Relation to Temperature

The minimum and maximum temperatures to support plant growth generally lie between 40 and 97°F. The temperature at which optimum growth

Fig. 4-21. *The "greenhouse effect" produced by the earth's atmosphere.*
[Adapted from Galston, *Life of the Green Plant,* Prentice-Hall, Englewood Cliffs, 1961.]

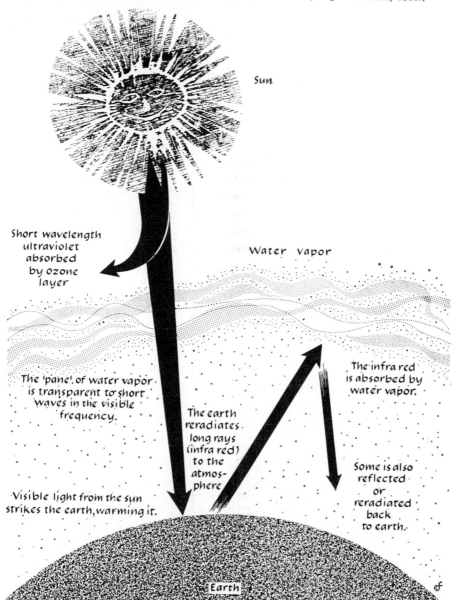

Sun

Short wavelength
ultraviolet
absorbed
by ozone
layer

Water vapor

The 'pane' of water vapor
is transparent to short
waves in the visible
frequency.

The earth
reradiates
long rays
(infra red)
to the
atmos-
phere

The infra red
is absorbed by
water vapor.

Some is also
reflected
or
reradiated
back
to earth.

Visible light from the sun
strikes the earth, warming it.

Earth

occurs varies with the plant and differs with the stage of development (Fig.
4-22). In addition, different parts of the same plant vary as to the minimum
temperature that they will withstand. Roots of cold-acclimated plants are
more sensitive to low temperature than stems; flower buds are more tender
than leaf buds.

A number of growth processes show a quantitative relationship to temperature. Among these are respiration, part of the photosynthetic reaction,
and various maturation and ripening phenomena. In addition, plant processes such as dormancy, flowering, and fruit set are temperature critical. The
optimum temperature for plant growth depends, then, on the species and
variety, and on the particular physiological stage of the growth process.
Plants grown under uniform, constant temperature do not grow or produce
fruit as rapidly as do plants grown under alternating night and day temperatures. Most plants require a lower night than day temperature. Some
plants require cold temperature to complete their annual or life cycle. This
is discussed more fully in the following chapter.

There are various types of injury associated with extremes in temperature.
Temperatures close to or below the freezing point of water may cause permanent damage, resulting in death. This is dramatically seen after the first
fall freeze, when most herbaceous plants are killed. Cold injury brought
about by freezing is thought to be due to the formation of ice crystals, which
cause mechanical injury to the cell. Another possibility is that such crystal
formation causes desiccation of the cell. The withdrawal of water from the
cells results in protein precipitation. Cold injury during the winter is also

Fig. 4-22. *Optimum night temperature varies with the species and with the
stage of development in the life cycle.*

[Adapted from F. W. Went.]

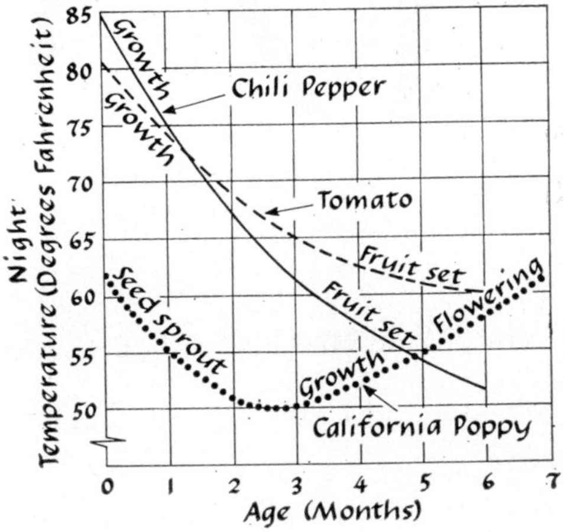

associated with tissue desiccation brought about by decreased water absorption from the roots. This type of *winter kill* is a common injury to evergreens where transpiration during the winter is a contributing factor. Evergreens may be protected from winter kill by covering them with plastic, which cuts down on transpirational losses.

Some plants are found to be sensitive to temperatures slightly above freezing. This *chilling injury* is noted in peanut, velvet bean, sweet potato, and in the cucurbits.

Plants that are resistant to cold injury (*hardy* plants), as compared to those susceptible to cold injury (*tender* plants), appear to have an increased proportion of unfreezable (*bound*) water in the cells, an accumulation of soluble carbohydrates, and a lower water content. The free water associated with succulent tissue freezes at 32°F. The *osmotically held* water, caused by an increase in sugar-like substances, has a lowered freezing point depending on the concentration and acts as an "antifreeze." The "bound," or colloidally held, water freezes at a still lower temperature. The winter injury that occurs in grapes after an unusually heavy production (often due to inadequate pruning) is associated with a low sugar content of the tissues, which renders them susceptible to cold injury. Thus, differences in cold resistance of particular plants may be induced by methods which tend to increase sugar accumulation. This will be discussed under hardening in Chapter 7. The variation in cold resistance among plant species is probably related to their ability to bind water in nonfreezable forms. The greater the proportion of bound water, the hardier the plant.

The "heaving" of soil due to alternate freezing and thawing injures the plant by the mechanical ripping of the root system. This may be overcome by procedures such as mulching that tend to prevent premature thawing. A substantial portion of freezing injury is associated with unseasonably high temperatures in the winter. In temperate regions unseasonably high temperatures in late winter often initiate growth prematurely. This renders the plant extremely susceptible to subsequent cold weather. This is often noticed on the southern side of trees (in the Northern Hemisphere), where insolation is greatest. Similarly, the early blooming of fruit trees brought about by unseasonable warm weather is feared because of the increased danger of frost injury to flower buds.

High-temperature injury is often related to desiccation. The "burning up" of plants during unusually hot weather is usually a result of excessive water loss in transpiration as compared with water uptake. This is very noticeable when unusually warm, dry, windy weather occurs after transplanting. Soil surface temperatures under these conditions may be extremely high and interfere with root growth. Young transplants often "burn off" at the soil line. Extremely high air temperatures (115–130°F) may be lethal to the plant as a result of the coagulation of protein. The cessation of growth under hot weather is a reflection of an altered metabolic balance. When the respiration rate increases faster than that of photosynthesis, there will be a resultant depletion of food reserves. As in all biologic processes the critical temperatures vary with the material.

The Plant in Relation to Light

Plants grown in the absence of light but provided with a source of food from storage organs (for example, seed, tuber, or bulb) are yellow, and have

Fig. 4-23. *Etiolated (left) and light-grown (right) bean seedlings.*
[Adapted from Bonner and Galston, *Principles of Plant Physiology*, Freeman, San Francisco, 1952.]

greatly elongated, spindly stems (Fig. 4-23). The same plants, when provided with light, develop green color associated with the development of chlorophyll and the initiation of photosynthesis, and assume the normal stem structure. The morphological expression of light deficiency is called *etiolation,* and is related to the effects of light on auxin distribution and synthesis. The dependence of chlorophyll development on light is utilized in the production of *blanched,* or white, asparagus and celery. In Europe there is a preference for white asparagus and celery. Asparagus is dug instead of cut to obtain blanched spears. Blanched celery is produced by mounding the base of the growing plant with some opaque material such as soil or paper. In the United States, self blanching types are grown that are naturally somewhat lighter and produce a thicker stalk, which shades the inner portion of the plant.

Some anthocyanin pigments also require light to develop. The Sinkuro variety of eggplant only develops purple pigment in the presence of light, and the fruit is white under the calyx. Similarly, apples produced on the inside of the tree do not develop as intense a pigmentation as do those on the outside. Apple fruits can be made to develop slogans with the use of a tape containing a transparent and opaque surface (Fig. 4-24).

Light influences a great many other plant responses. These include ger-

Fig. 4-24. *Light influences the formation of some anthocyanin pigments. These labeled apples were produced by affixing the tapes shown below to the fruits on the tree before the natural formation of pigment.*
[Courtesy Purdue Univ.]

mination, tuber and bulb formation, flowering, and sex evpression. This effect of light on plant development is often related to the length of the light and dark periods (*photoperiod*). These aspects of light will be discussed in the following chapter.

Quality and Quantity of Light

The radiant energy required by plants is confined almost entirely to the visible spectrum. Growth is optimum when the entire range of the visible spectrum (that is, white light, sunlight) is provided. Light energy, described in terms of particles called *photons* (quanta), is inversely proportional to the wavelength. Thus, visible light of different wavelengths, which we see as different colors, provides different energy requirements. The light reactions of the plant (photosynthesis, phototropism, photoperiodism) are based on photochemical reactions carried on by specific pigment systems that respond to various wavelengths (Fig. 4-20). For example, the portion of the visible spectrum that results in phototropism are the violet, blue, and green regions of the spectrum. The red portion, most effective in photosynthesis, is ineffective in phototropism. The pigments that absorb wavelengths effective in phototropism are yellow, perhaps carotenoids or flavanoids. It is intriguing to consider that these pigments manufactured by plants provide animals with compounds involved in their photoreceptive reactions (vision)!

Light quantity or intensity refers to the concentration of light waves. It can be expressed in terms of electrical energy (watts) per unit area or in terms of luminosity (footcandles). Since these units are used to express intensity, they are not completely satisfactory when considering plant irradiation. The footcandle, a measurement of luminosity, is the intensity of radiation based on the sensitivity of the human eye. Thus, the same energy at a wavelength of 5550 Å will have a higher footcandle rating than light with a wavelength of 6500 Å because the eye is less sensitive to this part of the spectrum. The use of radiation intensity in terms of power units, such as watts per unit area, also does not take into account the spectral composition. This must be kept in mind when interpreting intensity requirements. The range in light intensity over the earth is enormous. Light intensity at full sun is a billion times brighter than starlight. The intensity of various light conditions expressed as footcandles is shown in Table 4-7. The different light reactions of the plant vary in their requirements with respect to both the intensity required to initiate the reaction and the effect of the intensity on the rate of the reaction.

Table 4-7. *Intensity values in footcandles for various light conditions and plant photoreactions.*

LIGHT CONDITION OR PHOTOREACTION	FOOTCANDLES
Starlight	0.0001
Moonlight	0.02
Photoperiodic induction (cocklebur)	0.3
Indoors near window	100
Overcast weather	1000
Maximum photosynthesis (individual leaf)	1200
Direct sunlight	10,000

Light and Photosynthesis

The rate of photosynthesis is related to the availability of the raw materials, water and carbon dioxide, and to the energy available in the form of light and heat. These simple requirements are abundantly provided in the temperate and tropical areas of the earth and sea.

The photosynthetic rate is proportional to the intensity of light up to about 1200 footcandles. Chlorophyll thus is able to efficiently use only a portion of the incident light energy on a sunny day, which may be over 10,000 footcandles. However, due to shading effects, a maximum amount of light intensity is required to provide all of the leaves in a plant with optimum amounts of energy. The rate of photosynthesis is sharply curtailed during low light intensity with cloudy weather. Not all plants, however, respond to high light intensity. Some require as little as one-tenth of full sunlight. These differences in light intensity requirements enable the classification of plants as sun plants or shade plants.

Only about 1% of the light received by the leaf during sunny days is utilized in photosynthesis. The remainder is reflected, reradiated, transformed into heat, or utilized for transpiration (Fig. 4-25). The energy stored by the plant is represented by all of the past (oil, coal) and present plant growth.

The photosynthetic reaction is specific in its light-quality requirements. Chlorophyll absorbs the red and blue portions of the spectrum, permitting the green light to go through. Thus, chlorophyll appears green. The absorption qualities of the chlorophylls of higher plants show a higher absorption of the red light than the blue.

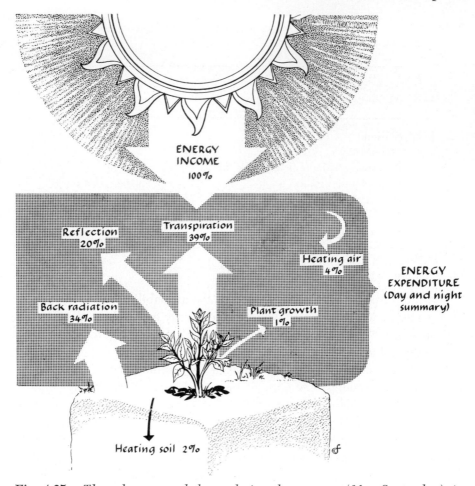

Fig. 4-25. *The solar energy balance during the summer (May–September) in southeast England. The energy expenditure is expressed as the percentage of the total that is sufficient to evaporate 36 in. of water.*

[Adapted from Penman, in *Sprinkler Irrigation Manual,* Wright Rain, Ringwood, England, 1956.]

The intensity and quality of light reaching the plant varies with the season, the latitude, and the weather conditions affecting the water vapor in the atmosphere. Thus, during the winter, light often becomes a limiting factor in greenhouses, although heat is provided through combustion of previously captured energy. The Northern areas, which are in almost continuous light during part of the year, provide abundant photosynthesis where temperature is not limiting. The enormous size of the potatoes and cabbages produced in Alaska is due to the abundant light energy provided in this region during the summer.

Air

Air is not usually considered a limiting factor in plant growth. There is relatively little variation in the composition of the atmosphere, and air movement tends to keep these gases in equilibrium. Under optimum growing conditions and high light intensities, carbon dioxide availability may limit photosynthesis. However, the tremendous volume of air (0.03% CO_2) normally provides sufficient carbon dioxide in relation to the available light. Furthermore, there is a limit to the amount of carbon dioxide a plant will tolerate. The addition of carbon dioxide to the air is being tried in carnation greenhouses in Colorado, where the natural light intensity is very high. The use of artificially applied carbon dioxide would be necessary for optimum production of algae, which has been suggested as a means of providing food for an overcrowded world.

The quality of the air is becoming an important factor in plant growth. This is especially true for horticultural operations which are close to urban and industrial areas. For example, smog, which contains partially oxidized hydrocarbons, can be injurious to plants as well as to people.

The availability of oxygen in the soil is often a critical factor in plant growth. Poorly aerated soils have a low oxygen and high carbon dioxide content. This reduces respiration in roots and limits root growth, resulting in a reduction of water and nutrient uptake by limiting the absorption surface and impeding the active absorption process. High carbon dioxide levels also have a toxic effect to roots. The death of large trees when their roots are covered over with extra soil is a dramatic example of the effects of an altered oxygen to carbon dioxide ratio in the soil.

Aquatic plants, or plants adapted to marshy or boggy conditions, may be structurally altered such that aeration of the roots is supplied from leaves. Other hydrophobes apparently have adapted in some manner to low oxygen concentrations. Oxygen and carbon dioxide levels have a great effect on fruit and plant storage. This topic will be discussed in Chapters 5 and 11.

Selected References

Bonner, J. and Galston, A. W. *Principles of Plant Physiology.* Freeman, San Francisco. 1952. (An outstanding, modern approach.)

Levitt, J. *The Hardiness of Plants.* Academic, New York. 1956. (An excellent review of cold-, heat-, and drought-hardiness.)

Lyon, T. L., Buckman, H. O., and Brady, N. C. *The Nature and Properties of Soils*. 6th ed. Macmillan, New York. 1960. (A basic text on agricultural soils.)

Meyer, B. S. and Anderson, D. B. *Plant Physiology*. Van Nostrand, New York. 1952. (A valuable reference work.)

Sinnott, E. W. *Plant Morphogenesis*. McGraw-Hill, New York. 1960. (An analysis of morphological change associated with plant development and differentiation.)

CHAPTER 5

Plant Development

By CHARLES E. HESS, *Purdue University*

After a consideration of the plant in terms of physiological processes, it is now possible to consider the organism as an integrated mechanism capable of an irrevocable increase in size and complexity. Starting with the germination of a seed, the developmental history of a plant will be traced through juvenility, maturity, flowering, and fruiting. At fruiting the essential cycle of the plant growth is completed. In perennials, the plant is ready to recycle after a period of quiescence. In annuals, fruiting is a signal to the organism to enter the final phases of plant growth—senescence and death (Fig. 5-1).

VEGETATIVE PHYSIOLOGY

Germination

Germination includes all the sequential steps from the time the seed imbibes water until the seedling is self sustaining (Fig. 5-2). In the simplest concept, germination involves the enzymatic conversion of complex reserve substances to simple soluble substances that are readily translocated to the embryonic plant. Here some substances are oxidized through respiration, and release energy; others are utilized in synthesis. Externally, the seed must be provided with ample supplies of oxygen to satisfy the respiratory requirements and of water to provide a medium for enzymatic activity and synthesis. The temperature of the environment must be such that the biochemical processes of degradation and synthesis can operate. Although light is not usually required, in some plants (for example, lettuce) it can either trigger or inhibit the germination process.

127

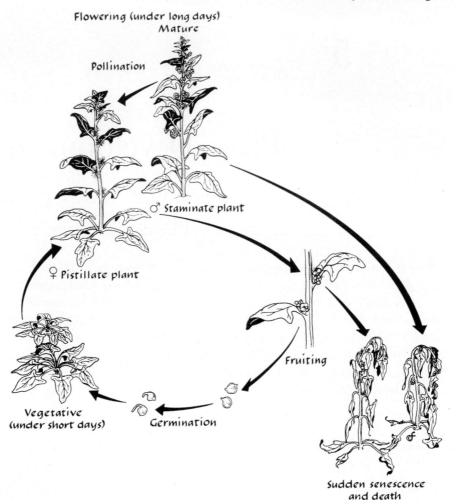

Fig. 5-1A. *Developmental history of a herbaceous annual (spinach). The seed of spinach quickly germinates under proper environmental conditions for growth. If the seedling is grown under short days it forms a distinct vegetative stage (rosette). Under long days, the stem elongates to form a seedstalk and initiates flowers. Since spinach is normally dioecious, staminate and pistillate flowers form on separate plants. Soon after the staminate plants flower, and soon after the pistillate plants fruit, they undergo rapid senescence and die.*

Seed Dormancy

Seed that is viable and yet fails to germinate in the presence of favorable environmental conditions is said to be dormant. The cause of dormancy may be *physical* or *physiological*.

Physical dormancy takes the form of hard, impervious seed coats, which provide a barrier to the entrance of water and, in some plants, oxygen. The legume family provides the greatest number of examples of this type of dormancy. Under natural conditions these seeds do not germinate until soil microorganisms or weathering have sufficiently weakened the seed coat to permit the entrance of water. Thus germination may require a number of years rather than only one season. In horticultural practice, seeds having an

Fig. 5-1B. *Developmental history of a woody perennial (peach). The peach seed germinates only after a period of cold treatment. The juvenile stage lasts about 2–3 years. The yearly cycles must be interrupted by a period of cold. Usually flower buds are initiated in the third or fourth year and open in the following spring. The plant may live for 50–60 years, and undergoes a very gradual deterioration. However, the plant may be rejuvenated from buds close to the base of the tree. If vegetative growth is continually budded onto new rootstocks the "original" plant may remain, in effect, immortal.*

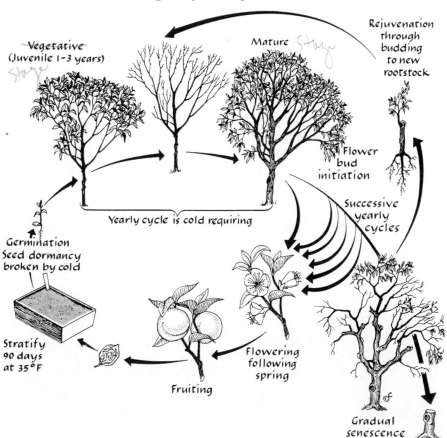

Vegetative
(Juvenile 1–3 years)

Mature Stage

Rejuvenation through budding to new rootstock

Flower bud initiation

Successive yearly cycles

Yearly cycle is cold requiring

Germination
Seed dormancy
broken by cold

Stratify
90 days
at 35°F

Flowering
following
spring

Fruiting

Gradual
senescence

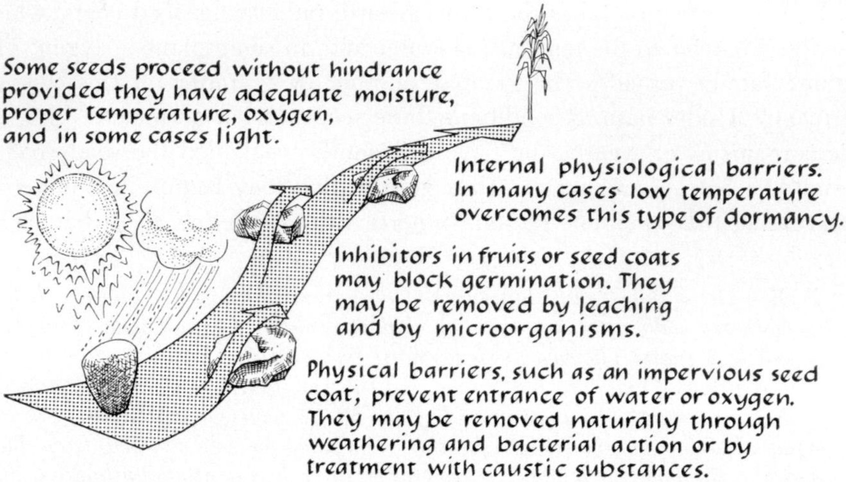

Some seeds proceed without hindrance provided they have adequate moisture, proper temperature, oxygen, and in some cases light.

Internal physiological barriers. In many cases low temperature overcomes this type of dormancy.

Inhibitors in fruits or seed coats may block germination. They may be removed by leaching and by microorganisms.

Physical barriers, such as an impervious seed coat, prevent entrance of water or oxygen. They may be removed naturally through weathering and bacterial action or by treatment with caustic substances.

Fig. 5-2. *Germination is the route from seed to seedling. Barriers to germination (dormancy) may prevent its occurrence even though favorable environmental conditions for growth are present.*

impervious coat are scarified or artificially worn or weakened in order that germination can take place uniformly and without delay (see Chapter 9).

Physiological dormancy may be caused by inhibitors—substances that block the germination process. They may be present in the flesh of the fruit, in the seed coat, or even in the endosperm of the seed. Examples of dormancy caused by inhibitors are quite common in horticultural crops. Germination of seed within a tomato is a rare occurrence, yet as soon as the flesh of the tomato is removed and the seeds are rinsed, germination takes place without delay. This inhibition of germination is due not to the low pH or high osmotic values of the tomato flesh but to a specific chemical entity. Although the inhibitor in tomato fruit has not been isolated and characterized, there is evidence that it belongs to a group of compounds known as the unsaturated lactones. A naturally occurring member of this group is coumarin.

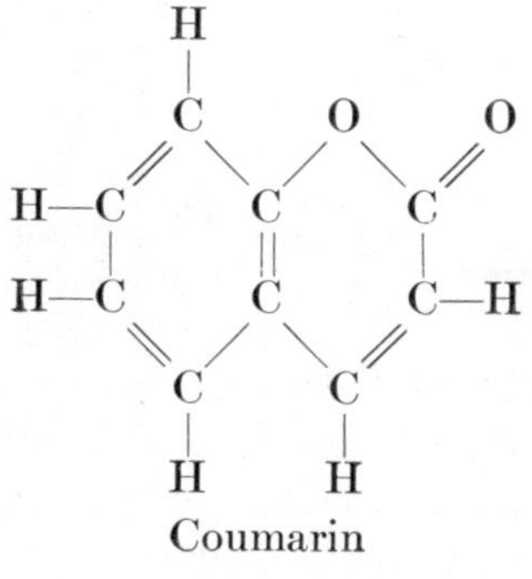

Coumarin

The mode of action of such substances as coumarin consists in blocking or inactivating enzymes essential to the germination process. For example, it has been shown that the activity of α- and β-amylases is blocked in the presence of a germination inhibitor. The amylases are essential for the hydrolysis of starch; that is, the conversion of complex insoluble carbohydrates to simple soluble forms. As with dormancy imposed by the impervious seed coat, inhibitors delay and extend the period during which germination takes place. Leaching by rain and degradation by microorganisms are examples of how germination inhibitors are removed from the fruit and seed coats.

Physiological dormancy may also be due to internal factors such as an immature embryo. In some seeds at the time the fruit is ripe, the embryo consists of only a few undifferentiated cells. The seed of the American holly (*Ilex opaca*) is an example. Therefore, an *afterripening* process must occur during which the embryo differentiates at the expense of the endosperm. In other seeds, particularly in woody species of the temperate zone, the causes of internal dormancy are more complex. In addition to the inhibitors that block germination, a germination stimulator is also required, which is produced as a prerequisite for, or concurrently with, germination. Both the removal of the blocking action of the inhibitor and the production of the stimulatory substance occur during a condition known as cold stratification. The prerequisites for cold stratification are the presence of moisture and a temperature above freezing but below 50°F. A temperature of approximately 41°F appears to be optimum. The fate of the inhibitors during the cold stratification period is not completely clear, but the production of a germination stimulator has been demonstrated.

The morphological site of internal dormancy is primarily in the plumule. In some seeds, however, it is found in the radicle; in others both the plumule and the radicle are dormant. Under such conditions it is often necessary to expose the seed to alternating cold and warm conditions. For example, with *Viburnum* it is necessary to provide a warm temperature (70–80°F) for the radicle to develop. Exposure to low-temperature stratification is then necessary. As a result, the inhibitor content decreases, and growth-promotive substances increase. Germination then takes place when the seeds are returned to warm conditions.

More complex are the germination requirements of the tree peony (*Paeonia suffruticosa*). The seed must first be exposed to low-temperature stratification to break radicle dormancy. Then a warm temperature is required for the radicle to develop. As soon as it emerges, the seed must be returned to low-temperature stratification to break plumule dormancy. After the second stratification period, the seed germinates upon return to warm temperatures.

The fact that the germination of a seed is blocked by one form of dormancy does not exclude the possibility that another form may also be present. Such a condition is called *double dormancy* and is characteristic of several members of the legume family. A well-known example is the redbud (*Cercis canadensis*). Both physical and physiological blocks to germination are present, the former being a seed coat that is impervious to water; the latter, an internal dormancy that is broken by exposure to cold. The sequence of events to which seeds with double dormancy are exposed is very precise. The physical barrier to germination must be removed before any attempt is made to remove the physiological barrier. If a seed coat is impervious, water essential for biochemical reactions cannot enter, and cold treatments to remove inhibitors or to promote the synthesis of a stimulator will not be effective. In nature, seeds with double dormancy often require two years for germination. The first year is required for soil microorganisms and weathering to remove the physical barrier by rendering the seed coat permeable to water and oxygen. The seed is not yet ready to germinate, however, because the internal dormancy has not been broken. During the second winter internal dormancy is broken, and germination occurs the following spring.

Dormancy of seeds is a biological mechanism that provides protection against premature germination when environmental conditions may not be favorable for seedling growth. Thus, in nature, seeds that have a cold-requiring internal dormancy need an exposure to the low-temperature conditions of winter. Seeds from woody plants of the temperate zone will not germinate during the late fall to face the unfavorable growing conditions of winter, but are internally delayed until the following spring.

The germination of seeds of most of our common vegetable crops are often not blocked by either physical or physiological forms of dormancy. In contrast, such plants as the woody ornamentals and many weed species possess, almost without exception, one or more of the major types of dormancy. Thus, it would appear that dormancy mechanisms may be eliminated through an intensive breeding program.

Juvenility

A seed is considered germinated when it has produced a plant that, under proper environmental conditions, is potentially capable of continuous and uninterrupted growth. From the time this stage is reached until the first flower primordium is initiated, the plant is considered to be in a vegetative phase of growth. If during the vegetative phase the plant cannot be made to flower, regardless of the environmental conditions imposed upon it, it is said to be juvenile. The juvenile phase is characterized by the most rapid rate of growth of the overall organism, and in some plants, by distinct morphological and physiological features. The juvenile phase varies in length from one to two months for annuals to a period of few years for the fruit trees. Some plants, such as bamboo, require scores of years.

Although a definitive physiological study is still wanting, some concepts of the nature and causes of the juvenile phase have been obtained by studying plants in which a distinct morphological or physiological change is associated with the transition from juvenility to maturity. Among the morphological features that are associated with juvenility, and which are lost or altered at maturity, are the presence of thorns (pears), leaf lobing (ivy) or the lack of lobes (*Philodendron*), and the angle of the branches with respect to the main axis of the plant (spruce). One physiological feature that is associated with juvenility, and which appears to be applicable for all plants, is the ability of the plants to readily initiate adventitious roots. Another

Fig. 5-3. *Morphological differences between juvenile and mature phases of growth in the English ivy. In the juvenile stage the leaves are lobed, and growth is horizontal. When the plant becomes mature the leaves are entire, and shoots grow upright and bear flowers.*

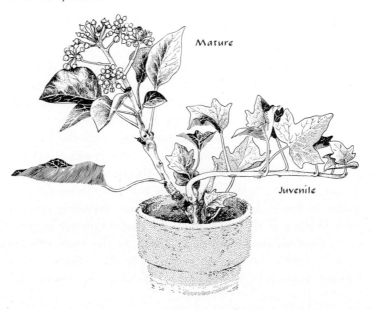

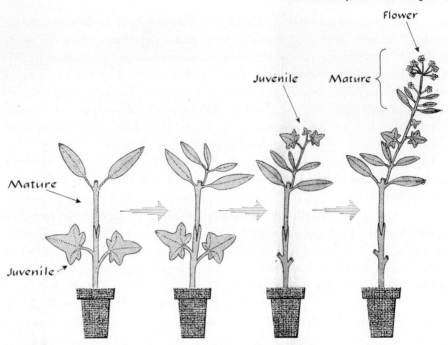

Fig. 5-4. *Induction of juvenility and reversal to the mature state by grafting.*

specific physiological characteristic of juvenility is geotropism, as exemplified by English ivy (*Hedera helix*). In its juvenile phase of growth *Hedera
helix* is a trailing vine, climbing only with support. In the mature stage of
development the new growth is negatively geotropic, growing away from
the ground (Fig. 5-3).

One physiological concept of juvenility postulates that the apical meristem, although constantly laying down new cells, actually goes through an
aging process. This assumes that no correlative growth substances are involved. A more likely hypothesis is that the cause of juvenility is due to the
presence of substances emanating from the seed or from the juvenile root
system. An explanation for the transition from the juvenile to the mature
state is that the "juvenile factor" gradually becomes exhausted as the plant
grows or is rendered ineffective as the distance from the apex to the root
system increases. Some support for this postulation of a disappearing substance is found in grafting experiments involving mature shoots and a
juvenile stock of *Hedera helix*. If the mature branch is grafted on a juvenile
stock, juvenile shoots develop at first on the mature branch. After a few
weeks' growth the juvenility gradually disappears, and the shoot again
becomes mature (Fig. 5-4). This particular experiment lends support to the

"exhaustion" concept, which assumes that the new shoots on the mature scion first utilize the "juvenile factors" in the stock. As growth proceeds the juvenile factors become exhausted, and the mature phase is then resumed. Although there is evidence for the presence of a "juvenile factor," it has not been isolated.

Bud Dormancy

Vegetative growth is not a continuous process but is associated with periods of arrested development. One type of arrested growth is brought about by unfavorable environment. For example, the growth of bluegrass, a common turf species, ceases under moisture stress and top growth may die under continued drought. When conditions are more favorable growth resumes from underground rhizomes. Many plants similarly survive periods of temperature extremes by undergoing a period of quiescence.

Bud dormancy, as is true of seed dormancy, implies that growth is temporarily suspended even though all the external conditions normally required for growth are provided. For example, woody plants of the temperate climates develop vegetative buds at each node throughout the growing season. The lack of growth of these buds after formation is initially an expression of apical dominance controlled by auxin distribution (see Chapter 7). At this time, these buds can be induced to grow by pruning, which removes the growth inhibiting apical meristem. With the onset of autumn, however, the buds develop a true dormant condition and will not grow even if the plant is moved to a warm greenhouse. The degree of dormancy varies not only between species but also between buds on the same plant. The flower buds of many trees such as peach, cherry, and apple have a lower chilling requirement than do the vegetative buds, and therefore flower before the leaves emerge. In *Forsythia* the cold requirement is so low that it may be seen to flower in the fall after a brief period of cold weather.

In woody plants of the temperate climates, the onset of dormancy is conditioned by short day length and low temperature. Bud dormancy in these plants is probably internally regulated by the formation of growth-inhibiting substances. It is broken naturally with cold temperatures. This cold reaction is localized, for if an isolated stem of a dormant plant is cold-treated while the remainder of the plant is kept at a warm temperature, only the dormancy of the treated stem buds are broken.

The survival value of dormancy is clear. A physiological mechanism that prevents growth is a biological check on the perversity of weather. If woody plants lacked internally imposed dormancy they might initiate growth un-

Fig. 5-5. *The effects of insufficient chill in the peach. Left. This peach seedling was photographed at the South Coast Field Station in California on May 31, 1961 when only 300 hours below 45°F had accumulated. The tree has a relatively long chilling requirement and shows severe injury as a result of insufficient chill. The tree has flowered and fruited because flower buds have a lower chill requirement than leaf buds. Right. The same seedling on June 6 at Yucaipa, where the minimum temperatures are significantly lower as a result of the 2500- to 2900-ft elevation, has leafed out normally.*
[Courtesy J. W. Lesley, University of California, Division of Agricultural Sciences.]

der favorable periods in the late fall only to have this succulent growth succumb to succeeding severe weather. After enough cold weather has proceeded to break dormancy, growth is limited only by favorable temperature.

The period of cold treatment required to break dormancy not only varies with the species but is sensitive to selection within species. For example, peaches have been selected for cold requirements that vary from 350 to 1200 hours below 45°F. Low-chill-requiring varieties are selected for southern areas where the periods of cold weather may be brief. If varieties having high chill requirements are grown too far south, they will leaf out poorly or not at all in the spring (Fig. 5-5). It is the cold requiring dormancy brought on by short day length that prevents the production of temperate fruit crops in subtropical regions.

Maturity

When a plant becomes potentially capable of reproduction it is said to be *mature*. The maturity of a plant can be unquestionably ascertained by the development of flowers. In many plants, however, physiological and morphological changes take place before the macroscopic expression of flowering becomes apparent. In English ivy, for example, leaf shape is greatly modified as the mature state is reached. Leaves change from a lobed condition in the juvenile state to an entire leaf in the mature state. The last leaf formed prior to the flower bud is almost reduced to a bract.

When the plant reaches maturity, it is capable of flowering but will not necessarily do so. The environment to which the plant is exposed at the time of maturity determines whether the plant will reach the ultimate in expression of the mature state—the flowering response.

REPRODUCTIVE PHYSIOLOGY

Flowering

Flowering is a term representing a wide spectrum of physiological and morphological events. The first event, the most critical and perhaps the least understood, is the transformation of the vegetative stem primordia into floral primordia. At this time subtle biochemical changes take place that dramatically alter the pattern of differentiation from leaf, bud, and stem tissue to the tissues that make up the reproductive organs—pistil and stamens—and the accessory flower parts—petals and sepals. Among the events that follow initiation are development of the individual floral parts, floral maturation, and anthesis.

Once a meristem has been biochemically signaled to change from the vegetative to the reproductive state, microscopic changes in its configuration become apparent (Fig. 5-6). Growth of the central portion is reduced or

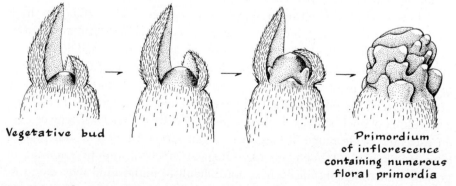

Vegetative bud

Primordium
of inflorescence
containing numerous
floral primordia

Fig. 5-6. *The transition of a vegetative bud to a floral primordia in the cocklebur.*
[From Bonner and Galston, *Principles of Plant Physiology*, Freeman, San Francisco, 1952; after Bonner and Thurlow.]

inhibited, and the meristem becomes flattened In contrast to the conical shape characteristic of the vegetative condition. Next, small protuberances develop in a spiral or whorl arrangement around the meristem. Although this phase of reproductive differentiation is quite similar to vegetative differentiation, a basic difference does exist in that there is no elongation of axis between the successive floral primordia as there is between leaf primordia. In most plants, once the transformation from the vegetative to the reproductive state has been made, the process is irreversible and the floral parts will continue development until *anthesis*—the point at which the flower is fully open—even though the environmental conditions that existed during initiation are changed. By the time anthesis takes place, meiosis has already occurred, and pollen and embryo sac development are complete. At this stage the plant is prepared for the next major step in its development—fruiting.

Carbohydrate:Nitrogen Relationship

Floral initiation has been studied primarily through manipulations of the plant's environment, particularly nutrition, light, and temperature. The rapid advances in the knowledge of the purely nutritive aspects of plant physiology in the latter part of the nineteenth century created an atmosphere in which it was believed that perhaps all aspects of plant growth could be explained or regulated by an alteration or adjustment of a plant's nutrition. This approach was culminated with respect to flower initiation by the concepts of Kraus and Kraybill who proposed, in 1918, that the initiation of flowering was regulated by the *carbohydrate:nitrogen* relationship of the plant. When tomato plants were grown under conditions favoring photosynthesis, and at the same time were supplied with an abundance of nitrogen fertilizers, vegetative growth was lush, and flowering was reduced. But when the nitrogen supply was reduced while photosynthesis was maintained at a high level, vegetative growth was reduced, and flowering was abundant. With the combination of low nitrogen and low photosynthesis both vegetative growth and flowering were reduced. This concept of nutritional control of flowering was readily accepted, and stimulated investigations on the effect of the carbon:nitrogen relationship in other plants. The results of such studies, however, indicated that plants will flower over an extremely wide range of carbon:nitrogen ratios. In view of our present appreciation of the tremendous physiological effects of minute quantities of growth-regulating substances, it is not difficult to understand why the gross ratios of total carbon compounds to total nitrogen compounds does not provide a consistent indication of the physiological condition of the plant.

This is not to say that the nutritional status of a plant lacks importance in regard to flower initiation. The nutritional status can directly influence the degree or quantity of flowering, but can only indirectly affect the qualifying event of initiation. As an example, it is possible by the continued removal of new growth to cause a tomato plant to initiate a flower when only the cotyledons are present (Fig. 5-7). It can be demonstrated that the presence of new growth has an inhibitory effect upon floral initiation. From these results it is tempting to suggest that the reason nitrogen reduces flowering in the tomato is only incidentally associated with the carbohydrate:nitrogen relationship. Perhaps the stimulation of new growth by nitrogen inhibits flower initiation. In support of this concept is the observation that almost any means by which growth can be reduced, such as bending a branch from an upright to a downward position, results in increased floral initiation.

The concept that flower initiation is triggered by minute chemical changes was suggested by Sachs in 1865. But because of the popularity of the nutritional concepts of growth control, Sachs' theories received little support. In 1920, two years after the Kraus and Kraybill hypothesis was published, a discovery was made that caused a revolution in the concepts of flower initiation, and provided direct support to the postulations of Sachs.

Fig. 5-7. *The presence of young leaves on tomato inhibits flower initiation.*
[Adapted from DeZeeuw, *Meded. Landbouwhogesch. Wageningen*, 54(1):1–44, 1954.]

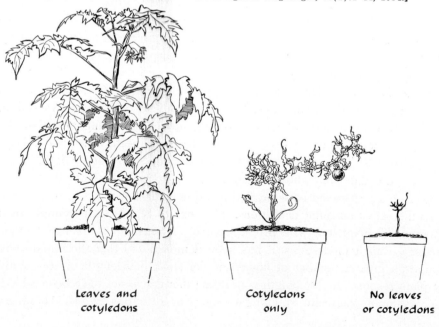

Leaves and
cotyledons

Cotyledons
only

No leaves
or cotyledons

Photoperiodic Effect

The discovery of photoperiodism by W. W. Garner and H. A. Allard, scientists of the United States Department of Agriculture, was made in conjunction with a breeding experiment. A new variety of tobacco was developed that flowered only in the greenhouse during the fall. Since most varieties of tobacco flower in the summer, Garner and Allard attempted to provide the new variety with environmental conditions that would cause it to initiate flowers in the summer in order to make additional crosses. But no matter what was used in an attempt to reduce vegetative growth and initiate flowering—altering the nutrition of the plant, allowing it to become potbound, withholding water—they all failed. An attempt was then made to vary an environmental factor that had not been previously considered, namely, day length. The result was the discovery that by artificially shortening the daily exposure to light during the summer, the new variety of tobacco could be made to flower as profusely as it did in the fall. Garner and Allard's research stimulated a great amount of investigation in the field now called *photoperiodism*—the growth response of a plant to the length of day, or more precisely, the length of the light and dark periods. It was soon found that a great number of plants responded to variations in day length. Some plants responded exactly as did the new variety of tobacco, but others responded in exactly the opposite way; that is, they flowered only when the days were long or were artificially lengthened. As the results of these many investigations accumulated, it became apparent that a majority of plants fell into one of three categories: *short-day*, *long-day*, and *day-neutral* plants. Short-day plants initiate flowers only when the day length is below about 12 hours. These include many of the spring- and fall-flowering plants, such as chrysanthemum, salvia, cosmos, and poinsettia. Long-day plants initiate flowers only in day lengths exceeding 12 hours. They include almost all of the summer-flowering plants of the temperate zones, such as beet, radish, lettuce, spinach, and potato. Day-neutral plants apparently can initiate flowers under any day length. These include the dandelion, buckwheat, and many tropical plants that either flower on a year-round basis or, if they do not, can be shown to be affected by other environmental conditions. The tomato is a typical example of a day-neutral plant, but with proper control of other environmental factors, under certain temperatures, it has been demonstrated that the tomato will initiate a greater number of flowers under short day length. As the study of plant response to day length continues other categories have been added. For example, there are nonobligate long- or short-day plants. These are plants that will flower regardless of the day length but which will flower earlier or more profusely when the day is either long or short. A petunia will flower either under long or short days but will flower better under long days. It is therefore classified as a nonobligate, long-day plant. In still another category are the plants that flower only after an alternation of day lengths and are known as "long-day, short-day plants." Such plants require first an exposure to long days and then to a period of short days.

The discovery of photoperiodism is particularly significant in that it clearly demonstrates the hormonal control of flower initiation. The mature or newly expanded leaf is the perceptor of changes in day length. In some plants the leaves need only to be exposed to one light-dark cycle of the proper day length to cause flower initiation. In the majority of plants several to many cycles are required. Once the leaves have received the photoperiodic message, they produce a substance, or a precursor of a substance, called *florigen*. Unfortunately, however, florigen remains only a name, for it has proven to be one of the most elusive of all plant-growth substances. Its transport from the leaves to the growing point can be demonstrated up and down stems, across graft unions, and from one plant to another, but the substance has not been isolated. A major advance that may lead to the identification of florigen is the recent isolation of the pigment system called *phytochrome* in the leaf, which specifically receives the photoperiodic message. This was discovered by H. A. Borthwick and Sterling B. Hendricks, scientists of the United States Department of Agriculture (USDA), and was first reported in 1959. Three important characteristics of photoperiodism aided in the discovery of phytochrome. First, interruption of the dark period with a small amount of light prevents flowering in short-day plants and permits flowering of long-day plants (Fig. 5-8). Interruption of the light period with brief intervals of darkness has no effect on flowering. The night-interruption reaction is extremely critical in some plants. It can be shown that a very weak light (0.3 foot-candles) is enough to interfere with the dark period in cocklebur. Second, red light is the most effective portion of the light spectrum producing the night interruption effect. Third, light from the far red portion of the spectrum can completely reverse the effects of the red light. Furthermore, the effect of the far red exposure is reversed again by exposure to red light. The direction of this "molecular shift" is determined by the light quality (that is, red or far red) of the final exposure. The reaction is completely reversible over a considerable period of time, as long as the time lapse between exposures does not exceed a specific amount. In summary, phytochrome is a pigment present in small amounts in all plants.

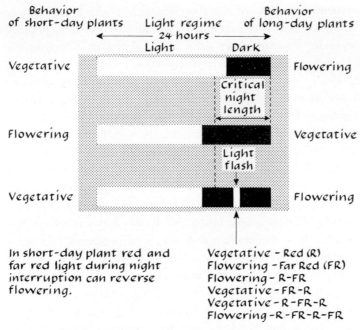

Fig. 5-8. *Photoperiodism refers to the control of flowering by the length of light and dark period. It is the length of the dark period rather than the length of the light period that is the critical factor. Short-day plants flower under periods of long night. Long-day plants flower under periods of short night. The flowering effect can be reversed by substituting red and far red light during night interruption.*

[Adapted from Galston, *The Life of the Green Plant,* Prentice-Hall, Englewood Cliffs, 1961.]

Under short-day conditions an interruption of the dark period with red light causes a molecular shift in phytochrome that brings about flowering in long-day plants and prevents flowering in short-day plants. The reason for this differential response is not known. The action of far red light can reverse the red effect. In addition, this shift is also influenced by the length of the dark period and by temperature. This may explain the light-temperature relationship in photoperiodism and may explain why the light break is most effective at the middle of the dark period.

Phytochrome appears to have many effects upon growth and development. It has been shown to be responsible for the promotion and inhibition of germination in seeds of some plants. In lettuce, seed germination can be inhibited or promoted by alternating red and far red light. Although all seeds contain phytochrome, many plants do not require this "light signal" to germinate.

Although the discovery of phytochrome has made a very significant contribution toward explaining the mechanism of flower initiation, a vast amount of experimentation must be done before the substances specifically involved in the transition of the apical meristems from the vegetative to the flowering condition can be isolated and their mode of action determined.

The emphasis placed upon photoperiodism should not be interpreted as being an indication that it has exclusive control over flowering. Temperature, for example, has both an indirect and a direct effect upon flower initiation. It can influence flowering indirectly by modifying the plant response to a given photoperiod. Thus, a poinsettia will initiate and develop flowers in 65 days when grown under short-day conditions at 70°F. When grown under the same conditions at 60°F, however, 85 days are required before initiation occurs. A more striking example is that of the strawberry. At temperatures above 67°F the June-bearing strawberry behaves as a short-day plant and will not initiate flowers in day lengths longer than 12 hours. At temperatures below 67°F its response is that of a day-neutral plant, and the plant will initiate flowers even in continuous illumination.

Vernalization

The direct effect of temperature upon flowering was recognized over a hundred years ago by the American worker Klippart. He described a process whereby it was possible to "convert" winter wheat into spring wheat (winter wheat is planted in the fall and produces a crop the following year; spring wheat produces a crop in the same year it is planted). The process consisted essentially of reproducing the process that occurs in the field. Klippart partially germinated the winter wheat and then prevented further development by maintaining the seed at a temperature near freezing. The treated seed was planted in the spring, and it produced a crop in the same year. Therefore, the normal biennial habit of the winter wheat had been eliminated, or, more correctly, the cold requirement was satisfied. Klippart's research did not receive much attention until his work was repeated by the controversial Russian agronomist Lysenko. The phenomenon was characterized as being the effect of temperature, during one or more of the developmental phases of plant growth, upon future flowering behavior, and was named *vernalization* by Lysenko. Since Lysenko's work in 1928, a considerable amount of research has been devoted to mechanisms of the cold response. A vernalized plant, that is, a plant which has been given a cold treatment, can be grafted on to a nonvernalized plant, and both will flower. The implication is that a substance has passed from the vernalized plant, across the graft union, to the nonvernalized plant. A similar experiment has been conducted with annual and biennial forms of the same plant, such as henbane. The annual form requires no cold treatment to flower, and when grafted onto the biennial form causes the latter to flower. Apparently the annual form produces the flowering stimulus without a cold treatment. In wheat, this difference between annual (spring) and biennial (winter) forms of wheat has been shown to be controlled by a single gene, which might indicate that a single compound is involved. Although the flower-inducing substance produced during vernalization has not been isolated, a clue to its identity is found in the fact that the cold requirement of some plants can be partially or completely replaced with gibberellic acid.

Further evidence that temperature can have a profound affect upon flowering is provided in the phenomenon of devernalization. Plants exposed to a cold period of the proper temperature ($41°F$) for a sufficient period of time (usually at least six weeks), such that they would normally flower, can be reverted back to their original nonflowering condition by exposure to high temperature. Onion growers take advantage of the devernalization on a commercial scale. Onion sets are stored during the winter at temperatures near freezing to retard spoilage. The onion sets are vernalized at this temperature, and if they were planted directly from cold storage in the spring, the set would quickly flower, and no bulb would be formed. Therefore, the onion sets are exposed to temperatures above $80°$ for 2–3 weeks before planting. The sets, now being devernalized, will not flower but will form bulbs.

Although photoperiodism and vernalization appear to have many similarities, and are definitely interrelated, the stimuli produced in the two responses to environment do not seem to be identical. Evidence for this supposition is taken from experiments in which it is possible to separate the effect of vernalization from those of photoperiodism. For example, most biennial plants when supplied the required exposure to low temperature still will not flower unless they are placed under the proper day length. Similarly, where gibberellins replace the cold requirement, flower initiation will not occur unless the day length is correct.

In addition to these temperature effects it has been shown that the alternation of warm and cool temperatures also influences flowering. This is the phenomenon of *thermal periodicity*. The classic example is the tomato, which will initiate more flowers when grown at a cycle of $80°F$ during the day and 63–68°F during the night than when grown at higher or lower night temperatures. This phenomena has been utilized in greenhouse tomato culture.

Moisture Effects

Moisture is another environmental factor which may influence flower initiation. For example, if *Rhododendrons* are subjected to a period of rainy weather during the fall, which is when this plant normally initiates flower buds, most of the buds will be vegetative. Many other woody plants respond similarly. It can be regularly observed that flowering in the spring is much more abundant after a dry summer and/or fall than after a wet summer and fall. Those who emphasize the nutritional role in flower initiation interpret this effect of moisture as being due to a favorable carbohydrate:nitrogen relationship. In rainy weather, the production of carbohydrates is reduced to a level that is too low to provide the balance necessary for flowering. As pointed out before, however, this interpretation appears to be an oversimplification of a rather complex problem.

Fig. 5-9. *The crocus flowers in the early spring from buds initiated the previous summer.*
[Photograph by J. C. Allen & Son.]

Time of Flower Initiation

The time at which the initiation of flowers takes place is of particular importance to the horticulturalist. Many perennial plants, both woody and herbaceous, initiate flower primordia from several to many months before flowering (Fig. 5-9). In the apple, for example, flower buds are initiated from June to August, depending upon the variety. Flowering occurs during the following spring. In June-bearing strawberries the flowers are initiated in August and September, when the days become short. Attempts to obtain two crops from plants that normally produce one have been made in Holland. The plants are subjected to short day length immediately after the first crop is harvested rather than waiting for it to occur naturally in late summer or fall.

Sex Expression

The environment, besides having a profound influence upon flower initiation, can also influence the subsequent differentiation of the flower. This phenomenon is best seen in sex expression. In the normal sequence of events, the first flowers produced in the cucurbits are male. (Fig. 5-10). As growth continues there is an alternation of male and female flowers; eventually only female flowers are initiated. If the plants are grown under long-day conditions and cool temperatures there is an increase in the ratio of female to male flowers. The effect of nutrition, photoperiod, and temperature has been demonstrated to affect sex expression in many plants.

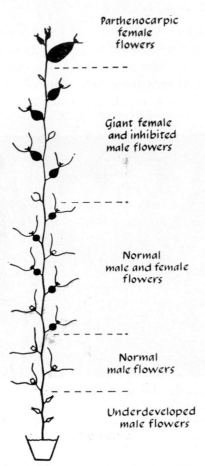

Parthenocarpic
female
flowers

Giant female
and inhibited
male flowers

Normal
male and female
flowers

Normal
male flowers

Underdeveloped
male flowers

Fig. 5-10. *The normal sequential development of male and female flowers on the acorn squash.*

[Adapted from Nitsch, Kurtz, Liverman, and Went *Am. J. Botany,* **39**:32–43, 1952.]

Fruit Development

Fruit development can be conveniently divided into four phases: (1) initiation of the fruit tissues, (2) prepollination development, (3) postpollination growth, and (4) ripening, maturation, and senescence. The origin of the fruit is found in the initiation of the floral primordia, which usually develops concomitantly with the flower. The increase in fruit size in the prepollination phase of development is primarily the result of cell division. After pollination, cell enlargement is responsible for the major portion of size increase. However, in some large-fruited plants (for example, watermelon and squash) cell division continues for some time after pollination, the final size being a consequence of both an increase in cell number and in cell size. The stimuli and nutrients for prepollination growth are supplied primarily by the main body of the plant. In plants having perfect flowers the stamen primordia are often differentiated before the ovary primordium, and have been shown to be a source of growth stimulus. Surgical removal of the immature stamens in the flower bud adversely affects the growth of the ovary if the operation is performed at an early stage of development. Extraction of the unripe anthers reveals the presence of large amounts of auxin.

Pollination

One of the most critical points in the growth and development of a fruit is pollination. Pollination has at least two separate and independent functions. The first is the initiation of the physiological processes which culminate in "fruit set" or, more precisely, in inhibition of fruit or flower abscission. The second function of pollination is to provide the male gamete for fertilization. That these two functions are indeed separate can be demonstrated by the use of dead pollen. In the orchid the use of dead pollen results in fruit set and some growth, but fertilization is not possible. A more precise demonstration of the multiphase function of pollen is the use of a synthetic auxin (Fig. 5-11). Here again fruit set is obtained. The fact that water extracts of pollen are also effective in inducing fruit set has led to the postulation that the pollen contains an auxin. But the minute

Fig. 5-11. *Other than providing the male gametes, pollination prevents abscission of the flower. This role of the pollen may be replaced by the application of auxin.*

[From Bonner and Galston, *Principles of Plant Physiology*, Freeman, San Francisco, 1952; after Avery and Johnson.]

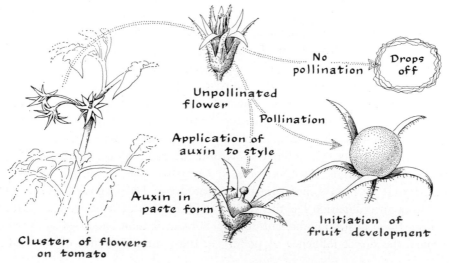

amount of auxin present in the pollen that lands on a stigma usually cannot account for the auxin response obtained. Instead it seems that the pollen contributes either an enzyme that converts auxin precursors present in the stigma to auxin or provides a synergist that renders effective the auxin already present.

Even though pollination takes place, and fruit set is obtained, fertilization is not absolutely assured. Sometimes pollen does not germinate, or if it does, the pollen tube may burst in the style. The germination of pollen is dependent upon the presence of a medium of the proper osmotic concentration (as shown by the effect of various sugar concentrations upon germination) and is stimulated by the presence of certain inorganic substances such as manganese sulfate, calcium, and boron. In the lily it has been shown that the highest concentration of boron occurs in the style and stigma.

In addition to the presence of organic and inorganic substances present in and on the stigma, which stimulate germination, there is also evidence for the existence of substances that chemically attract the growth of the pollen tube. If, for example, a slice of lily stigma is placed on an agar medium containing sucrose and boron, and is surrounded by a ring of pollen placed at a distance from the stigma, all the pollen tubes will grow in the direction of the stigma.

If the growth of the pollen tube is very slow the style, or even the entire flower, may absciss. This may be artificially prevented, however, by the application of auxins such as α-naphthalene acetamide. This technique is particularly valuable to plant breeders, who through the use of auxins are now able to obtain seed from strains of petunia, cabbage, and marigold, which otherwise were considered self sterile. When fruit set and growth are obtained either by pollination or by the application of an auxin, but fertilization does not take place, the fruit is said to be "parthenocarpic." Although no seeds are present, seedlike structures may develop, as in the case in some seedless varieties of holly, oranges, and grapes.

The effect of pollination on fruit set and the influence of the resultant seed on fruit growth make pollination a crucial phase in the production of many fruit crops. For example, in apple and pear, where genetic incompatibility prevents self pollination within the same clone, more than one pollen-fertile variety must be present to assure pollination. As pollen is transferred by insects, bees are often reared for this purpose (Fig. 5-12).

Although pollination has the two major functions of fruit set and fertilization, there is still another interesting but uncommon effect called "*metaxenia*," the direct influence of pollen on the maternal tissues of the fruit.

Fig. 5-12. *The effect of pollination on fruit set and the influence of the resultant seed on fruit growth make pollination a crucial phase in the production of many crops grown for their fruits. For example, in apple and pear, where genetic incompatibility prevents self-pollination within the same clone, more than one pollen-fertile variety must be present to assure pollination. Since pollen is transferred by insects, bees are often reared for this purpose.*
[Photographs by J. C. Allen & Son.]

In the date palm, a dioecious plant, the pollen affects, in addition to fruit set and pollination, the size of the fruit and date of ripening. This influence of the pollen variety can be demonstrated by using one strain of pollen to fertilize a number of female inflorescences of different date varieties. This effect is in contrast to the direct effect of pollen on embryonic or endosperm tissue, referred to as *xenia*. The different colored kernels of Indian corn are a good example of xenia.

Post Fertilization Development

After fertilization, the plant enters into a phase of physiological activity that is second in intensity only to germination. The developing fruit no longer depends primarily upon the parent plant for a source of growth stimuli but are instead received from developing seed within the fruit. The role of the seed can be empirically demonstrated by observing that misshapen fruits result from uneven distribution of seeds. In many fruits direct correlation exists between either weight or length and seed number. This effect of the seed on fruit development is mediated through chemical substances. For example, extracts of immature seeds can stimulate growth of unpollinated tomatoes. Furthermore, it is possible to correlate various physiological events in the development of a fruit with the presence of growth substances. It has been demonstrated that the auxin levels reach a low at the time of flower drop, and particularly during the natural abscission of partially developed fruit that occurs when a heavy crop is obtained in fruit trees, known in horticultural terminology as the "June drop." The relationship between natural auxin level and fruit development is shown in Fig. 5-13. The growth of the strawberry receptacle also has been

Fig. 5-13. *The relationship of internal auxin levels and fruit drop in the apple.*

[Adapted from Luckwill, *J. Hort. Sci.*, 28:14–24, 1953.]

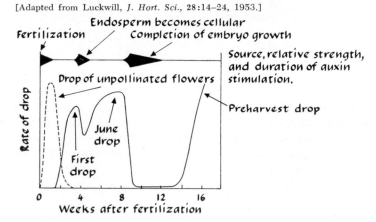

Growth of receptacle
induced by one
achene

Growth of receptacle
induced by three
achenes

Normal growth of
receptacle induced
by many achenes

Fig. 5-14. *Developing seeds are a source of stimulus for fruit growth. In the strawberry, when all the achenes except one are removed, only the receptacle tissue directly under the achene will enlarge. If additional achenes remain, additional areas of the receptacle will develop. The stimulus from the seeds can be replaced in part by the application of auxin.*

[From Bonner and Galston, *Principles of Plant Physiology*, Freeman, San Francisco, 1952; after Nitsch.]

prevented by removal of the achenes—one-seeded fruits. If one or two achenes were left intact the receptacle would grow only in the area directly under the achene (Fig. 5-14). The achenes were extracted and found to contain high levels of auxin, whereas the receptacle tissue was comparatively low in auxin content. Finally, the addition of an auxin in the form of indoleacetic acid (IAA) dramatically stimulated the growth of an acheneless receptacle. Indoleacetic acid has been demonstrated to be at very high levels in immature corn kernels. More recent studies indicate that there are present in the developing seeds many growth-promoting substances that stimulate fruit growth, such as several auxins, gibberellin-like compounds, and substances capable of stimulating cell division. The embryo and the endosperm appear to be the primary sources of the growth substances.

Nutrition and Fruit Growth

Although the control center of fruit growth is located in the seed, the raw materials for fruit development are supplied by the plant. Thus, the nutrition and moisture availability of the plant directly affect fruit size. It has been calculated that at least 40 leaves on a mature apple tree are required to support the growth of one apple. If the forty to one ratio is substantially reduced by an abnormally high fruit set, the quality and size of the individual fruits is greatly reduced. Therefore, it is now a common orchard practice to artificially reduce the number of fruit. This is known as *fruit thinning*, and will be discussed in Chapters 7 and 8.

Ripening

A final, dramatic physiological event marks the end of maturation and the beginning of senescence of the fruit. This is the *climacteric*. It is characterized by a marked and sudden rise in the respiration of a fruit prior to senescence, and takes place without the influence of external agents. The respiration rate then returns to a level equal to or below that which existed prior to the climacteric. The climacteric is associated not only with the quantitative burst in carbon dioxide production but also with qualitative changes related to ripening, such as pigment changes. The transition from green to yellow in certain varieties of apple, pear, and banana takes place during or immediately following the climacteric. The peak of acceptability, or "edible ripeness," of pears coincides with the peak of the climacteric. In apple, banana, and avocado, maximum acceptability is reached immediately after the climacteric. Finally, a marked increase in the susceptibility of fruits to fungal invasion follows the climacteric.

The occurrence and causes of the climacteric are currently under study. Almost all fruits studied exhibit a characteristic rise in respiration after the harvest, with the exception of most citrus fruits. The lemon, when held in an atmosphere containing at least 33% carbon dioxide, will exhibit a climacteric. The degree and duration of the rise varies considerably between species, from a short intense peak for the avocado to a longer, less definite peak for the apple. Explanations for the climacteric rise in respiration are varied. One hypothesis holds that, prior to the climacteric rise, the acidity of the cytoplasm decreases to a critical level, which in turn increases the permeability of the cell membranes. Then, fructose, which previously had been accumulated in the vacuole, can move back into the cytoplasm and provide a substrate for increased respiration.

A second hypothesis involves adenosine diphosphate (ADP) and adenosine triphosphate (ATP), compounds that are related to energy transfer in the cytoplasm. During respiration, a part of the energy released is preserved in the conversion of ADP to ATP; that is, the addition of a phosphate to ADP in the presence of energy results in the formation of a high-energy bond. This bond can later be broken to release energy for use in synthesis. The rate of respiration may be limited by the amount of ADP available for accepting a high-energy phosphate bond. It is postulated, therefore, that during fruit maturation, when there is rapid cell enlargement and a high demand for protein synthesis, there is a shortage of ADP. But as the fruit matures, ADP becomes available, and the respiration rate increases. Evidence for this hypothesis is that the addition of ADP to tissues of immature fruit causes an increase in respiration, but as maturation progresses the response decreases until it is completely lost during the climacteric.

As with any physiological event, temperature has a profound effect upon maturation and the climacteric. For example, a comparison of respiration has been made between apples held at 36°F and apples held at 73°F. The maximum respiratory activity is 5–6 times as high at 73°F as at 36°F, and it takes 25 times as long to reach the climacteric at the lower temperature. However, the total amount of CO_2 liberated during the time between harvest and the end of storage life was approximately the same for both temperatures, equivalent to 16–20% of the reserve carbohydrates initially present in the fruit. In pears a pattern was established similar to that for apples at the two temperature extremes, but the rates of CO_2 evolution were much higher and the storage life much shorter.

SENESCENCE

Senescence refers to the erosive processes that accompany aging prior to death. This process is one of the most baffling and least understood of the developmental processes.

Senescence in plants may be *partial* or *complete*. *Partial* sensecence refers to the deterioration and death of plant organs such as leaves, stems, fruits, and flowers. Examples are the death and abscission of cotyledons in bean plants, the death of two-year-old raspberry canes, or the death of the entire shoot of tulip in the early summer. *Complete* senescence refers to the aging and death of the entire plant except for the seeds. The termination of the life cycle of true annuals and biennials is often sudden and dramatic. After fruiting, whole fields die in a synchronized pattern during the early or middle part of the growing season (for example, spinach, corn). In contrast, the senescence of such perennial plants as the apple or peach appears as a gradual erosion of growth and viability. In addition, perennials can be rejuvenated. Mature apple trees may be revitalized by severe pruning and fertilization or by encouraging the growth of adventitious buds at the base of the tree. The senescence of annual plants can be shown to be relatively irreversible, and is associated with flowering and fruiting. Spinach plants kept vegetative under short days will not senesce. After having been induced to flower they will surely die.

The older concepts explaining the senescence of annual plants are associated with a depletion hypothesis. It is suggested that during flowering

Fig. 5-15. *The separation of bolting and flowering effects on senescence. Treatments from left to right: (1) short day; (2) short day + gibberellic acid; (3) long day; (4) long day + gibberellic acid. Note that the phenomenon of bolting does not lead to senescence unless it is associated with flowering induced by long days.*
[From Janick and Leopold. *Nature*, **192**:887–888, 1961.]

and fruiting essential metabolites are drained from the main plant and accumulate in the fruit and seed. By the time the fruit is mature the plant is depleted to the point that further growth is impossible, and death rapidly follows. It can be shown that the removal of fruits can significantly postpone senescence and death. It has also been observed that the greater the number of flowers or fruits on an individual plant, the more rapid is senescence and death.

However, the depletion concept of senescence is an oversimplification of a complex process. Unpollinated pistillate plants and staminate plants of a dioecious plant such as spinach also senesce. In these plants senescence can be postponed by the removal of developing flowers, but death cannot be averted. Clearly, there is no depletion of the plant to account for this effect. It can further be shown that the seed stalk formation that accompanies flowering is distinct from senescence, since spinach plants induced to bolt through the use of gibberellic acid, but kept vegetative, do not senesce (Fig. 5-15). Apparently, the biological signal that causes an annual plant to senesce and die is associated only with the flowering process and is merely accentuated through fruiting. The relationship between the senescing signal and flowering is not at all clear.

Selected References

Crocker, W. and Barton, L. V. *Physiology of Seeds.* Chronica Botanica Co., Waltham, Mass. 1953. (A comprehensive review.)

Leopold, A. C. Senescence in plant development. *Science*, **134**:1727–1732. 1961. (An interesting discussion of the problem and significance of senescence in plants.)

Murneek, A. E. and Whyte, R. O. *Vernalization and Photoperiod*. Chronica Botanica Co., Waltham, Mass. 1948. (A famous collection of papers on this subject.)

Plant Growth Regulation. Fourth International Conference. Iowa State Press, Iowa. 1961. (An excellent collection of papers. Note especially the paper by P. F. Wareing and T. A. Valliers, which presents a new interpretation of the mechanisms of dormancy in seeds that require cold-stratification.)

Salisbury, F. B. Photoperiodism and the flowering process. *Ann. Rev. Plant Physiol.*, **12**:293–326. 1961. (A recent, well-annotated review.)

Schaffalitzky De Muckadell, M. Juvenile stages in woody plants. *Physiol. Plant.*, **7**:782–796. 1954. (A review article.)

PART II

The Technology
of Horticulture

CHAPTER 6

Controlling the Plant Environment

As man increases his dominion over the earth he must not only satisfy his own narrow limits of survival but must control the environment of his plants. This may involve providing moisture where none may be expected to occur naturally or may require building elaborate structures that literally house plants over their entire productive life. The environmental factors most amenable to modification are soil, light, temperature, and moisture.

Although the modification of the environmental factors affecting plant growth are discussed more or less individually in this chapter, their inter-relationships must be kept in mind. For example, temperature and light interact in their effects on plant growth and development. Thus, temperature must be considered not only in relation to day-night fluctuations but with respect to day length. Similarly, soil fertility and water availability are intimately related. The alteration of one factor very often affects another. For example, the control of temperature in a greenhouse by shading affects light availability. The successful culture of the plant depends on the proper synchronization of these environmental modifications. This chapter involves a discussion of environmental control in relation to plant growth. The control of environment in relation to storage is discussed in Chapter 11.

SOIL MANAGEMENT

The soil provides support for the plant and is the storehouse of plant nutrients and water as well as of oxygen for root growth. The ability of the soil to support plant growth is often referred to as its *productive capacity*. The soil's productive capacity must be considered in terms of fertility and physical condition. It is not enough that the nutrients necessary for growth be contained in the soil; they must be released in a form readily available to the plant. Furthermore, the soil must be conserved; it is a renewable, but not an easily replaceable, natural resource. Soil management is concerned with the sustained use of land and with economic crop production.

Maintenance of Soil Fertility

Soil fertility, the nutrient supplying capacity of the soil, involves the amount and availability of plant nutrients (see Chapter 4). The recognition of soil fertility as a factor in crop response is recorded in ancient Greek writings, as is the supplemental use of manure on soils to improve plant growth. The use of cover crops, the mixing of soils, and the addition of lime and salts to increase the productivity of soils are found in Roman agricultural treatises. Nevertheless, it was not until well into the nineteenth century that the role of inorganic nutrients in soil fertility was understood. The study of soil fertility today is intimately involved with microbiology, chemistry, and physics.

The maintenance of soil fertility is concerned with adjusting the current supply of available nutrients to optimum levels for economic crop production. The inherent fertility of the soil is related to the factors that contributed to its formation, namely, the parent minerals from which the inorganic content of soil was formed, the topography, the climate, the natural vegetation, and time. The fertility of "virgin" soil—soil that has not

Fig. 6-1. *Influence of man on the fertility and organic matter of the soil.*

[Adapted from Jenny, *Factors in Soil Formation,* McGraw-Hill, New York, 1941.]

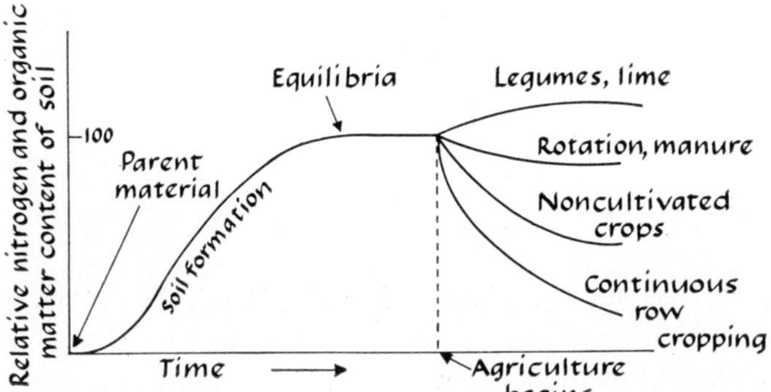

been disturbed by cultivation—reaches an equilibrium such that the nutrients released equal those which are lost. The inherent fertility of virgin soils, which varies greatly, may become depleted when the soil is brought under cultivation (Fig. 6-1). This is brought about by crop removal (Table 6-1) and mineralization of organic matter. In addition, the removal of a

Table 6-1. *Approximate amounts in pounds per acre of soil nutrients removed by fruit and vegetable crops.*
[Data from American Plant Food Council.]

		NUTRIENT (IN ELEMENTAL FORM) REMOVED (LB/ACRE)					
CROP	ACRE YIELD	NITRO- GEN	PHOS- PHORUS	POTAS- SIUM	CAL- CIUM	SUL- FUR	MAG- NESIUM
Apples (fruit)	600 bu	34	3	32	3	12	5
Beans (seed)	40 bu	86	7	28	5	5	4
Cabbage (heads)	20 tons	120	14	133	16	32	5
Onions (bulbs)	1000 bu	154	26	121	18	48	12
Peaches (fruit)	500 bu	30	3	73	3	4	5
Potatoes (tubers)	600 bu	126	19	150	7	14	14
Spinach (tops)	1000 bu	88	10	35	17	8	10
Sweet potatoes (roots)	400 bu	53	7	93	7	9	13
Tomatoes (fruit)	20 tons	80	9	117	16	5	9
Turnips (roots)	500 bu	64	13	72	14	20	5

permanent plant cover, row cropping, and the loss of soil structure by cultivation facilitate erosion by water and wind. The nutrients lost may be replaced by supplemental additives in the form of fertilizers and manures. Nitrogen also may be added by the use of a leguminous crop through the process of nitrogen fixation. Chemical fertilizers are often the most economical source of nitrogen.

Fertilization as a Horticultural Practice

Fertilization refers to the addition of nutrients to the plant. The primary objective of crop fertilization is to achieve an optimum plant response. This may not necessarily be the greatest response; in commercial crop production it is that point at which the value of the increased response is equal to the cost of the additive (Fig. 6-2). Fertilization beyond this level

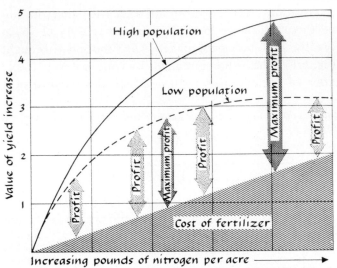

Fig. 6-2. *The yield response diminishes with increasing quantities of fertilizer. The optimum rate is obtained when the value of the yield response is just equal to the last increment of fertilizer added. At this point the profit is maximized. But the response to fertilizer may depend on other factors. As is shown above, increasing the plant population changed the response curve and made a higher rate of nitrogen profitable.*
[Adapted from Soil, USDA Yearbook, 1957.]

must be considered a wasteful practice. Not only is an excess subject to loss by leaching and volatilization but may be destructive to crops as a result of toxic accumulations. Overfertilization of greenhouse soils has become a serious problem.

Materials that supply nutrient elements to plants are known as *fertilizers*. Those that supply nitrogen, phosphorus, and potassium, the major plant nutrients, are called *complete fertilizers*. The grade, or analysis, of these fertilizers is the percent by weight of nitrogen (expressed as elemental N), phosphorus (expressed as P_2O_5), and potassium (expressed as K_2O) *in that order.* (The reason phosphorus and potassium are not expressed in their elemental form is historical. A movement is in progress to have this changed.)

An 80-lb bag of a 5-15-30 fertilizer will contain 4.0 lb of N, the amount of phosphorus in 12 lb of P_2O_5, and the amount of potassium in 24 lb of K_2O. The fertilizer ratio is simply the analysis expressed in terms of the lowest common denominator. A 6-10-4 analysis has a 3:5:2 ratio; 10-10-10 analysis has a 1:1:1 ratio. Fertilizers are referred to as low-analysis fertilizers when the amount of available nutrients is below 30% and as high-analysis fertilizers when the amount of available nutrients is 30% or above. Because of the weight and extra handling involved, low-analysis fertilizers tend to be more expensive per nutrient unit than high analysis fertilizers. High analysis fertilizers, however, require special accuracy and care in their application. Although by law the analysis of nitrogen, phosphorus, and potassium must be stated on the fertilizer bag, many fertilizers contain, or are restricted to, other plant nutrients.

Fertilizers may be classified as *natural organics* or *chemicals*. Natural organics (for example, manure, blood, fish scraps, cottonseed meal) are compounds derived from living organisms. Chemical fertilizers, such as ammonium nitrate and superphosphate, are synthesized from inorganic minerals. Recently a number of forms of nitrogen-containing compounds have been synthesized, for example, urea and cyanamid. Urea can be synthesized directly from the air, which requires only a source of electrical power. Although these are organic compounds in the chemical sense, they are not necessarily derived from living systems. The nutrients in natural organic fertilizers, and some synthetic organics such as "ureaforms," undergo gradual chemical transformations to available forms. These fertilizers therefore provide a means of extending the period of nutrient availability to accommodate the need of the growing plant.

Modern fertilizers can be compounded to satisfy the different needs of the user. Thus they may not only be made up of different nutrients but may be a mixture of organic and inorganic forms. In this way some or a portion of the applied nutrients can be made available immediately whereas the rest can be released slowly, commensurate with the current needs of the crop. Whether a slow-releasing fertilizer or a number of applications of a fast-releasing fertilizer should be used depends on the economics involved. At present, slow-releasing fertilizers tend to be expensive on a per nutrient basis.

The physical characteristics of fertilizer materials vary greatly. Although many fertilizers are solids, they may be applied in dissolved form as a liquid, as in irrigation water. Nitrogen may be applied in the ammonia form as a gas. In addition to soil application, nutrients may be applied directly through the foliage. Nitrogen can be efficiently applied through the leaves by spraying them with urea. The application to the foliage of such trace elements as manganese and boron has also proved practical.

LEVEL OF FERTILIZATION. The kind and level of fertilization is based on crop need in relation to current fertility levels and the alternative sources of plant nutrients. The prediction of plant-nutrient needs has been one of the main goals of plant fertility studies. The techniques that are now used consist in correlating plant response with chemical tests on the soil or with tests made on the plant tissues themselves. However, the total nutrient content of the soil does not give a true picture of nutrient availability. The available nutrients are related to the exchangeable cations, the soil reaction or pH, and the organic cycles. Some biological assays of the soil have been made by utilizing the response of sensitive plants or microorganisms. The relationship between these tests, soil type, and climate have been correlated for many crop plants. Quick tests have been developed, although these are often not too accurate. In many plants severe deficiencies of certain nutrients produce characteristic responses in the plant called *deficiency symptoms*, which often can be used to diagnose the trouble (Table 6-2). The good plantsman will not permit nutrient shortages to become this severe.

Table 6-2. *A key to plant-nutrient deficiency symptoms.*

[From McMurtrey, in *Diagnostic Techniques for Soils and Crops*, American Potash Inst., Washington, D.C., 1950.]

SYMPTOMS	ELEMENT DEFICIENT
A. Older or lower leaves of plant mostly affected; effects localized or generalized.	
B. Effects mostly generalized over whole plant; more or less drying or firing of lower leaves; plant light or dark green.	
C. Plant light green; lower leaves yellow, drying to light-brown color; stalks short and slender if element is deficient in later stages of growth.	Nitrogen
CC. Plant dark green, often developing red and purple colors; lower leaves sometimes yellow, drying to greenish brown or black color; stalks short and slender if element is deficient in later stages of growth.	Phosphorus
BB. Effects mostly localized; mottling or chlorosis with or without spots of dead tissue on lower leaves; little or no drying up of lower leaves.	
C. Mottled or chlorotic leaves, typically may redden, as with cotton; sometimes with dead spots; tips and margins turned or cupped upward; stalks slender.	Magnesium
CC. Mottled or chlorotic leaves with large or small spots of dead tissue.	
D. Spots of dead tissue small, usually at tips and between veins, more marked at margins of leaves; stalks slender.	Potassium
DD. Spots generalized, rapidly enlarging, generally involving areas between veins and eventually involving second-	

Table 6-2. *Continued*

SYMPTOMS	ELEMENT DEFICIENT
ary and even primary veins; leaves thick; stalks with short-ened internodes.	Zinc

AA. Newer or bud leaves affected; symptoms localized.
  B. Terminal bud dies, following appearance of distortions at tips or bases of young leaves.
    C. Young leaves of terminal bud at first typically hooked, finally dying back at tips and margins, so that later growth is characterized by a cut-out appearance at these points; stalk finally dies at terminal bud.   Calcium
    CC. Young leaves of terminal bud becoming light green at bases, with final breakdown here; in later growth, leaves become twisted; stalk finally dies back at terminal bud.   Boron
  BB. Terminal bud commonly remains alive; wilting or chlorosis of younger or bud leaves with or without spots of dead tissue; veins light or dark green.
    C. Young leaves permanently wilted (wither-tip effect) without spotting or marked chlorosis; twig or stalk just below tip and seedhead often unable to stand erect in later stages when shortage is acute.   Copper
    CC. Young leaves not wilted; chlorosis present with or without spots of dead tissue scattered over the leaf.
      D. Spots of dead tissue scattered over the leaf; smallest veins tend to remain green, producing a checkered or reticulating effect.   Manganese
      DD. Dead spots not commonly present; chlorosis may or may not involve veins, making them light or dark green in color.
        E. Young leaves with veins and tissue between veins light green in color.   Sulfur
        EE. Young leaves chlorotic, principal veins typically green; stalks short and slender.   Iron

    The relationship between fertility level and plant performance varies with the species and the nutrient involved. For example, 100–150 lb of nitrogen applied prior to planting will promote optimum production of tomatoes on mineral soils, whereas this level of nitrogen will reduce muskmelon yields as a result of decreased production of perfect flowers. However, the plant response to fertility level can be discussed in general. At one end of the scale are *deficiency levels*, in which plants show definite symptoms of a lack of nutrients. At somewhat higher levels, although they may not show obvious deficiency symptoms, plants may respond in yield. This has been termed *"hidden hunger."* At levels above which no response to fertilizers may be demonstrated, the plant may continue to show an increasing level of nutrient absorption. This is termed *"luxury consumption."* At abnormally high levels growth is reduced, and death may even occur. Maximum production presumably occurs in that state of soil fertility in which a slight luxury consumption exists.

The level of crop response to fertilization is related in part to the productive capacity of the soil. Crops on soils of low productive capacity show a maximum response at a lower level of fertility than on soils of high productive capacity. Productive capacity is based on long-term nutrient availability and soil condition. Owing to the nature of forces in the soil that establish an equilibrium between the soil and the soil solution, optimum fertility cannot be achieved in one quick step. When larger amounts of fertilizer are placed on soils of a low productive capacity, much of it is wasted. These excess nutrients may be leached, may be tied up in forms unavailable to the plant, or may be unequally distributed throughout the soil in relation to plant needs. However, continued applications of fertilizer at the level of optimum plant response tend to increase the productive capacity of the soil, ultimately raising its yield potential.

Fig. 6-3. *As excess of soluble fertilizers applied to growing plants such as turf grasses may burn the foliage or may kill the entire plant.*
[Courtesy W. H. Daniel.]

PLACEMENT AND TIMING. One of the important factors in the use of fertilizer is proper placement and timing. This involves efficiency of plant usage, the prevention of injury, and convenience and economy of application. To be effective, fertilizer must be applied where and when the plant needs it. Single yearly applications may not be sufficient for some nutrients, such as nitrogen, and may not be necessary for others. Concentrated applications of highly soluble fertilizers cannot be applied to growing plants, especially when young, because of salt injury (Fig. 6-3). In perennials, or in long-season annuals, it may be more efficient to carefully control nutrient availability throughout the season, and for this reason repeated applications are made. This is especially important with nitrogen fertilization, where losses of excess amounts must be considered.

There are various methods of placement. Fertilizers may be applied prior to planting by scattering it uniformly over the surface of the ground (*broadcast application*). It may be dropped behind the plow at the furrow bottom (*plow-sole placement*), or placed in a band under or to one or both sides of the seed (*band placement*) during planting (Fig. 6-4). Another mode of application consists in applying fertilizer directly over the crop after emergence (*top dressing*) or beside the row (*side dressing*). Side dressed applications of fertilizer are often made along with a cultivation and are thus mixed into the soil. Fertilizer may also be applied along with mechanical transplanting, either as a band under the plant or dissolved in the supplemental transplanting water (*starter solution*).

The timing of fertilizer applications depends upon the nutrient and the crop as well as on the soil type and the climate. Nitrogen fertilizers must be supplied as close to the plant as possible to be of any use. The nitrate forms of nitrogen are water soluble and move rapidly within the soil. Although the ammoniacal forms of nitrogen are held on the soil colloids, they become "mobile" as soon as they are converted to the nitrate form. Thus, nitrogen often becomes deficient, especially in sandy soils. Soils high in applied organic matter may be temporarily short of nitrogen as a result of the high buildup of microorganisms that pre-empt available soil nitrogen in their own bodies. In addition, the nitrogen

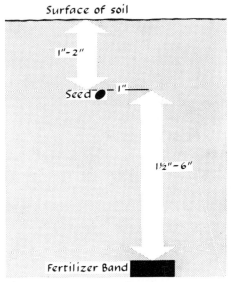

Fig. 6-4. *The proper placement of fertilizer band for many vegetable crops. Large amounts of fertilizer banded too close to the seed may inhibit growth because of salt injury. Fertilizer placed too far away may be insufficient to stimulate the early seedling growth that is so important to optimum plant performance.* [Adapted from Soil, USDA Yearbook, 1957.]

concentration in the soil solution may be relatively low in the spring especially in cold or wet, poorly drained soils, owing to a lack of nitrification by aerobic bacteria and to excess denitrification by anaerobic bacteria. Consequently, many crops show a response to spring applications of nitrogen. It is unwise to apply all of the nitrogen at planting because of possible injury, thus it is often also applied as a side dressing during growth.

In perennial fruit crops such as apple and peach, excess nitrogen is associated with poor fruit color and soft fruit, as well as with undesirable vegetative growth that occurs late in the season, which leaves the plant vulnerable to winter injury. Consequently, nitrogen is usually applied only once, early in the spring, in order that any excess will have been used up by summer. In small-fruit crops that ripen early in the summer, such as the strawberry, nitrogen is not applied to bearing patches in the spring because of the undesirable effect of fruit softening.

In contrast to nitrogen, phosphorus moves very little in the soil. Consequently, the total quantity needed during the season can be applied at one time. Because of the high phosphorus requirement of seedlings it is important that adequate levels be made available close to the seed or transplant. The use of starter solution, transplanting water supplied with liberal phosphorus (about 1500 ppm), is recommended for many transplants. The phosphorus is supplied by soluble phosphate salts such as mono- or diammonium phosphate and monopotassium phosphate. A popular starter solution uses three pounds of a mixture of diammonium phosphate and monopotassium phosphate (10-52-17 analysis) per 50 gallons of water. When an extensive root system is established, the plant requirements are satisfied by lower levels of phosphorus. Phosphorus applications are often banded under the seed to achieve the same effect (Fig. 6-5). Perennial plants usually do not respond to phosphorus application because the root systems are extensive and active throughout most of the growing season.

Because of the low mobility of phosphorus and the low efficiency of uptake by plants (less than 25%) it has been found profitable to build up soil phosphorus levels prior to planting horticultural crops. Once phosphorus levels are brought up, supplemental additions of phosphorus need not be frequent. In turf, for example, there is practically no net loss of phosphorus.

Potassium salts are intermediate in mobility to phosphorus and nitrogen. Owing to their solubility, potassium salts cannot be placed close to seeds or plants in any great amounts. Since potassium is not as critical for seedling growth as nitrogen or phosphorus, broadcast applications are usually made before planting.

Regulation of Soil Reaction

Soil reaction, so important to nutrient availability and root growth, is an important phase of soil management. Although plants vary in their response to pH (Fig. 6-6), most horticultural crops do well with a pH between 6.0 and 6.5. A group of "acid-loving" plants of the Ericaceae

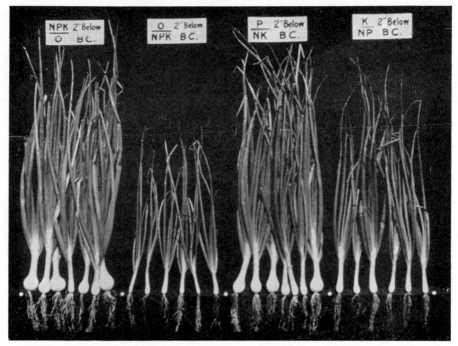

Fig. 6-5. *Response of onions to fertilizer placement. In all cases equal amounts of fertilizer were added, either banded 2 in. below the seed or broadcast over the surface of the soil. The greatest response was obtained when the fertilizer was placed below the seed, where it was available to the young plant. The treatment series indicate that phosphorus is the critical nutrient with respect to placement.*

[Courtesy J. F. Davis.]

(rhododendrons, gardenias, azaleas, camellias, cranberries, blueberries) require conditions of low *p*H (4.5–6.0). A low soil reaction may be used to control soil diseases in crops that prove less sensitive to low *p*H than the corresponding disease-producing organism. Thus, potatoes may be grown at *p*H 5.2 to control scab, a disease caused by a fungus that is not adaptive to acid soils. Potatoes, however, perform equally well at a higher *p*H in disease-free soil.

The natural reaction of soils is due to the interaction of climate with the parent materials of the soil. In general, acid soils are common where the precipitation is high enough to leach appreciable amounts of exchangeable bases from the surface layers. Thus, in the humid climates, the areas of most intense horticulture, soil acidity is often a problem. Soil alkalinity occurs generally in the more arid regions, where there is a comparatively high degree of cation accumulation. Alkaline soils may result in a high

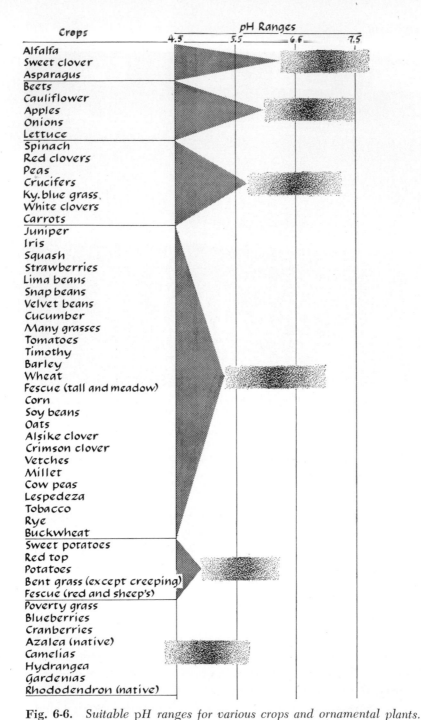

Fig. 6-6. *Suitable pH ranges for various crops and ornamental plants.*

[Adapted with permission of the publisher from *The Nature and Properties of Soils* by Lyon, Buckman, and Brady, 5th ed., copyright 1952 by the Macmillan Company.]

170

salt accumulation (salinity). This can be a problem in the irrigated soils of the American Southwest.

Soils become acid because the basic cations on the soil colloid are replaced by hydrogen ions. This process can be reversed, and the soil pH increased, by adding basic cations, for example, calcium, magnesium, sodium, and potassium. Calcium is the most economic cation for increasing soil pH. In addition, calcium has other beneficial effects. It is an essential element in plant nutrition; it is thought to promote good soil structure by promoting granulation; and it encourages certain soil microorganisms, especially the nitrifying and nitrogen-fixing bacteria. The addition of calcium or calcium and magnesium compounds to reduce the acidity of the soil is known as *liming*. Although the term lime refers correctly to CaO, it is used in the agricultural sense to include oxides, hydroxides, carbonates, and silicates of calcium or calcium and magnesium. Soil liming has resulted in significant increases in plant growth. The amount of liming required depends upon the degree of pH change desired, the base exchange capacity of the soil, the amount of precipitation, and the liming material and its physical form in relation to particle size.

Soil may be made more acid by placing hydrogen ions on the soil colloid. This is done by adding substances that tend to produce strong acids in the soil. Some nitrogen fertilizers will increase soil acidity, but elemental sulfur is by far the most effective substance to use for this purpose. In warm, moist, well-aerated soils, bacterial action converts sulfur to sulfuric acid.

Maintenance of Soil Condition

Tilth

The importance of good physical condition of the soil (*tilth*) in relation to plant growth is a significant part of soil management. Soil structure and texture have a direct effect on the water-holding capacity and aeration of the soil. This influences root growth, as well as the soil microorganisms which play an important part in making available the nutrients in organic matter. Crusting and puddling of the soil are indications of poor tilth (Fig. 6-7).

The physical condition of the soil is largely conditioned by the amount of organic matter. Organic matter may be maintained, and in some cases increased, in field soils by altering crop rotation and by adding supplemental organic matter in the form of manure. In potting soils organic matter is often added in the form of peat. Recently the use of chemical

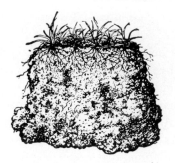

Fig. 6-7. *A puddled soil (left) compared with a well-granulated soil (right).*

[Adapted with permission of the publisher from *The Nature and Properties of Soils* by Lyon, Buckman, and Brady, 5th ed., copyright 1952 by the Macmillan Company.]

soil conditioners such as Krilium have been suggested, although this has not proven practical. The problem of maintaining soil condition is complicated because most cultivation practices, contrary to first impression, do not aid in improving soil structure. Even the gains made by distributing plant material through the soil may be more than offset by compaction, by the loss of organic matter as a result of oxidation, and by erosion. Clay soils in particular must be handled carefully to maintain soil structure. If they are cultivated when too wet the soil becomes puddled. The use of heavy equipment (such as mechanical harvesters) on wet, clay soils seriously impairs soil structure and often leads to compaction problems. This is less of a problem on sandy or peat soils, where soil structure is generally not an issue.

Increasing Organic Matter

Organic matter affects both the fertility and physical condition of the soil. Organic matter acts as a storehouse of nitrogen and other nutrients, and greatly influences the exchange capacity of the soil. It improves the physical condition of the soil by increasing the water-holding capacity, so important to sandy soils, and by increasing aeration, which is especially necessary in clay soils.

The accumulation of organic matter reaches an equilibrium in undisturbed soil. Because the organic material of the soil is largely under the control of biologic and climatic forces one must differentiate between a temporary and a long-term increase in organic matter. Unfortunately it is easy to reduce the organic matter of a soil, yet it is relatively difficult to build it up. The major loss of organic matter comes about from increased oxidation as a result of cultivation and from crop removal.

Perhaps the best way to increase the long-term organic matter is through the extended use of a legume or grass sod (Fig. 6-8). The organic matter produced as a result of root disintegration is protected from excessive oxidation by the constant cover and lack of cultivation. Permanent orchard plantings are kept in good tilth by the use of sod. Mixtures of shallow- and deep-rooted grasses, such as Alta fescue (shallow-rooted) and Ladino clover (deep-rooted) are often used to obtain a resilient floor under heavy equipment as well as to prevent compaction and to improve drainage. Sods, of course, have certain disadvantages. They are not generally used in peach culture because of frost injury (see Chapter 12) as well as the loss of precise control over nitrogen levels. In annual and perennial plantings organic matter can be built up by rotating row crops with legume sods. A standard soil management for potatoes in the northern United States involves a three-year rotation of potatoes, grain, and clover. The grain is used to control weeds and to act as a "nurse crop" for the establishment of the clover.

The plowing down of a growing crop as a "green manure" temporarily increases the organic content of the soil, but this practice cannot be expected to increase the long-term organic matter. The buildup of high populations of microorganisms may actually reduce the net organic matter content of the soil through an unexplained breakdown of the more resistant organic fraction. The rapid breakdown of a green manure does release tied up nutrients. But materials like millet or sudan grass, which have a high car-

Fig. 6-8. *Good soil structure under an alfalfa sod. Note how the roots have penetrated the soil.*

[Photographed by J. C. Allen & Son.]

bon content in relation to their nitrogen or protein content, may create a temporary nitrogen shortage because of the utilization of the available nitrogen by microorganisms. Nitrogen must then be added to compensate for this shortage. Sweet clover and other legumes that have a high nitrogen content in proportion to carbon compounds are destroyed faster by microorganisms and release a steady supply of nitrogen.

The use of grasses or legumes planted in mid- or late summer provides the advantages of a sod for part of the year. These *cover crops* are probably of most value in preventing winter erosion. They are usually plowed under in the spring as a green manure. This should be done early to prevent the loss of excessive moisture from the soil.

The use of manures to supplement soil organic matter is at present an expensive procedure. Manure is probably more valuable for its nutrients than for its contribution of organic matter. Similarly, the use of mulches indirectly adds to organic matter, although only in the upper surface of the soil. Their greatest contribution, however, lies in reducing the amount of cultivation, which in effect limits the oxidation of organic matter.

Soil Conservation

Agriculture operates in a finite and decreasing land area over the world's favored climates. Its basis is a layer of topsoil that averages only seven inches over the earth's surface. This mantle cannot be exploited indefinitely; it must be conserved and refurbished.

Although the reduction of productive capacity through the loss of fertility and structure is considerable, the most serious problem is erosion. Nutrients can be added by fertilization, but the loss of topsoil cannot be so easily or quickly remedied. The loss of soil due to wind and water is a national problem. It contributes to silt-clogged rivers, alternate drought and flood, dust bowls, and poverty. Yet soil conservation need not be practiced for purely altruistic reasons. Soil conservation yields immediate rewards in terms of plant performance and must be considered the basis of sound soil management.

Erosion of the soil is a natural process influenced by climate, topography, and the nature of the soil itself. Where permanent and undisturbed plant cover exist, erosion is more or less gradual and in equilibrium with soil-formation processes. Accelerated erosion comes about in the absence of plant cover. Areas which as a result of climate or topography are unable to support a permanent plant cover undergo a "geologic" erosion, such as found in the Grand Canyon. The accelerated soil erosion brought about by

Fig. 6-9. *Mountain runoff has severely eroded this vineyard in Santa Fe, California.*
[Courtesy USDA.]

agricultural cultivation or overgrazing comes about through the action of water in humid climates (Fig. 6-9) and of wind in arid climates.

The maintenance of vegetative cover is basic to soil management. Vegetative cover retards erosion by breaking and cushioning the beating force of the rain (Fig. 6-10), increasing the absorptive capacity of the soil, and holding the soil against both water and wind. The soil cover increases the infiltration of water through the soil by preventing the clogging of the soil pores by fine surface particles. The techniques used for increasing soil cover include sod culture (as in orchards), proper rotation, cover cropping, and mulching.

Fig. 6-10. *The beating force of a raindrop striking wet soil. Soil particles and globules of mud are hurled in all directions.*
[Courtesy U.S. Soil Conservation Service.]

Water erodes the soil by literally carrying it away. The carrying power of water increases with its speed and volume. The volume of water depends upon the amount of rainfall and the rate at which it is absorbed by the soil. The speed with which this water moves is directly related to the slope of the land and the amount of cover. Any technique that either increases absorption or reduces the speed of the runoff will prevent soil erosion.

The absorptive capacity of the soil may be increased by deep plowing, by increasing the organic matter of the soil, or by increasing drainage. Thus, the burning or removal of organic matter is a poor conservation practice. Where natural drainage is poor, tiling may be necessary to remove water and provide air.

The control of erosion by reducing the speed of runoff may be accomplished in a number of ways. Most basic is contour tillage, in which plowing, cultivation, and the direction of the "row" follows the contour of the land rather than the slope of the land. This affects the speed and power the surface water attains and thus the ability of the tilled soil to absorb water (Fig. 6-11). The use of *intertillage,* or *strip cropping;* which alternates strips of sod and row crops planted along the contour, helps to slow runoff by interposing barriers with high absorptive capacity. The alternating of sod with row cropping serves to achieve the benefits of rotation. On steeper slopes, where greater amounts of surface water must be accommodated, the use of

Fig. 6-11.   *Contour planting of a field of pineapple in Hawaii.*
[Courtesy Dole Corp.]

Fig. 6-12. *A terraced peach planting on a fine sandy loam. The terrace ridges have been left in rye cover in order to protect the land against wind erosion.*
[Courtesy U. S. Soil Conservation Service.]

waterways, permanently sodded areas, facilitates water removal and minimizes erosion.

Where contour cultivation and strip cropping are not sufficient to check erosion, *terraces* constructed on the contour must be used. Terracing, an ancient idea, consists in cutting up a slope into a number of level areas. Terraces appear as steps on the hillside. Although the "steps" of ancient terraces were made of stone, modern terraces are made by building low, rounded ridges of earth across the sloping hillside (Fig. 6-12). Terracing slows down the speed of surface runoff, and although it is designed primarily to prevent erosion, it facilitates the storing of available water. Thus, terracing is an important practice in areas of low rainfall.

Fig. 6-13. *Farm windbreak of evergreens.*
[Photograph by J. C. Allen & Son.]

Some of the erosion caused by wind, especially in open prairies or plains, may be checked by planting *windbreaks*—one or more rows of trees or shrubs planted at right angles to the prevailing winds (Fig. 6-13). The effectiveness of the windbreak is local and is related to the thickness and the height of the trees. The maintenance of a permanent plant cover in conjunction with windbreaks effectively reduces wind erosion where it is a problem. On organic soils, small grain rows are used as temporary windbreaks to protect vegetable seedlings.

WATER MANAGEMENT

Water management in agriculture is concerned with the regulation and use of water to effect plant growth. It involves the control of excess as well as deficient moisture conditions and the conservation of water. Because of the close association between water and soil the control of moisture must be an integral part of soil management.

Irrigation

"And a river went out of Eden to water the garden; and
from thence it was parted, and became into four heads."
GEN. 2:10

The great ancient civilizations of Egypt, Babylon, China and the Incas in the New World were dependent upon irrigation for the abundant agriculture necessary to support their large populations. Uncontrolled river flooding gave way to complex systems of water distribution that involved ditches, canals, and waterways. Mechanical devices such as the dragon wheel and Archimedes' screw provided artificial movement of water. Although irrigation has long been a vital part of the agriculture of the semiarid, subtropical climates, it has not been widely practiced in the humid temperate climates until recently. At present, supplemental irrigation is increasing as a component technology of horticulture. This has been brought about by improvements in irrigation technology, such as increased pump efficiency, lightweight tubing, and sprinkler systems.

Types of Irrigation

There are three general methods of land irrigation: *surface irrigation, sprinkler irrigation,* and *subirrigation.* In *surface irrigation* the water is conveyed directly over the field, and the soil acts as the reservoir for moisture. In *sprinkler irrigation* water is conveyed through pipes and is distributed under pressure as simulated rain. In *subirrigation* the water flows underground as a controlled water table over an impervious substratum and provides moisture to the crop by upward capillary movement.

SURFACE IRRIGATION. The application of water by surface irrigation is utilized in arid and semiarid regions where the topography is level (Fig. 6-14). The water is conveyed to the fields in open ditches at a slow nonerosive velocity. Where water is scarce, pipelines may be used, since they eliminate losses due to seepage and evaporation. The distribution of water is accomplished by various control structures or by siphons. The flow of water must be carefully controlled, for not only may water be expensive, but excessive leaching of water-soluble nutrients and erosion of soil may occur with too rapid a flow. Drainage canals must be provided to remove waste water and eliminate ponding. The advantages of surface irrigation over sprinkler irrigation are lower power requirements and reduced water loss by evaporation. But since the system depends on gravity flow, it is inefficient in distribution because more water is supplied close to the source. Another serious objection to surface irrigation is the deleterious effect that it has on soil structure. Heavy soils become puddled under the heavy load of water, resulting in a loss of soil aeration and in subsequent baking and cracking when the soil dries out.

Fig. 6-14. *Furrow irrigation in a lettuce field in the Salinas Valley, California.*

[Courtesy Ansel Adams and Wells Fargo Bank, San Francisco.]

The distribution of water over the field in surface irrigation may be accomplished either by flooding the entire field in a continuous sheet (*flood irrigation*) or by restricting the water to some type of furrow (*furrow irrigation*). The field must be almost level, otherwise low spots will get too much water, and high spots will get none. Flood irrigation is common in horticultural crops that are tolerant of excessive water, as are cranberries. Furrow irrigation is the most widely used method of applying water to row crops. Although furrow irrigation is fairly efficient in water utilization, it requires high labor costs. Constant supervision is required to prevent furrow streams from uniting and forming large channels. In rolling land, and with closely growing crops, water may be applied to small furrows that guide rather than carry the water. This is referred to as *corrugating irrigation*. Soakers (perforated hoses that allow water to seep into the soil at a low, uniform rate) provide a form of surface irrigation that can be employed in greenhouses and in home grounds and gardens.

SPRINKLER IRRIGATION. Sprinkler irrigation, although not new, has come into widespread use since 1945, owing to the introduction of light aluminum pipe, quick couplers, and improved nozzles. Until then, sprinkler systems consisted of permanent "overhead" installations that were confined to use in small market gardens. Portable, light-weight pipe has put sprinkler irrigation into a prominent position in agricultural technology. It has proved practical as a means of providing supplemental water in the so-called "humid" climates. The advantages of sprinkler irrigation lie in the even and controlled application rate. Although in arid climates evaporation may be higher with sprinkler than with surface irrigation, the controlled application rate results in a more efficient use of water. The slower rate of application reduces runoff, erosion, and disturbed soil condition. In addition, sprinkler irrigation can be used on land that is too steep to permit the proper use of other methods, and makes full use of land by eliminating the need for a permanent distribution system. The limitations of sprinkler irrigation lie in the high initial cost. although operational labor costs are reduced. The power requirements are

Fig. 6-15. *Three large diesel engines of this type provide power for sprinkler irrigation on a large Midwestern sod farm.*
[Courtesy International Harvester Corp.]

Fig. 6-16. *Sprinkler irrigation is practical as a result of portable, lightweight, aluminum pipe. The sprinkler pattern must be overlapped about 40% to achieve uniform application of water.*
[Courtesy USDA.]

high, for water pressures of 15–100 lb./in.^{2} must be maintained (Fig. 6-15). The chief operational difficulty is high wind, which disturbs the sprinkler patterns and results in uneven water distribution.

Sprinkler irrigation equipment operates with nozzles or perforated pipe. Rotating sprinkler heads, the most widely used type, apply water to circular areas at rates of 0.2 in./hour to over 1.0 in./hour (Fig. 6-16). In order to obtain proper coverage the overlap should be one-fourth to one-half of the wetted circle.

SUBSURFACE IRRIGATION. Subsurface irrigation involves creating and maintaining an artificial water table. In order for such a system to function properly, the ground must be level, and subsurface soil must be permeable enough to permit the rapid movement of water laterally and vertically. A barrier, such as an impervious layer, must be available to prevent the loss of water through deep percolation. A distribution system of ditches and laterals permits the artificial water table to be raised or lowered by pumping water into or out of the system. There are, however, relatively few places in the United States where these specialized conditions exist. A good example is the San Luis Valley of Colorado, an important potato producing area. Subirrigation is also common in organic soils.

The level at which the water table is maintained in organic soils has many ramifications. The most favorable plant growth is achieved with a water table of 24–36 in. from the surface of the soil, the tolerance varying somewhat with the plant. For example, such crops as mint and celery require a

water table of about 18 in. The water table also affects organic soil subsidence, which is the "loss" of soil due to drying, settling, compaction, slow
oxidation, and wind erosion. The rate of subsidence increases as the water
table drops. One of the problems associated with a high water table, however, is caused by excessive, unexpected rainfall. Unless the water table can
be quickly lowered, uncontrolled flooding may result and cause extensive
crop damage.

Determining Irrigation Requirements

Irrigation, while often capable of yielding enormous benefits, may be a
wasteful, and even a harmful practice, if applied incorrectly. The determination of when and of how much water to supply in relation to crop production is one of the main problems in irrigation. In a sense this requires
that an accounting system be established that will determine whether or not
the available water will meet crop needs in spite of loss due to evaporation,
transpiration, runoff, and percolation. The net deficiency not compensated
by natural precipitation may be made up by irrigation. The timing of application can be extremely critical because of the nature of the plant requirements in relation to stage of growth. In snap beans, for example, moisture
stress during flowering and pod formation seriously depresses the yield as
a result of flower abscission and ovule abortion.

There are two approaches to the determination of irrigation requirements.
One concerns the measurement of soil moisture, from which the available
moisture is determined. The other involves calculating the status of water
availability from meteorological data.

The accurate determination of soil moisture is an essential tool for determining irrigation requirements. Although the experienced person can evaluate soil moisture from the "feel" of the soil (Table 6-3), this rough test
varies with the soil and the person making the test. There are now various
objective methods available. Soil moisture may be calculated from the
weight of soil taken before and after oven drying. This gravimetric procedure is exact, but it is slow and laborious. More rapid methods are based
on the ability of a sorption block made of gypsum or other porous material
to absorb water in proportion to the amount present in the soil. The percentage of the soil moisture in the plaster block may be determined by
weight or by direct measurement of the electrical conductance or resistance
between electrodes inserted in the block. Another device called a tensiometer gives an indication of water availability. It consists of a porous cup
filled with water and attached to a vacuum gauge or mercury manometer
that measures the tension at which the water is held to the soil. In addition,

Table 6-3. *Feel chart for the determination of moisture in medium- to fine-textured soils. With sandy soil, the balls are more friable' and fragile through-- out the whole range.*
[From Strong, in *Sprinkler Irrigation Manual.* Wright Rain, Ringwood, England, 1956.]

DEGREE OF MOISTURE	FEEL	PERCENT OF FIELD CAPACITY
Dry	Powder dry	None
Low (critical)	Crumbly, will not form a ball	Less than 25
Fair (usual time to irrigate)	Forms a ball, but will crumble upon being tossed several times	25–50
Good	Forms a ball that will remain intact after being tossed five times, will stick slightly with pressure	50–75
Excellent	Forms a durable ball and is pliable; sticks readily; a sizable chunk will stick to the thumb after soil is squeezed firmly	75–100
Too wet	With firm pressure can squeeze some water from the ball	Over field capacity

other sophisticated procedures are available that are based on the thermal properties or on the neutron-scattering potential of the soil. At present the gravimetric method must be considered the most accurate. The rapid soil-measuring devices (for example, the tensiometer and the irrometer) have not proved altogether successful, owing in part to the random variation of soil moisture, the difficulty of achieving intimate contact of the sorption block with the soil, and the problem of determining proper placement in the root zone for measurement.

Meteorological and climatological data offer a powerful tool for measuring the status of available water. The procedure involves the calculation of *consumptive' use*—the water lost by evaporation and transpiration—which is probably the best index of irrigation requirements. Consumptive use varies with a great number of factors: temperature, hours of sunshine, humidity, wind movement, amount of plant cover, the stage of plant development, and available moisture.

High rates of water consumption are associated with a high percentage of plant cover and with hot, dry, windy conditions. Because optimum plant performance is associated with an adequate uninterrupted supply of water, the peak requirements must be considered. Crops have the highest water requirements in the fruiting or seed-forming periods (Fig. 6-17). An approx imate relationship between the peak moisture use of horticultural crops and climate is given in Table 6-4. Plants differ in their water requirements largely in relation to their ground-covering ability and their depth of rooting (Table 6-5). The relationship between water requirements and depth of rooting might be somewhat less than expected because deep-rooted plants obtain their greatest percentage of moisture from the upper surface of the root zone.

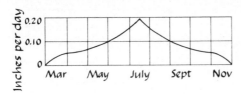

Fig. 6-17. *Rate of water use of peaches in a cool, dry climate.*

[Adapted from Strong, in *Sprinkler Irrigation Manual*, Wright Rain, Ringwood, England. 1956.]

The amount of available moisture provided by rain may be very much less than the total rainfall. Owing to soil evaporation and the slow rate of infiltration, showers that provide less than $\frac{1}{4}$ in. during the hot summer days may contribute very little to available soil moisture. On the other hand, a high proportion of water from heavy precipitation may be lost by runoff. The effectiveness of precipitation therefore depends upon the intensity, as well as upon the amount, in relation to temperature and the absorbing capacity of the soil.

It has been possible to determine a satisfactory consumptive-use index for a particular area by using monthly averages of mean temperature and

Table 6-4. *Average peak moisture use for common irrigated horticultural crops (inches per day).*

[From Strong, in *Sprinkler Irrigation Manual*. Wright Rain, Ringwood, England. 1956.]

CROP	COOL CLIMATE HUMID	COOL CLIMATE DRY	MODERATE CLIMATE HUMID	MODERATE CLIMATE DRY	HOT CLIMATE HUMID	HOT CLIMATE DRY
Potatoes	0.10	0.16	0.12	0.20	0.14	0.24
Tomatoes	0.14	0.17	0.17	0.22	0.23	0.27
Beans, field	0.12	0.16	0.16	0.20	0.20	0.25
Vegetables	0.12	0.15	0.15	0.19	0.20	0.23
Deciduous orchard	0.15	0.20	0.20	0.25	0.25	0.30
Deciduous orchard with cover	0.20	0.25	0.25	0.30	0.30	0.35
Citrus orchard	0.10	0.15	0.13	0.19	0.18	0.23

hours of sunshine. Empirically derived constants are available for adjusting these values for different crops. Any water deficit can be calculated by subtracting the consumptive-use requirements from the available water present. Potential evapotranspiration (the combination of evaporation and transpiration when the surface is completely covered with vegetation and there is an abundance of moisture) can be calculated by using the Bellani black-plate atmometer, a relatively simple instrument used to measure evaporation (Fig. 6-18), and by estimating the percentage of ground cover.

Because all of the irrigation water applied is not available to the crop, the amount applied must be based on *irrigation efficiency*, the percentage of irrigation water applied in relation to that which becomes available for consumptive use. Water should be applied to bring the soil up to field capacity at a depth commensurate with the bulk of the feeder root system. The rate must be consistent with the absorptive properties of the soil. Irrigation is best applied when the water tension in the zone of rapid water removal goes above four atmospheres or when 60% of the available water in the root

Table 6-5. *Normal root zone depths of mature irrigated crops grown in a deep, permeable, well-drained soil.*
[From Shockley, in *Sprinkler Irrigation Manual*, Wright Rain, Ringwood, England. 1956.]

CROP	ROOT DEPTH (FT)	CROP	ROOT DEPTH (FT)
Alfalfa	5–10	Grass Pasture	3–4
Artichokes	4	Ladino Clover	2
Asparagus	6–10	Lettuce	$\frac{1}{2}$
Beans	3–4	Onions	1
Beets (Sugar)	4–6	Parsnips	3
Beets (Table)	2–3	Peas	3–4
Broccoli	2	Potatoes (White)	3–4
Cabbage	2	Potatoes (Sweet)	4–6
Cantaloupes	4–6	Pumpkins	6
Carrots	2–3	Radishes	1
Cauliflower	2	Spinach	2
Citrus	4–6	Squash	3
Corn (Sweet)	3	Tomatoes	6–10
Corn (Field)	4–5	Turnips	3
Cotton	4–6	Strawberries	3–4
Deciduous Orchards	6–8	Walnuts	12 plus
Grain	4	Watermelons	6

zone is depleted. The amount of water that can be efficiently utilized is primarily related to the soil fertility level. The maximum benefits of irrigation are dependent upon the existence of a readily available nitrogen supply.

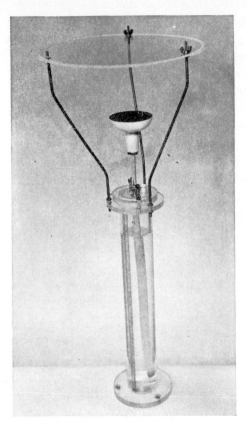

Fig. 6-18. *The Bellani black-plate atmometer measures evaporation. Potential evapotranspiration can be calculated by taking readings with this instrument and estimating total plant cover.*
[Courtesy W. H. Gabelman.]

Drainage

Drainage is the removal of excess gravitational water from the soil. Under conditions of good natural drainage, surplus surface and soil water is rapidly removed to streams and rivers. The poor natural drainage of some areas is a result of several factors. Such areas may have a high natural water table due to an impervious layer that prevents downward percolation, resulting in *waterlogged soils.* Others may be low-lying in relation to surrounding drainage and receive more water than can be removed. Some areas are subject to flooding brought about by the overflow of streams and rivers. Flooding can be averted either by building protective levees or controlling the rate of water movement. This is accomplished as a part of a program of upstream watershed management through the control of excess runoff or by the construction of dams and reservoirs to restrict the flow in times of excess water movement.

The facilitation of natural drainage is both a land reclamation and a cultural practice. The permanent drainage of wetlands has been a significant factor in the expansion of agriculture in the eastern United States, where some of the most productive cropland was formerly "worthless" marsh and swamp. Not all wetlands are suitable for drainage, but they still remain valuable for wildlife, forest, and recreational use. As a cultural practice, drainage consists in removing the excess water which interferes with plant development and with the performance of such operations as tillage and harvesting. It is necessary when the natural removal of water by runoff, percolation, and evapotranspiration is too slow. Drainage extends the potential growing season by permitting earlier tillage in lands that are consistently wet in the spring.

Excess water can be removed by surface and subsurface drainage. Surface drainage refers to the removal of surface water by development of the slope of the land. Subsurface drainage is accomplished by the construction of open ditches and tile fields to intercept ground water and carry it off. The water enters the tiling through the joints, and drainage is achieved by gravity feed through the tiles. The problem of drainage design, which involves the depth, size and number of drains to be installed, is concerned with the physics of ground water movement.

Water Conservation

Water is of national concern. For a nation to prosper an abundant source of high quality water must be available for agricultural and industrial use as well as for human consumption and sanitation. The misuse of water resources leads to alternate flood and drought, problems that affect all of us.

Water conservation implies the proper stewardship of our water resources as a whole. It may involve large programs to control flooding, develop hydroelectric power, and facilitate navigation. These are problems that require national effort. Water conservation also involves the control of water resources on a smaller scale. It must therefore be a part of the water management of every individual enterprise.

Soil management practices developed for the efficient utilization of water involve the control of soil erosion and the conservation of soil moisture by the control of soil runoff and the increase of the water absorption capacity of the soil. It may include practices such as mulching or the close mowing of sod in orchards, which are designed to reduce the removal of water from the soil. Because horticultural crops are high users of water, the extreme practices of dryland farming, such as fallowing, to conserve moisture without resorting to irrigation are usually not practical. In fallowing, the ground is left unplanted for a whole year and, in an effort to build up soil moisture, is cultivated only to eliminate weeds. In order for horticultural crops to be grown where water is insufficient, irrigation is essential. But irrigation depends on large sources of water. Hence, where organized irrigation facilities are not available, and where lakes or streams with sufficient flow do not adjoin the property, a source of water supply must be developed. Irrigation wells offer one possibility. These are large volume wells capable of supplying the high quantities of water required. Storage ponds or reservoirs are becoming increasingly important as a source of irrigation water. They are usually made by constructing an earth dam across a gulley or an intermittent or spring-fed stream (Fig. 6-19).

Fig. 6-19. *Artificially created storage ponds are an important source of irrigation water.*
[Courtesy U.S. Soil Conservation Service.]

The problem of water rights have social as well as economic implications. These implications are reflected in our laws. The *Riparian law*, the common law involving water rights with respect to rivers and streams, has established a legal framework for disputes concerning water diversion and distribution. In this common law, property rights do not involve complete water rights except for personal use. Neither the landowner nor anyone else owns the water or may divert it from its normal flow. However, because of differences in water availability from one region to another, the common law has been modified throughout the United States. The right to use water from streams for irrigation is variable and depends on state law. Similarly the right to pump underground water for irrigation differs widely from state to state. The legal codes must be clearly understood in situations concerning irrigation and drainage procedure.

TEMPERATURE CONTROL

Plant growth shows a marked response to small changes in temperature, and if extremes in temperature persist for even short periods of time, they will lead to irreversible changes of state, resulting in death to the plant in whole or in part. Methods for the control of temperature in the culture of horticulture crops vary greatly. For the great majority of crops there is no active control, but rather an adaptation through selection of location, site, and choice of plant. This is discussed further in Chapter 12. For some field grown horticultural plants an active attempt may be made to modify and ameliorate extremes in temperature through cultural practices such as mulching and various techniques of frost control. The regulation of temperature in greenhouse culture can be complete, involving artificial heating and cooling.

Cultural Practices

Mulching

Mulches are insulating substances spread over the surface of the soil (Fig. 6-20). Although one of their chief purposes is the regulation of soil temperature, they serve many other functions. Mulches conserve soil moisture because they reduce evaporation by lowering the soil temperature and by increasing the absorptive capacity in the upper layer of soil. Erosion is reduced as a result of decreased surface runoff and the shielding effect of the mulch to driving rain. Mulch is commonly applied for this reason to newly planted lawns and seed beds, especially on sloping areas. Mulches may control weeds and eliminate the need for cultivation by smothering weed growth and cutting off light from the soil surface. It offers protection to flowers and fruit from mud-splattering rain. This is especially important in low-growing crops such as strawberries. In addition, mulches may be a source of organic matter and nutrients to the soil. Mulching is often desirable for its own sake, since its pleasing appearance provides an attractive background for flowers or plant material.

Fig. 6-20. *Corncobs make an inexpensive mulch for apple orchards in the Corn Belt states. The mulch is spread around the drip line of the tree.*

Mulches may be applied during the active growth (*summer mulch*) or be restricted to late fall to provide cold weather protection (*winter mulch*). Although the benefit of the summer mulch is attributed to a number of factors (for example, moisture conservation and weed control) the principal benefit of winter protective mulch is its influence on temperature.

The temperature-stabilizing affect of summer mulches is due to insulation, heat absorption, and shading. The surface of bare, dark-colored soils on a sunny midsummer day may be 30° higher than air temperature. The reduction in soil temperature attained as a result of mulching appears to increase nutrient availability, and improves root growth and, ultimately, the performance of many plants.

The temperature-regulating effect of a winter protective mulch is two fold. One effect is to temper extremely low winter temperatures. This is achieved through the insulation effect provided by the mulch, which conserves ground heat. The other effect is to stabilize and buffer soil temperature and prevent recurring freezing and thawing, which rips and injures plant roots through soil heaving. During winter warm spells in cold climates, a mulch tends to keep the ground frozen by providing insulation and shading. Thus, not only does a mulch "warm" the plant under extreme winter weather, but it also keeps it cold during unseasonable warm spells. By keeping them under a winter mulch, spring-flowering plants may be delayed from early blooming to avoid the damaging effect of spring frost.

Fig. 6-21. *Mechanized mulching of strawberries.*
[Courtesy Friday Tractor Co., Hartford, Mich.]

The application of winter mulch is usually made after a light freeze so as not to delay dormancy. Tender plants, such as roses, may be protected by mounding the crown with soil. After the mound is frozen it is covered with an insulating organic mulch. Winter mulching is a standard practice in strawberry culture. After the plants have become dormant in the fall, but before heavy, injurious freezes, the entire planting is usually covered with 2–3 in. of straw (Fig. 6-21). The plants are uncovered in spring, when growth can no longer be prevented. The excess straw is then moved to the middle of the rows, where it serves to keep the fruit clean. If frost is expected during flowering, recovering the plant achieves a measure of protection.

Most mulching materials consist of plant refuse or by-products: leaves, straw, sawdust, corn cobs, peat, tobacco stems, pine needles, wood chips, or paper. The main values of summer mulches are relatively independent of the material. Inorganic substances such as rockwool or gravel are effective. A good mulch must be economical, available, and easy to handle. It must also be stable in order that it will not easily wash or blow away. Mulches used around the home must be nonobjectionable as to odor and appearance.

Some of the problems associated with mulching materials arise from their tendency to act as sources and harborers of plant pests—weeds, disease-producing microorganisms, and rodents. Because of the disease problem, the refuse of the plant being protected should not be used as mulch. Straw that has been improperly handled may contain weed or grain seed, which may contribute to the weed population the following spring. Fresh straw should be prespread and moistened during warm weather to induce germination before being used. The use of mulch in orchards must be accompanied by rigid methods of rodent control, lest rodents build up to damaging populations in the favorable environment that a deep mulch affords.

Many mulching materials are highly inflammable and present a fire hazard. Straw mulch in particular should not be placed too close to buildings. Unless partially decomposed, fresh leaves make unsatisfactory mulch because they tend to pack closely, and may smother plants. Although organic mulches decompose and will eventually contribute plant nutrients, the high carbon content of many of these materials may contribute to nitrogen deficiency. This is especially true if the mulch is plowed under. This can be avoided by applying extra nitrogen.

Frost Control

A number of techniques are used to avoid the destructive consequences of spring frost. Spring frost may be avoided by late planting. Although frost conditions may be predicted on a probability basis, it is not always practical to plant at the last frost-free date. Even this date is only a statistic. The spring culture of seedlings in protective structures circumvents frost filled weather. Frost control for perennial plantings, however, must depend on more substantial procedures.

The judicious choice of location and site remain the main bulwark against frost. Cultural practices used in the control of frost involve techniques that either encourage the conservation of heat or add heat directly. The conservation of heat is brought about by any method that will increase daytime absorption of heat by the soil or prevent its loss at night. This can be accomplished by using hot caps (Fig. 6-22), by cultivating, or by fogging. The addition of heat can be accomplished in a number of ways, for example, by using heaters, by flooding, by spray irrigation, or by artificial air movement. These methods will be discussed more fully along with the meteorological aspects of frost in Chapter 12, Horticultural Geography.

Plant-growing Structures

Cold Frames

An inexpensive form of temperature control for seedlings and transplants during the early spring is achieved with the *cold frame*. A cold frame is

Fig. 6-22. *Hot caps protect early tomatoes in California's San Luis Rey district. The hot cap is made of a translucent paper and acts as a miniature greenhouse.*
[Courtesy USDA.]

an enclosed ground bed, usually sunken, with a removable sash. Heat is provided through the trapping of solar energy. Temperatures inside the cold frame increase relative to the air during the day when the sash is in place due to the "greenhouse effect" (see Chapter 4). Heat is stored in the soil during the night, and plants can be protected even though outside air temperatures dip below freezing. With especially low temperatures, insulating material such as straw is sometimes placed over the sash. Temperatures are maintained during the day by raising or removing the sash. Cold frames are commonly used for starting early transplants from seed or as a means of hardening off greenhouse-grown transplants.

Hotbeds

Hotbeds are essentially cold frames provided with a supplemental source of heat. Additional heat may be provided by fermentation, hot water, steam, or electricity. Fermentation heat is provided from decaying organic matter, most commonly strawy manure, placed under the plants. The use of hot air, steam, or hot water systems are usually arranged to heat the soil by conduction. Electrical heating also provides ground heat through the use of a soil-heating cable. Thermostatically regulated electrical heating provides precise temperature control. Such systems can be easily installed; the operating cost depends upon electrical rates.

Greenhouses

Greenhouses (in England they are referred to as glass houses) are more or less elaborate, permanent structures equipped not only to regulate temperatures but to provide increased environmental control of plant growth (Fig. 6-23). Because of the great amount of control that must be achieved in greenhouses, this type of culture becomes an extremely specialized operation.

In ordinary greenhouses temperature is regulated through a heating and ventilation system similar to that of the hotbed. A central coal or oil furnace supplies the heat. In Europe, portable "steam plants" are available. Peripheral steam heating is the most commonly used distribution system, although heating pipes may be placed under benches in large greenhouses. Ventilation is provided at the sides and top of the structure. Automatic controls are available for both heating and ventilation.

Temperature control during cold seasons is a matter of adjusting heating and ventilation to take maximum advantage of solar heat. In warmer

Fig. 6-23. *Greenhouse carnation production. The majority of carnations produced in the United States are grown under glass.* [Photograph by J. C. Allen & Son.]

weather, however, it becomes increasingly difficult to maintain reasonable temperatures for plant growth with an ordinary ventilation system. Some greenhouse cooling is achieved by shading the glass with a whitewash spray. The whitewash is made in such a way that it will weather off naturally by fall. Fan and pad cooling provides an economical system for lowering summer greenhouse temperatures. Cooling is achieved by the evaporation of circulated water through excelsior or some other high-surface material (Fig. 6-24). Fans opposite the cooling "pads" draw the cooled air across the greenhouse. The efficiency of the system increases as the humidity goes down. Even in the hot, humid, midwestern United States, temperatures can be kept at least on a par with the outdoor shade.

The use of refrigeration equipment is not economical for commercial greenhouse cooling, although it is used to obtain uniform temperatures for experimental conditions. Refrigeration equipment is widely used in greenhouses for storage purposes.

Plastic films have proved to be a quick and inexpensive substitute for glass and have found a ready market for cold frames, hotbeds, small sash houses, and greenhouses (Fig. 6-25). However, although glass greenhouses have a high initial construction cost, they still compare favorably with plastic greenhouses in price on a long-term depreciation basis. The light-absorbing qualities of plastic are similar to those of glass. At present, a number of different types of plastic coverings are available. These vary from polyethylene films to the more rigid plastics. Since some polyethylene films disintegrate under the influence of ultraviolet light during the summer, they must be replaced each fall. This provides a unique advantage in that, with the plastic removed, the summer cooling problems are eliminated entirely. Ultraviolet-resistant polyethylene is now available. Shade cloth may be substituted for plastic on the frame during the sum-

Fig. 6-24. *Fan and pad greenhouse cooling installation. Note cooling pads in foreground.*

[Photograph Acme Engineering and Manufacturing Corp., Muskagee, Okla.]

Fig. 6-25. *Plastic greenhouses are a convenient, inexpensive structure. The poly-ethylene plastic is removed in the spring, when temperatures get too high, and is replaced in the fall. The frame can then be covered with shade cloth and the structure converted to a shade house. (Above) A scissor-type, truss-rafter, plastic greenhouse in the process of being covered. (Below) A gothic-rafter, plastic greenhouse. The insulated pipe carries steam from the green-house range.*

[Courtesy P. H. Massey, Jr.]

mer. This means of temperature control is, of course, not possible with the more permanent plastic coverings.

Shade Houses

Shade houses may either be large walk-in structures or low, covered open frames. Although shading is commonly used to reduce temperature, it is also used to protect shade loving plants such as chrysanthemum, hy-drangea, azalea, and various foliage plants from leaf damage caused by high light intensities. This is accomplished through the use of such ma-terials as lath or screening. In addition, various types of "shading cloth" are available, which can be used to cut down light intensity by different amounts.

Propagation beds are often located in shade houses to reduce excessive transpiration. Owing to the inadequacy of their root systems, excessive heat is especially injurious to newly rooted cuttings and transplants. Less watering is required under shade, since transpiration and soil evaporation are reduced.

LIGHT MODIFICATION

The control of light has become a significant part of the technology of horticulture. The manifold effects of light must be considered in terms of quality, intensity, and duration in their relation to the many physiological processes involved.

Satisfying Photosynthetic Requirements

Plant growth depends on the fixation of carbon during photosynthesis. Although most plants grow best in the high light intensities of full sun (5000–10,000 footcandles), a single leaf is light saturated at about 1200 footcandles. The higher intensities are needed, however, to provide sufficient light energy to compensate for leaf shading. Growth is much reduced at lower light intensities. Most plants cannot grow below 100–200 footcandles, the level of light in an average room. The *compensation point* is that light intensity at which plants will maintain themselves but will not grow. Foliage plants grown for decor are selected for their ability to maintain themselves at this level. For optimum appearance they must usually be replaced within the year unless more light is provided for growth. During the winter the light intensity available above plants in a greenhouse is often between 300 and 1000 footcandles. As a result of this low light intensity and the short day length, plant growth is often severely limited.

Because of the high energy requirements of photosynthesis and the present-day cost of power, it is not economically feasible to use supplemental light to increase photosynthesis in most situations. The use of supplemental illumination for this purpose is practical in the greenhouse only where large numbers of "valuable" plants, such as seedlings, are grown in a small area. Supplemental light is used widely to increase growth in experimental studies or for indoor decorative plantings when cost is not a direct factor.

In outdoor cultivation the efficiency of light utilization may be increased by such cultural practices as spacing, training, and pruning. These techniques are discussed in the following chapter. Rows running in an east-west direction will utilize light more efficiently than will rows running in a north-south direction, where plants will shade each other. In most situations, however, the direction of the row is usually governed by the prevailing slope of the land or by convenience.

Control of Day Length

The control of day length by utilizing either supplemental illumination or shading has become a standard practice in florist crop production. The artificial lengthening of the day, or interruption of the dark period, makes it possible to promote flowering in long-day plants or to prevent or delay flowering of short-day plants. Similarly, under natural long days, shading prevents flowering of long-day plants and promotes flowering in short-day plants. In the culture of chrysanthemums, the most important florist crop in the United States, it is standard practice to control flowering by manipulating the photoperiod. The extension of the photoperiod by illumination is economical on a commercial basis because of the low light intensity required for the process. In this way plants can be induced to flower "out of season." The commercial control of flowering makes it possible to produce a continuous supply of many florist crops. It allows flower production to be synchronized more closely with market demand, which, in the United States, is governed by season and holiday. The alteration of photoperiod is a valuable tool for the breeder, who may wish to cross plants that do not normally flower simultaneously.

An increase in photoperiod is achieved by extending the day length to about 17–18 hours. The same effect can be achieved, however, by interrupting the middle of the dark period for about 3 hours. Thus, in terms of power, alteration of the dark period is more efficient than extending the day length. This effect can be made even more efficient by the use of brief light flashes (4 sec/min).

The reduction of photoperiod is achieved by using black cloth. Because of the low intensity of light required, care must be taken to completely darken the plant. The common procedure used for indoor and outdoor culture involves the use of a curtain built on a track.

Light Sources

Artificial light sources differ greatly in their spectral distribution (Fig. 6-26). Tungsten lamps, which emit light by heating their filament to extremely high temperatures ($2850°K$), produce a continuous spectrum from blue to infrared. The radiation within the visible spectrum lies mainly in the red and far red, although the greater part of the overall emission is in the invisible infrared. Fluorescent lamps emit light from both low pressure mercury vapor and fluorescent powder. Their emission spectrum contains both the continuous spectrum from the fluorescent material and the line spectrum of the mercury vapor. Light from ordinary fluorescent lamps is low in red and deficient in far red. This is why fluorescent bulbs are cool. It should be emphasized that different types of lamps and light sources will vary as to their spectral distribution. For example, fluorescent lights are available that will produce light richer in red.

Because of the energy lost in heat (the infrared radiation), tungsten lights are rather inefficient, since only about 5% of the energy input is transformed into the light range required by plants (4000–7000 Å), as compared to over 15% for fluorescent lights. Consequently, fluorescent lights are more efficient in providing the high energy required for the acceleration of photosynthesis. Fluorescent lights have not been widely used in greenhouses, however, owing to the high cost of ballasts and installation.

Fig. 6-26. *Spectral emission of tungsten filament lamps and daylight fluorescent lamps as compared to the spectrum of the sunlight reaching the earth. The weak line spectra of the mercury discharge from the fluorescent lamps is not shown. The chart offers no quantitative comparison with respect to the energy output of the sources.*
[Adapted from data of General Electric Co.]

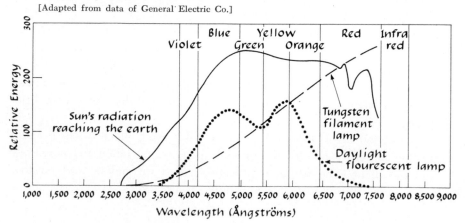

Tungsten lamps have proven very efficient for controlling flowering and for promoting vegetative growth in many woody plants, because the net red light so important in the photoperiodic effect is high. Fluorescent light that is weak in red is preferable for supplemental illumination of plants that react strongly to the far red with respect to elongation and become etiolated and spindly. Tungsten light is used where elongation is desirable, as in asters or hyacinths.

In order to achieve satisfactory growth in complete artificial light, the best results are obtained with a combination of light sources. Tungsten and fluorescent lights complement each other to produce a spectrum closer to that of sunlight than does either separately. In experimental growth chambers, where high intensities are desirable, combinations of tungsten, fluorescent, and mercury lamps may be used. Special precautions must be taken to dispose of the infrared radiation (heat).

Selected References

Russell, E. W. *Soil Conditions and Plant Growth.* 9th ed. Longmans, Green and Co., New York. 1961. (The ninth edition of the most famous work on agricultural soils. The first seven editions were written by Sir John Russell.)

Soil. USDA Yearbook, 1957. (A broad, nontechnical treatment.)

Sprinkler Irrigation Manual. Wright Rain, Ringwood, England. 1956. (This treatise on sprinkler irrigation contains some outstanding articles by English workers.)

Water. USDA Yearbook, 1955. (An excellent discussion of water in relation to agriculture.)

Van der Veen, R. and Meijer, G. *Light and Plant Growth.* Macmillan, New York. 1959. (A brief but valuable book on light and its modification in relation to plant growth and development. The examples used are largely horticultural.)

Went, F. W. *The Experimental Control of Plant Growth.* Chronica Botanica Co., Waltham, Mass. 1957. (Studies of controlled plant growth carried out at the Earhart Laboratory. Particularly valuable for the climatic responses of individual crop plants.)

CHAPTER 7

Directing Plant Growth

The growth of plants may be modified to suit man's desires. These modifications may be achieved by direct manipulation of the plant itself, in contrast to interference with the plant's environment. The direct control of growth by pruning and grafting are among the oldest of horticultural practices. Recently, however, chemical substances (*growth regulators*) that affect growth and development have been discovered.

The direct modification of growth is effectively limited by our knowledge of plant development. The more complete our knowledge and the more refined our techniques, the more sophisticated is our control. It becomes possible to affect not only the amount of growth, but the form and pattern of growth, as well as differentiation in such physiological processes as flowering and rooting.

PHYSICAL CONTROL

Growth may be controlled by purely physical methods. Physical techniques that direct the shape, size, and direction of plant growth are known as *training*. Training is in effect the orientation of the plant in space. This may involve merely providing a support on which plants naturally grow and, in addition, may include the bending, twisting, or fastening of the plant to the supporting structure (Fig. 7-1). Training often is associated with the judicious removal of plant parts, or *pruning*. Pruning may also be performed for other purposes, for example, to adjust fruit load, the subsequent change in form being only incidental.

The object of altering the spatial form or size of a plant is to improve its appearance or usefulness. Certain woody shrubs can be trained to resemble a great variety of shapes, limited only by the skill of the plantsman.

Topiary—beautiful to some, ugly to others—illustrates the plasticity of the growing plant (Fig. 7-2). The usefulness of a particular spatial arrangement may result from the increased efficiency of light utilization or from the facilitation of cultural operations, such as harvesting or disease control. Furthermore, training and pruning may enhance productiveness and quality.

Training and Pruning as Horticultural Practices

 Training and pruning are well-known, but by no means universal, practices. Herbaceous annuals or biennials are usually grown without any attempt to alter their growth patterns. The lack of training is not so much a matter of satisfaction in their performance, but of practicality. Since there are usually many plants in relation to the space involved, it is not possible to handle each one individually. Perennials, and especially woody plants,

Fig. 7-1. *Training orientates a plant in space and is an integral part of the culture of many plants. A. Tomatoes are twisted around twine to maximize space in greenhouse production. Tomatoes grown for early market in the field may be trained to wooden stakes. B. Grapes trained to the 4-cane Kniffen system. C. Hops are trained to 18-ft trellises.*

A   B   C

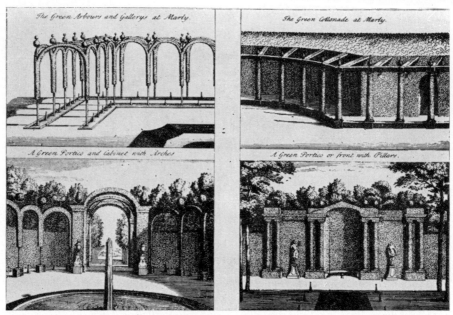

Fig. 7-2. *An example of topiary art from* The Theory and Practice of Gardening *by Alexander Le Blond, translated by John James in 1728. Topiary refers to the art of training plants to resemble unnatural, ornamental shapes. This type of "bush sculpture" was very popular in the seventeenth and eighteenth centuries for ornamental plantings, but is no longer in fashion.*
[From Wright, *The Story of Gardening*, Garden City Publ. Co., Garden City, New York, 1938.]

are often trained to some degree. Each individual is relatively valuable, since there are few plants per unit area, and since they are grown for extensive periods of time (the productive life of an apple orchard may be forty years). As plant size continually increases, the control of growth through pruning becomes a necessity. The framework of a woody tree in relation to pruning is shown in Fig. 7-3.

Physiological Responses to Training and Pruning

The orientation of the plant in space has a marked physiological effect on growth and fruiting. Fruit trees planted on an inclined angle of about 45° have been shown to become dwarfed and to flower earlier. The training of branches in a horizontal position encourages the same effect. This decrease in growth rate and increase of flowering occurs naturally when the weight of a heavy crop load bends a limb down. Thus, fruiting acts as a triggering device to keep the plant reproductive. A clear explanation of

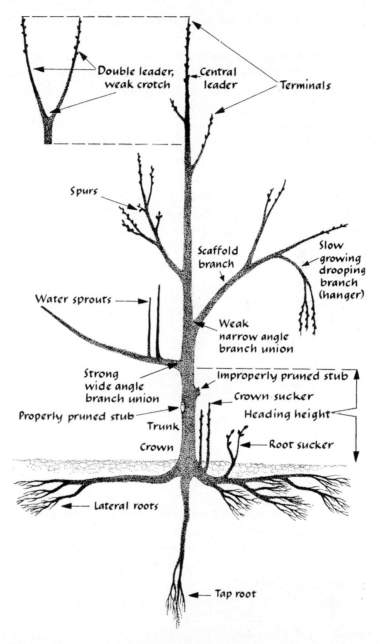

Fig. 7-3. *The plant framework in relation to pruning termi-nology.*

[Adapted with permission of the publisher from *The Pruning Manual* by Chris-topher, copyright 1954 by the Macmillan Company.]

this phenomenon has not been made. It has been suggested, however, that the effect is due to a disturbance of the normal auxin movement, which in turn affects phloem transport. This assumes that gravity effects the pattern of auxin distribution across the stem. The effect of the disruption of phloem transport on growth and fruiting is discussed later in this chapter.

The plant response to pruning is a result of the altered relationship of the remaining plant parts and the disturbed pattern of auxin production. The effect differs to some extent, depending on whether the plant is dormant or growing when pruned.

Altered Plant Part Relationship

An explosion of vegetative growth normally occurs after extensive shoot pruning. This is due to the fact that severe shoot pruning radically alters the balance between root and shoot. The flush of growth following pruning is caused by the diversion of water, nutrients, and stored food from an undisturbed root system into a reduced bud area (Fig. 7-4). Although there is also some reduction in the amount of stored food (along with some reduction in photosynthetic area), this is negligible because reserve food in the form of sugars and other carbohydrates are stored mainly in the roots and older portions of the shoot, especially during dormancy.

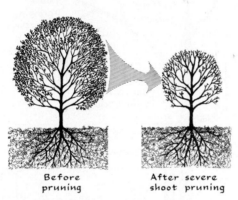

Before pruning   After severe shoot pruning

Fig. 7-4. *Shoot pruning alters the balance of root and shoot and results in increased growth of the remaining parts.*

The increased growth that occurs after extensive pruning might indicate that the technique has a rejuvenating effect. But the additional growth does not compensate for the removed portion of the plant; the plant pruned of vegetative growth never quite makes up the loss. Thus, pruning is in reality a dwarfing process, although some plant parts may be selectively increased.

Pruning and Flowering

In general, severely shoot-pruned plants, especially if they are young, tend to remain vegetative. Conversely, root pruning encourages flowering. This can be explained in a number of ways. It has been interpreted by an extension of the carbohydrate:nitrogen-balance "theory" of flowering (see

Chapter 5). This assumes that the severely shoot pruned plant draws on its carbohydrate reserve in the promotion of growth. The resulting low carbohydrate:nitrogen balance encourages vegetative growth. Root-pruned plants reduce nitrogen accumulation but, by slowing down vegetative growth, conserve carbohydrates. The carbohydrate surplus supposedly promotes flowering. Another equally valid explanation may be that actively growing leaves produce substances which inhibit flowering. Thus, a rapid increase of vegetative growth would be antagonistic to flowering. The encouragement of flowering by root pruning is a direct result of slowing down vegetative growth. The precise relationship, however, is unclear; the explanation awaits a more precise elucidation of the flowering process.

Auxin Unbalance

APICAL DOMINANCE. The role of the apical meristem in inhibiting the growth of dormant buds (bud break) behind it is known as *apical dominance*. This dominance of the apical meristem differs with the species in question. Thus, the actively growing bamboo is basically an unbranched stem, whereas the shrub Pfitzer juniper grows as a many-branching structure. Both the degree of branching and the subordination of lateral growth

Fig. 7-5. *Apical dominance refers to the effect of the apical bud in inhibiting bud break below. Removal of the apical bud encourages lateral breaks. The growth of lateral buds can be inhibited by auxin application to the cut portion of the stem.*

[Adapted from Bonner and Galston, *Principles of Plant Physiology*, Freeman, San Francisco, 1952.]

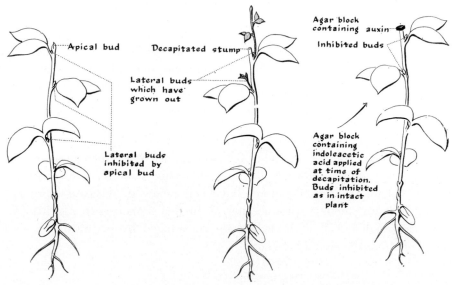

to the main growing stem, the *central leader,* appear to be functions of *apical dominance.*

The branching of shoots (and roots) has been shown to be influenced by auxin, which is produced in greatest abundance in a vigorously growing apex. A high concentration of auxin moving down from the stem tip has been shown to inhibit lateral bud break. Rapidly growing, unbranched shoots called watersprouts have very high auxin levels and represent an extreme example of apical dominance. Removal of the stem tip results in an increased amount of lateral bud break and of subsequent branching, usually directly below the cut (Fig. 7-5). This is explained by the destruction of the auxin-producing meristem, although it must be admitted that the precise relationship is not established. Thus, pruning that merely removes the tip of the stem (*heading back*) can create new form changes by the destruction of apical dominance (Fig. 7-6). Similarly, pruning that merely removes laterals but leaves the stem tip undisturbed (*thinning out*) not only eliminates branching but by increasing the vigor of stem tip, and presumably its auxin content, limits future lateral bud break.

Fig. 7-6. *These coleus plants are of the same age, and were grown under the same conditions with the exception of pruning. Removal of the apical meristem of the plant on the right has stimulated the growth of lateral shoots.*
[Courtesy E. R. Honeywell.]

BRANCH ANGLE. There is also evidence that the angle of branching is controlled by auxin. Branches produced below an actively growing, auxin-producing apex form a wider angle with the main stem than do branches formed where the growing point has been removed. A heavily pruned, young fruit tree tends to produce narrow-angled branches. In peach pruning, wide-angled scaffold branches are encouraged by permitting growth of a bud from the stub (Fig. 7-7).

Fig. 7-7. *Wide-angled scaffold branches are encouraged by proper pruning in the peach. Left. The central leader was summer pruned (pinched) above a bud during the first growing season to channel growth into selected scaffold branches and to encourage wide-angled attachment. Right. During winter pruning, the central leader was cut to a stub. The stub will be removed in a few years.*
[Courtesy of F. H. Emerson.]

Pruning Techniques

Heading Back and Thinning Out

The two basic pruning cuts, heading back and thinning out, are illustrated in Fig. 7-8. Heading back consists in cutting back the terminal portion of a branch to a bud, whereas thinning out is the complete removal of a branch to a lateral or main trunk. The heading back of a stem destroys apical dominance and is usually followed by the stimulation of several lateral bud breaks, depending on the species and the distance from the tip that the cut is made. To encourage spreading growth, the branch is usually cut back to an outside bud. Heading tends to produce a bushy, compact

Heading Thinning

Fig. 7-8. *Heading encourages lateral growth. Thinning results in a more open structure.*

plant. The shearing of a hedge is an extreme example of this type of pruning. Heading back actively growing plants is referred to as *pinching*.

Thinning, in contrast to heading, encourages longer growth of the remaining terminals. The net result of thinning is a reduction of laterals. Thinning of weak growth tends to "open up" the tree. It usually results in producing a larger rather than a bushier plant. The rejuvenation of older trees by reducing, and thereby stimulating, the remaining growing points is accomplished by thinning. The thinning out of growing wood is referred to as *deshooting*.

Timing of Pruning

"Prune when the knife is sharp."
                    OLD SAYING

The time to prune is influenced by a number of factors, including convenience, the species involved, and the effect desired. Although it is best to keep some plants more or less continually pruned, this is seldom practical. Fruit trees are usually *dormant pruned*. Not only is this convenient in the cycle of orcharding, but the framework of the plant can be more easily seen with the foliage off. Where winter temperatures are low, the pruning operation is usually delayed until the severest weather is past in order to reduce winter injury in fresh cuts. The pruning operation is best not carried on into the growing season because of the additional loss of translocated foods. *Summer pruning* of new growth makes it possible to avoid structural faults before too much growth is wasted. This is especially important when the tree is young. By proper heading little photosynthetic area need be lost. However, extensive dormant pruning has been shown to be less devitalizing than summer pruning. In addition, pruning wounds made in the early spring heal better than those made at other times of the year. Extensive pruning should be avoided in the late summer since this may initiate abundant, succulent vegetative growth, which may render the plant subject to winter injury. However, diseased growth or dead wood is best pruned away at once regardless of the season. This wood, besides being unattractive or dangerous, may become a harboring place for disease-producing pests.

It is only sensible to synchronize the time of pruning such that it does not interfere with the principal functions of the plant. Thus, ornamental flowering shrubs that bloom from buds laid down the previous year should be pruned after bloom. Similarly, it would be absurd to make large cuts on limbs of fruit trees supporting a maturing crop.

Objectives of Pruning

Pruning to Control Size

Probably the most obvious effect that pruning has on perennial plants is in the control of plant size. Since perennials grow continually, an optimum size can be maintained only by the selective removal of plant parts. Thus, the lawn is cut, the hedge is clipped, and shrubs and fruit trees are pruned in an effort to keep the plant within bounds (Fig. 7-9).

The size may be controlled for esthetic or utilitarian reasons. In fruit production, where crops are hand picked, large tree size makes harvesting, as well as spraying, extremely difficult. Certain pruning techniques can be used to effectively lower large trees over a period of years without excessive injury.

The compensating effect of pruning on growth may increase the size of particular plant parts. This diversion of growth may be utilized to achieve an actual increase in height or spread, even though total growth is reduced. The selective removal of buds, flowers, or fruits to increase the size of the remaining parts must be considered a specialized part of pruning. This is discussed further in Chapter 8. The pruning of flowers or fruits to increase fruit size is known as *thinning* (not to be confused with the pruning term *thinning out*). The removal of buds to increase flower size is known as *disbudding*.

Pruning to Control Form

The art of training and pruning to control plant form has received much attention in horticultural writings. In this context, form refers not only to

Fig. 7-9.   *The fairway is kept in bounds by constant mowing.*
[Courtesy International Harvester Co.]

the gross shape of the plant but to its structural makeup, which involves the number, orientation, relative size, and angle of branches. The natural form characteristic of different species may be greatly modified with pruning. Plants may be trained to grow upright or to spread, and branching may either be increased or decreased.

Woody plants, especially those bearing heavy loads of fruit, must be considered as structural units because they may be torn apart in a high wind. Structural strength in fruit trees is obtained by pruning to eliminate narrow-angled branches and to achieve a well-spaced arrangement of wide-angled scaffold branches. Narrow-angled branches are weak and tend to break under pressure because of the lack of continuous cambium and the inclusion of squeezed-off bark in the crotch (Fig. 7-10). For maximum strength, only one branch should develop at any point on the main stem, and the branches should be well distributed around the tree (Fig. 7-11). Owing to the increase in diameter of branches, it is necessary to select branches carefully when young.

The control of plant form may be utilized to achieve increased quality through better light distribution. The center of an unpruned apple tree is almost impervious to light and as a result produces few fruit, those that are produced being poor in color and quality. Opening up the tree is also

Fig. 7-10. *Narrow branch angles are weak because of the enclosure of bark and the formation of wood parenchyma in the crotch.*

[Adapted from Eames and MacDaniels, *An Introduction to Plant Anatomy*, McGraw-Hill, New York, 1947.]

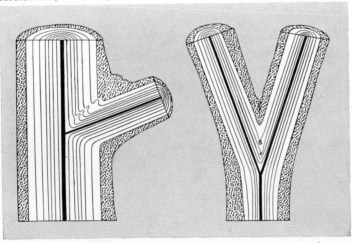

Wide angle branching   Narrow angle branching

Fig. 7-11. *For maximum strength scaffold branches of apple should be well spaced and evenly oriented around the tree. Left. In the unpruned tree the branches to be removed have been marked with paint. Right. The same tree after pruning.*
[Courtesy Purdue Univ.]

important for disease control in that it permits good spray distribution and facilitates rapid drying.

Mechanical harvesting of fruit crops requires specialized training and pruning to adapt the plant to the machine. For plants harvested by shaking, this involves the development of high trunks (to allow for a single "grab" by the machine when the tree is young) and only two or three main scaffolds for use when the tree is older. Mechanical harvesting of grapes by the use of a cutterbar requires special trellising and training of the vines.

Pruning for Plant Performance

ESTABLISHMENT OF TRANSPLANTS. The transplanting of large plants from natural growing sites is usually very difficult. Root pruning or repeated transplanting when the plant is young encourages a fibrous root system and allows the plant to be moved safely when large.

Proper root and shoot pruning greatly aids in reducing transplanting shock and promotes successful plant establishment. This is especially true in bare-rooted transplants. Light root pruning stimulates root initiation; shoot pruning conserves moisture by reducing the transpiration surface in relation to the root area.

PRODUCTIVITY AND QUALITY. Pruning is often a necessary step in the control of productivity. Where vigorous bud wood is desired, as in scion orchards, heavy pruning stimulates vegetative growth. On the other hand, where flower or fruit production is the desired aim, selective pruning that eliminates weak, nonproductive wood will aid in channeling the plants energy into flowering and fruiting. In addition, fruit and flower quality is greatly effected by the vigor of the wood it is borne on as well as its location in the tree. Shoot growth (suckers) on the understock of grafted plants must be continually removed to eliminate nonproductive growth. Similarly, forest trees may be pruned to produce knot-free lumber.

Training Systems

Training systems are carried on to control form throughout the life of the plant. Consequently, special attention must be given in the formative years. The objective is to obtain some predetermined shape in an attempt to achieve greater productivity, quality, ease of culture, or beauty.

Leader Training

The main considerations that determine form involve the point on the main stem from which branches form and the subsequent orientation of branches (Fig. 7-12). In the *central-leader* system of training, the trunk is encouraged to form a central axis with branches distributed laterally up and down and around the stem. The central axis, or leader, is the dominant feature of the tree's framework, and the main direction of growth is upward. In the *open-center*, or *vase*, system of training, the main stem is terminated, and growth is forced through a number of branches originating rather close to the upper end of the trunk. Special pruning is required to prevent a lateral from becoming dominant; that is, from forming a new central leader. Although the open-center tree is a lower tree than the central leader tree, it has inherent mechanical weaknesses, due to its narrow crotches and close branching. The *modified leader* system is somewhat intermediate between these two types.

An *espalier* is a railing or trellis along which plants (usually fruit trees or vines) are trained to grow flat. Plants trained in this manner are also referred to as espaliers. An espalier restricted to one shoot, or two shoots growing in opposite or parallel directions, is called a *cordon*. Because of extensive pruning labor required, tree fruits are not commercially grown as espaliers in the United States. Grapes, however, are commonly grown as espaliers, as in the widely used Kniffin system of training. Properly executed espaliers are extremely attractive as ornamentals. They are created with a combination of pruning and actual bending of shoots when succulent (Fig. 7-13). Such shoots will retain the imposed shape when lignification sets in.

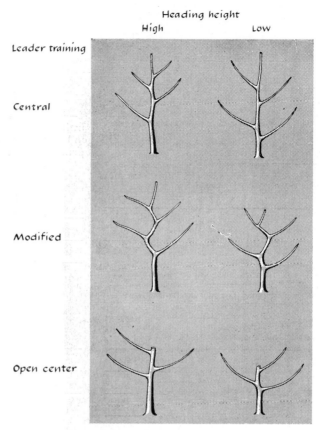

Fig. 7-12. *Training and tree form.*

Well-planned espaliers can be strong enough to be self-supporting, although frames are required in the early years.

The particular system by which a plant is trained depends to a large extent on the species. Peaches and apricots can be pruned to an open center because of the broad angle of attachment of the branches, which produce strong crotches. In addition, the central leader in peach trees is subject to winter injury. The reason for this is not clear, but it appears to be related to the failure of the central leader to harden off (Fig. 7-14). The narrow-angled branching of apples and pears makes the open center tree unfeasible, thus they are usually trained to either a central or modified leader (Fig. 7-15). Cherries and plums are trained to either the open-center or modified-leader system. Citrus and other evergreen fruits may be pruned lightly to establish a stronger framework, but usually little subsequent pruning is performed

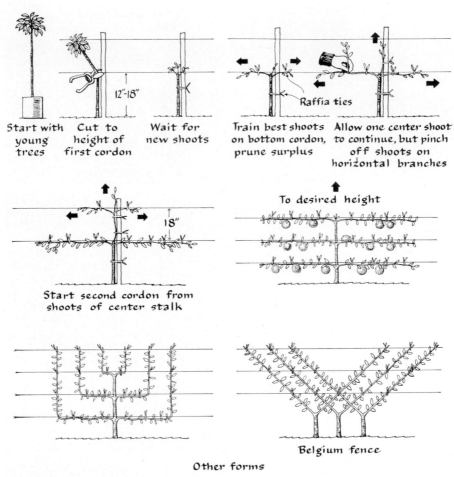

Start with   Cut to   Wait for   Train best shoots   Allow one center shoot
young   height of   new shoots   on bottom cordon,   to continue, but pinch
trees   first cordon   prune surplus   off shoots on
                                                                  horizontal branches

Start second cordon from
shoots of center stalk

Other forms

Fig. 7-13. *The creation of an espalier.*

[Adapted from Hudson, *Sunset Pruning Handbook,* Lane Book Co., Menlo Park, Calif., 1952.]

except to eliminate dead wood after a freeze. Mechanical hedgers are being tried on an experimental basis.

Renewal Pruning

To achieve superior performance in perennial plants grown for flowering or fruiting, pruning must stimulate the most reproductive growth. This involves the continuous renewal of growth that has reached its optimum reproductive age. Depending upon the species, this may be current, one-year-old, two-year-old, or older, wood.

The factors to be considered are (1) the time at which the buds are differentiated in relation to blooming and (2) the age of the wood that pro-

A   B

C   D

Fig. 7-14. *The peach is commonly pruned to an open center and is usually composed of two or three widely spaced, main scaffold limbs. A. A well-formed, three-scaffold crotch on a three-year-old tree. B. A six-year-old tree on which six scaffold branches were allowed to develop. All but two or three should have been eliminated at the start of the second year's growth. Note the weakness that has developed between the scaffold branches. C. A "two-story" tree showing severe winter injury as a result of delayed maturity. The center leader should have been removed at the start of the second season's growth. D. This tree was growing next to the one illustrated in C. The two-branched, wide-angled crotch shows no evidence of winter injury.*

[Courtesy Purdue Univ., from Extension Circular 426, 1956.]

A

B

C

D

E

F

duces the most abundant and highest quality buds. Flower buds may be initiated in the year of flowering, as in summer- or fall-blooming plants (for example, the rose and chrysanthemum), or on the previous year's growth, as in spring-flowering plants (for example, apple, lilac, peach, brambles). Those buds that differentiate the year previous to flowering may be produced on that year's new growth or on older wood. Many species form buds from spurs on older wood. Spurs may bear more or less irregularly for as long as twenty years. In apple, however, their most productive life is two to five years.

Plants that flower on current growth, as does the rose, are often severely dormant-pruned to encourage vigorous reproductive growth. If unpruned, the abundance of buds produces inferior individual blooms. The degree of pruning is related to the vigor of the plant; the more vigorous the plant the greater the number of buds that are retained. During the growing season, overvigorous canes that tend to remain vegetative are headed back. Roses grown for mass effect, such as climbers, are less severely pruned, although thinning of older growth is required to stimulate vigorous new canes.

The cutting of blooms in the summer serves to invigorate the remainder of the plant. Senescing flowers should be removed to prevent fruit development, since they drain nutrients from the plant.

Brambles (blackberry, raspberry) produce fruit on year-old canes. Although the roots are perennial, the canes are biennial, and either weaken severely or die out right after fruiting. Thus, pruning has a number of functions. Immediately after bearing, the fruiting canes are removed to encourage new shoot growth. In red raspberry (*Rubus idaeus*) new canes arise as root suckers, hence the old canes may be completely removed. Black raspberries (*R. occidentalis*) do not produce suckers, thus fruiting canes are removed above the crown. The dormant year-old canes are thinned if necessary and headed back to remove the weaker buds and to encourage branching. Black and purple raspberries are further pinched when summer growth is two or three feet tall to increase lateral branching.

Fig. 7-15. *An eight-year-old apple tree trained to a modified leader. A. Before corrective pruning. B. After corrective pruning. The removal of the main portion of the central leader has opened up the center of the tree. Many of the pruning cuts were made to correct structural weakness. C. Narrow-angled, forked branches should be eliminated. D. Closely spaced branches, especially those growing toward the center of the tree, should be removed. E. Intertwining branches should be corrected. Note that limb-rub injury has girdled the branch. F. Watersprouts should be removed. This watersprout growing within a crotch would, if neglected, result in extensive injury.*
[Courtesy Purdue Univ.]

Renewal pruning is an important practice in controlling yield, size, and quality in grapes. Grapes bear fruit on the current growth from buds laid down the previous season. The greatest production is achieved from the fourth to eighth bud, and the quantity and quality of production is based on the vigor of the plant in relation to the number of remaining buds. If too many buds are left in relation to vigor, the crop will be small in size and poor in quality. If too few buds are left, yield will be reduced. A pruning formula has been devised for the Concord grape on the basis of plant vigor as determined by the weight of the prunings. Thirty buds are left for the first pound and ten buds for each additional pound of wood removed. This formula of "30 + 10" results in a "moderately" pruned vine, which gives optimum production in Ohio. In addition to fruiting canes, stubs of one or two buds, called *renewal canes,* are retained. These provide growth from which fruiting canes may be selected the following year. Thus, from a single trunk, growth is renewed each year (Fig. 7-16). Other training methods differ merely as to the form of the plant; the renewal principle is essentially the same.

The pruning of fruit trees is divided into stages. When the tree is young, pruning is principally a training operation to control form in order to produce a structurally sound framework. Because of the adverse effects on early bearing, pruning must be limited at this stage. After four to six years, when the major scaffold limbs are established, renewal pruning insures a continuing bearing surface of two- to four-year-old wood, from which the bulk of the crop develops.

The pillar system of training the apple—a system developed in England —is a good illustration of renewal pruning (Fig. 7-17). Under this technique, the tree structure consists of a single leader 10–12 feet high. The number of bearing units maintained depends upon the vigor of the tree. Each unit consists of a two-year fruiting limb, a one-year-old shoot, and the current growth. Dormant pruning consists of (1) removing the spent fruiting limb (now three years old), (2) heading back the two-year terminals of the limb, but leaving the fruit buds intact in anticipation of fruiting, and (3) thinning out all but a single year-old shoot. This pruning pattern is repeated each year; thus the productive two-year-old fruiting wood is continually renewed. High quality and annual production are achieved by controlling the bearing area. Close spacing of the trees (6 × 12 feet or 605 trees per acre) results in high production per acre. By controlling size, mechanical production practices may be facilitated, and harvesting greatly simplified. The pruning operation, although extensive, is routine; no decisions need to be made. Whether the pillar system will prove to be practical in the United

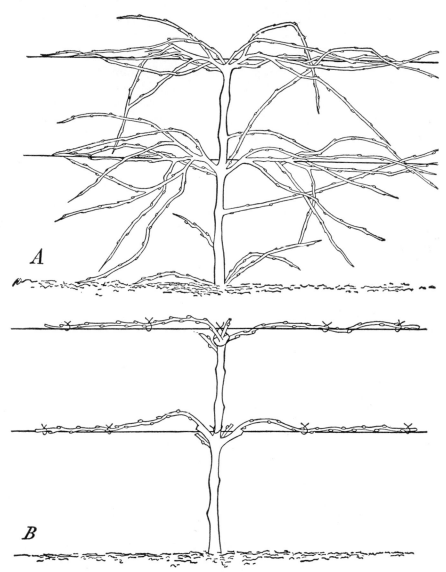

Fig. 7-16. *Concord grapes are commonly pruned in a renewal system. The sever-*
ity of pruning is related to the previous year's growth. A mature dormant vine
(A) before pruning, and (B) after pruning according to the four-cane Kniffin
system.
[From Farmers' Bull. 1870, USDA.]

States remains to be seen. The systems presently used in the United States
for pruning apples are renewal systems, but differ from the pillar system in
regard to the age of wood removed and the pattern of framework developed.

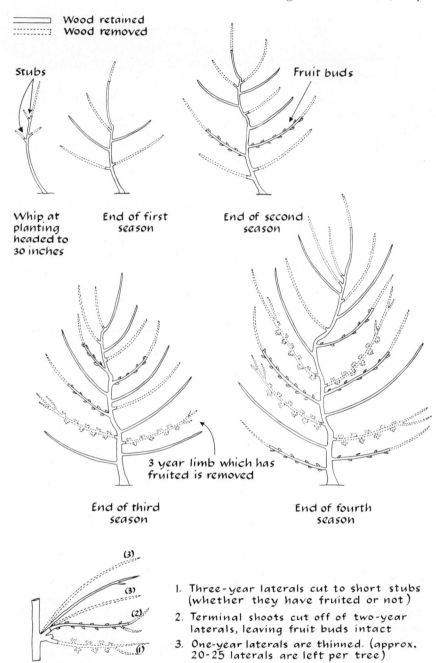

Fig. 7-17. *Pruning pillar apple trees.*

[Adapted from Weiss and Fisher, Canadian Dept. of Agriculture, 1960.]

BIOLOGICAL CONTROL

Graft Combination

Grafting is practiced to modify growth as well as for the propagation of plants. The interaction of two or more plants in a graft combination may affect growth and productivity. Moreover, disease resistance and hardiness may be achieved by the creation of a plant composed of more than one genetic component.

The practice of grafting as a means of growth control is used most extensively with fruit trees. Graft combinations of herbaceous plant material have not been fully explored, for unless the plant itself is relatively valuable, grafting is not an economical horticultural practice. In Japan, however, watermelon is grafted onto the gourd *Logonaria* to control Verticillium wilt, and eggplant is grafted onto *Solanum integrefolium* to increase productivity.

Fruit trees are normally composed of a "scion" variety grafted onto a rootstock, although more complex combinations are possible (Fig. 7-18). The rootstock may either be grown from seed as a unique plant (seedling rootstock) or may be asexually propagated (clonal rootstock). Some rootstocks,

Fig. 7-18. *Fruit trees are normally composed of two distinct parts, the rootstock and the scion variety. More complex trees may be made up of three or four components.*

[Adapted from Bonner and Galston, *Principles of Plant Physiology*, Freeman, San Francisco, 1952.]

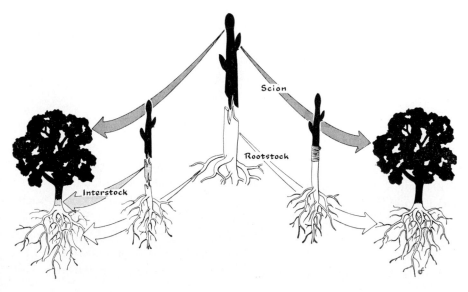

even though seed produced, are in effect clonal because of apomixis, as in citrus. Seedling rootstocks are often derived from a particular clonal variety. Thus, the "western" pear seedlings are usually derived exclusively from the Bartlett variety.

Restriction of Growth

The use of specific rootstocks to restrict the growth of the scion variety is an ancient practice. The degree of "dwarfing" achieved varies with the rootstock and with the species involved (Table 7-1). The physiological explanation of the dwarfing effect has not been fully established. Evidence exists that it may be related to a number of causes, among which are the restriction of upward translocation of inorganic nutrients through the rootstock, the restriction of downward phloem transport, or some physiological disturbance caused by graft incompatibility.

Table 7-1. *Some dwarfing rootstocks.*
[Adapted from Brase and Way, Bull. 783, New York Agricultural Experiment Station, 1959.]

FRUIT CROP	ROOTSTOCK	EFFECT
Apple	Malus clones	Complete range of dwarfing
	East Malling series	
	Malling Merton series	
	Malus sikkimensis "seedlings" *	Slight dwarfing
Pear	"Angers" quince clones	True dwarf
Sweet Cherry	"Stockton" Morello Cherry	Height reduced to half as compared to Mazzard stocks
Peach	*Prunus domestica* clones	Slight dwarfing
	Prunus institia clones	Slight dwarfing
Plum	*Prunus besseyi* clones	Slight dwarfing
Orange	Palestinian sweet lime seedling*	Slight dwarfing
	Sour orange seedling*	Slight dwarfing

* Apomictic

There are abundant sources of dwarfing rootstocks for the apple (Fig. 7-19). These rootstocks are all species of apple, many of which derive from old European clones grown under the names French Paradise and Doucin. These older clones were collected at the East Malling Station, England, and standardized by Roman numeral (EM I, EM II, or EM XI). Crosses involving EM IX and others with Northern Spy have produced a number of rootstocks of varying degrees of dwarfing, which were resistant to woolly

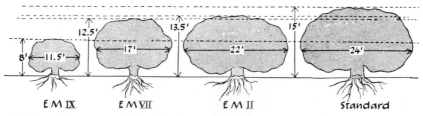

EM IX   EM VII   EM II   Standard

Fig. 7-19. *Comparative sizes of 17-year-old McIntosh on EM IX, VII, II, and standard seedling rootstocks.*

[Adapted from Circular 334, Ontario Dept. of Agriculture, 1958.]

aphis. These are standardized as the Malling Merton series (MM I, MM II, or MM VII). EM VIII and EM IX, are extreme dwarfing rootstocks. These rootstocks produce the dwarfing effect even if interposed between a "non-dwarfing" rootstock and a scion variety (Fig. 7-20). Thus, it is possible to avoid the shallow-rooted characteristics of EM IX, which produces poorly anchored trees, which are liable to tip over in wet ground after a strong wind, by using it as an *interstock* rather than a rootstock.

Pears are dwarfed by certain clones of quince that belong to a closely related genera (*Cydonia*). To avoid the graft incompatibilities of certain varieties of pear and quince, an interstock mutually compatible to both scion and stock is used as a "bridge." The pear variety

Fig. 7-20. *A comparison of fruiting and size of seven-year-old Delicious on seedling rootstock (left) and on Clark dwarf (right). The Clark dwarf is obtained by using a stem piece of Clark (a selection of French Paradise) as an interstock between the seedling rootstock and the scion variety.*

Hardy is often used as such a bridge. A "shield bud" of Hardy inserted under the scion bud serves the same function. Dwarfing rootstocks also exist for stone fruits.

Stimulation of Growth

Rootstocks may be used to compensate for poor root growth. The experimentally produced pear-apple hybrids had to be grafted on pear or apple to survive. The upright junipers (*Juniperus virginiana* varieties) have a poor root system, making them difficult to propagate. By grafting them onto the sturdy root system of *Juniperus glauca* Hetzi, a superior plant is created.

In apple, the use of Virginia crab as a rootstock or body stock to increase the vigor of the scion was once a common practice, but this is no longer recommended because of the sensitivity of Virginia crab to a virus disease known as "stem pitting" (Fig. 7-21).

Flowering and Productivity

The induction of flowering in the "nonflowering" Jersey group of the sweet potato by grafting to several species of related genera of the *Convolvulaceae* (morning glory) is a striking use of grafting to effect differentiation (Fig. 7-22). Apparently a specific flowering substance produced by the morning glory is transferred to the sweet potato. This substance is produced in the leaves of the morning glory species and is further effected by photo-period and temperature effects. This technique allows the use of hybridization as a breeding method for the sweet potato. It is of course unnecessary in the commercial production of sweet potatoes, since they are propagated from adventitious shoots that grow from the root.

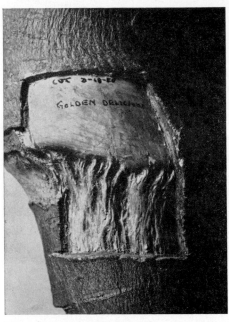

Fig. 7-21. *Symptoms of stem pitting virus on a Virginia crab apple bodystock. The scion variety, Golden Delicious, does not show the symptoms, but may carry the virus.*

[Courtesy R. B. Tukey.]

The age at which fruit trees will begin to bear can be affected by the rootstock. The severely dwarfing rootstocks of apple and pear also encourage early bearing. Dwarfing rootstocks have been utilized to induce fruiting in pears, which are notoriously late bearing, without a permanent dwarfing effect. Pears grafted or budded to quince are planted with the union 6–8 in. below the ground. Early fruiting is stimulated by the quince rootstock. Scion rooting, however, eventually overcomes the dwarfing influence of the quince rootstock.

Although the yield of dwarfed trees is smaller per tree than it is in the "standard" tree, their reduced size allows for closer spacing. This factor, coupled with the early bearing tendency, often results in greater per-acre yields with dwarf apples than has been achieved with "standard" trees on the standard spacing. There is evidence that some dwarfing rootstocks, with respect to fruiting, actually produce a more efficient tree than do seedling rootstocks. In general, dwarfing rootstocks seem to have no effect on fruit size.

In some instances the quality characteristics of the scion fruit have been shown to be effected by the rootstock. For example, the rough lemon rootstock lowers the sugar content of scion varieties of orange as compared to other rootstocks. In addition, rootstocks may affect such characteristics as blooming date and maturity.

Phloem Disruption

The induction of early fruiting and the control of growth by techniques that disrupt the phloem, just as girdling, scoring, or ringing are also ancient horticultural practices. Inverting a ring of bark accomplishes the same effect (Fig. 7-23). These

Fig. 7-22. *Sweet potato flowering after being grafted to a species of morning glory* (Ipomoea Nil).
[Courtesy S. Lam.]

practices, performed in early July (in the temperate regions of the northern hemisphere), are used to initiate flower bud formation in two- or three-year-old clonally propagated apple trees in order that they will flower and bear fruit the following year. Phloem disruption does not overcome seedling juvenility, but, like the use of dwarfing rootstocks, it is practiced to increase flowering on four-year-old apple seedlings. The injured phloem retards the downward movement of the synthesized organic materials. The induction of flower bud initiation is apparently due to the accumulation of some substance above the injured phloem, for a single branch can be induced to flower amid a barren tree. The effect is temporary, owing to the regeneration of phloem in the cuts, and to the seam in the inverted ring. Although the inverted ring effectively blocks the downward movement through the phloem, according to Karl Sax, the proponent of the technique, this one-way movement (polarity) may eventually be reversed.

The fact that phloem disruption also produces a dwarfing effect in addition to the induction of early flowering suggests that some types of rootstock

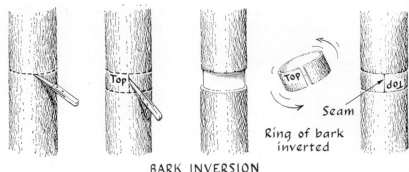

BARK INVERSION

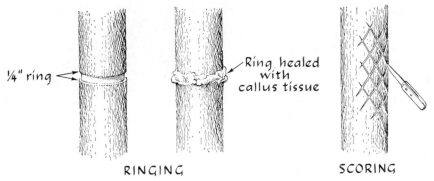

RINGING   **SCORING**

Fig. 7-23. *Dwarfing and the induction of early fruiting may be accomplished by phloem disruption.*

dwarfing may be related to the interference of downward phloem transport with the subsequent accumulation of organic substances. This, however, cannot explain the dwarfing effects of all rootstocks.

Hardening

Hardening in its broad sense refers to processes that increase the ability of a plant to survive the impact of unfavorable environmental stress. In its more restricted meaning hardening refers to processes that enable plants to withstand cold injury, just as the term hardiness is usually used to refer specifically to cold hardiness.

Cold hardiness is a variable characteristic that differs greatly with species. However, the development of hardiness within a plant varies in response to seasonal changes. For example, many plants that survive extreme winter freezing may be severely injured by spring frost. The natural change in hardiness in plants is related to temperature. The onset of cooler weather in the fall brings about a hardening and physiological toughening of woody and herbaceous plants. The increase in natural hardiness is due to an accumulation of sugars that increases the colloidally bound water. This is brought about by a slow-down of growth coincident with starch conversion or photosynthesis. Maximum cold hardiness is achieved in a cool, dry, sunny fall; the coolness and dryness discourage growth, whereas the sunshine favors photosynthesis.

The *hardening off* of transplants may be achieved by any treatment that materially checks new growth. This may be accomplished by gradually exposing the plants to cold, withholding moisture, or a combination of these two treatments. In general, about 10 days are sufficient to harden plants. This treatment is designed to produce a stocky, toughened plant in contrast to a soft, tender, "leggy" plant. Hardened plants are often darker green in color and, in the case of crucifers, have an increased waxy covering of the leaves. The induced cold resistance brought about by the hardening treatment in cool-season crops such as cabbage or celery may be considerable. Unhardened cabbage plants show injury at 28°F, whereas the hardened plants can withstand temperatures as low as 22°F. In warm season crops, such as tomato, the degree of cold hardiness imposed is slight, but hardening inures the plant to transplanting shock and hastens plant establishment under adverse conditions. The reduced growth rate enables the plant to withstand desiccation until the root system becomes established. Tender plants, which respire rapidly, have little chance of surviving warm, windy, dry conditions following transplanting. The cessation of growth under the hardening treatment, however, may severely interfere with subsequent performance, thus care must be taken to avoid overhardening. Under ideal transplanting conditions hardening may not be necessary.

CHEMICAL CONTROL

The control of plant growth and differentiation through the use of chemical substances is a modern development in horticulture, although examples can be found of the early use of various substances (for example, salt, wine, urine, germinating seeds) to this end. In general only a few isolated examples of these ancient practices have been shown to have a real physiological basis. The advances in this area have not come about through empirical methods but are instead largely a by-product of investigations into growth and development. This field was given great impetus by the impact of auxin studies on horticultural technology. A number of substances are now known that have a relatively broad spectrum of effects (for example, indoleacetic acid, maleic hydrazide, the gibberellins). Others merely mediate or block specific metabolic pathways. Substances such as colchicine have been used to achieve permanent genetic change (see Chapter 10). It can be assumed that, as knowledge expands in this area, an increasing number of growth-regulating substances will be found.

At present, the substances used to kill plants account for the greater part of chemical control. This is discussed further in the following chapter. The following section will review chemical substances that affect physiological processes of importance in horticultural practice.

Rooting

The rooting of cuttings has been shown to be influenced by auxin, although auxin is by no means the only substance involved. In the cutting, the natural auxin produced in young leaves and buds moves naturally down the plant and accumulates at the cut base along with sugars and other food materials. The natural formation of roots is apparently triggered by the accumulation of an optimum auxin level in relation to these substances. In a wide variety of plants, rooting is markedly increased by the addition of synthetic auxin. Although a wide variety of such compounds has been used, the greatest degree of success has been achieved with indolebutyric acid (Fig. 7-24):

—CH$_2$CH$_2$CH$_2$COOH

Indolebutyric acid

Fig. 7-24. *The potassium salt of indolebutyric acid markedly increases the rooting of* Chaenomeles *(flowering quince).*
[Courtesy J. S. Wells.]

Other auxins have a very narrow effective range of concentrations. Concentrations below the critical level are ineffective in root initiation, whereas those above the critical level not only inhibit both root growth and bud development but may cause gross morphological injury. Indoleacetic acid is ineffective, probably because it is readily destroyed by the plant.

Cuttings from many plants that are naturally difficult to root, such as apple, do not respond to auxin application. An interesting facet of this problem is that the transition of cuttings of some plants from "easy-to-root" to "difficult-to-root" is associated with the plant's change from juvenility to maturity. This may be due to the formation at maturity of inhibitors that block rooting. Thus, difficult-to-root, dormant grape cuttings become easy-to-root when leached with water to remove the inhibitor. Other plants become difficult-to-root not because inhibitors are present but because they become deficient in, or lack, certain required substances. If these substances are applied in combination with auxin, rooting can be promoted. This problem will be discussed further in Chapter 9.

Bolting

Bolting or seed stalk formation in biennial plants is induced by cold. Thus, carrots and onions do not flower unless growth is interrupted by a cold-induced dormancy. This cold requirement may be replaced under certain conditions by treatment with *gibberellins*, a group of substances whose primary morphological effects are associated with stem elongation. Gibberellins apparently replace or substitute for the natural compounds that are produced, or which accumulate, during the cold period and are responsible for bolting. Gibberellins will also induce bolting in those plants in which the process does not require cold but which are photoperiod sensitive, such as spinach. The bolting stimulus provided by gibberellins is independent of the flower-inducing stimulus. Thus, flowering in some chrysanthemums is dependent not only upon a short-day photoperiod but upon elongation induced by cold treatment. Gibberellins can replace the cold requirement, but the plants remain vegetative under long days. This use of gibberellins in promoting bolting has far-reaching effects in breeding, where time is often a limiting factor.

Gibberellins have the useful effect of facilitating normal seed stalk formation. For example, the heads of some lettuce varieties are so tight that the seed stalk cannot push through and may break or rot unless the head is cut, This is a desirable trait in crop production, but it interferes with seed production. Treatment with gibberellins can be used to encourage normal seed stalk formation in these lettuce types.

Flower Induction

The biochemical basis of flowering still remains unknown. That the triggering mechanism is hormonal, however, is indicated by the translocation of the photoperiodic stimulation from leaf to bud and across a graft union. It has been demonstrated that the suspected flowering hormone ("florigen") is not auxin, although auxin is involved in the process. Thus, auxin applied to many plants after the initiation of flowering may effectively promote flowering. Flower initiation of pineapple is induced by a number of compounds, among which are auxin and such unsaturated hydrocarbons as ethylene. This unique use of auxin to control flowering in pineapple is now a standard cultural procedure. At present, different auxin derivatives are utilized, for example, sodium naphthalene acetate in Hawaii, 2,4-D(2,4-dichlorophenoxyacetic acid) in the Caribbean area.

Fruit Set

Promotion of Fruit Set

The practice of chemically inducing fruit set has followed from studies involving the relationship of natural auxin to fruiting (see Chapter 5). The use of auxin derivatives to set fruit in the absence of pollination (parthenocarpy) has had some commercial utilization in the winter greenhouse production of tomatoes, where fruit set becomes difficult, and in fig and grape production. The auxin substances generally used for tomatoes are p-chlorophenoxyacetic acid and β-naphthoxyacetic acid. This practice is limited, however, since it causes fruit abnormalities, such as puffiness and premature softening. The use of auxins to set fruit in Calimyrna fig eliminates the need for male trees and the practice of caprification. However, the most effective auxin for fruit set (p-chlorophenoxyacetic acid) produces a seedless fruit that has not proved to be acceptable, and the auxin (benzothiazoll-2-oxyacetic acid), which permits the development of the seed coat, is not as effective for fruit set. The use of auxin sprays to promote fruit set in some grape varieties has eliminated the need for girdling. This has become a widely adopted practice in California for use with the Black Corinth and Thompson Seedless varieties.

Flower and Fruit Thinning

The removal of flowers and fruits to reduce crop loads has been referred to as thinning. The relationship of thinning to fruit quality and size is discussed further in Chapter 8. The reduction in crop load by *chemical thin-ning* has become a standard practice in a large part of the fruit industry. It is one of the best examples of the chemical control of growth. The physio-logical action of these chemicals consists in preventing the completion of fertilization or to induce embryo abortion, both of which result in natural abscission. Chemical thinning may be performed prior to fertilization (*flower thinning*) or after fertilization (*fruit thinning*).

The materials effective in thinning may be grouped into two types, de-pending on their mode of action. Flower-thinning compounds are composed of caustic and toxic substances (for example, phenols, cresols, dinitro-com-pounds) that kill off the blossoms or render them sterile. The principal effect of an interesting substance called Mendok (sodium dichloroisobutyr-ate) is to induce pollen sterility. This male gametocide has been used ex-perimentally in tomatoes (a self-pollinated crop) to induce sterility in the early clusters and thereby to concentrate fruit set. The concentrated ripen-ing of fruits would be desirable for "once-over" mechanical harvesting. The fruit thinning materials are auxin derivatives, which bring about thinning largely through embryo abortion. It is interesting to note that auxin, which sets fruit in some species, is used to remove fruit in others.

All auxins are not necessarily effective in thinning, and in fact only naph-thaleneacetic acid and its derivatives are effective in fruit thinning. This auxin is widely used in apples and is effective in peaches, pears, olives, and grapes, although *n*,1-naphthyl phthalamic acid has been more widely used in the stone fruits. Chemical thinning with auxin is also employed to prevent fruiting in trees used as ornamentals, where only flowering is desired and fruit is considered a nuisance.

The way in which auxin derivates cause embryo abortion is not clear. For example, the principal absorption of auxin is not through the fruit but through the foliage. The degree of thinning with auxin is greatly affected by the concentration used, the timing of application in relation to fruit de-velopment, and the species and variety, as well as by such environmental factors as temperature and humidity.

Preharvest Fruit Drop

The effect of auxin in inhibiting abscission has found an important hor-ticultural application in the control of preharvest fruit drop. The natural auxin, which prevents abscission and is provided by the seed, apparently decreases with fruit maturity. A number of synthetic substances are now used to delay fruit drop, among which are naphthaleneacetic acid, 2,4,5-

trichlorophenoxyacetic acid, and α-2,4,5-trichlorophenoxy propionic acid. Chemical preharvest drop control is widely used in the fruit industry for apple, apricot, pear, prune, almond, and citrus, and especially in varieties of these fruits that are prone to drop prematurely. It is an effective means of preventing fruit drop that is ordinarily accentuated after frost. The use of preharvest drop control to increase red color development after maturity is reached cannot be recommended because of the poor storage qualities of overmature fruit.

Dormancy

The modification of seed and plant dormancy promises to be an important area for chemical control. Although the control of seed dormancy has received relatively little attention, there has been a great deal of effort to prolong dormancy with respect to the storage of horticultural products. For example, the serious losses of potatoes and onions are associated with sprouting that occurs with the breaking of dormancy. High concentrations of auxin have been successful in prolonging dormancy. A number of other substances that prolong dormancy but which do not "kill" the tuber or bulb are being isolated. However, the use of many of these substances on foods is not feasible. The use of the growth inhibitor maleic hydrazide,

$$
\begin{array}{c}
\text{O} \\
\|\\
\text{C} \\
\diagup \quad \diagdown \\
\text{H—C} \qquad \text{N—H} \\
\| \qquad\quad | \\
\text{H—C} \qquad \text{N—H} \\
\diagdown \quad \diagup \\
\text{C} \\
\| \\
\text{O}
\end{array}
$$

Maleic Hydrazide

has been effective in inhibiting sprouting in onions and potatoes, even when applied to the growing plant. The extension of dormancy in woody plants to avoid damage by spring frost would provide great economic benefits.

Growth Promoters and Inhibitors

Chemical materials that promote or inhibit plant growth have promising uses in horticulture. For example, kinetin (6-furfurylamino purine) acts as a promoter of cell division and appears to have value in promoting callus formation. Similarly, the growth-stimulating effects of gibberellins are used to increase the size of celery. Substances that inhibit or retard growth are equally desirable. The effect of maleic hydrazide in slowing down the growth of turf to reduce the frequency of cutting has not proven practical in the field, but has stimulated a search for other compounds to this end. Recently, a number of compounds have been found that dwarf plants effectively by retarding stem growth. Examples are phosphon (2,4-dichlorobenzyltributylphosphonium chloride) and CCC (2-chloroethyl trimethylammonium chloride). Such substances show promise for use in reducing the height of many ornamental flowering plants without unduly interfering with flowering time or flower size (Fig. 7-25).

Untreated   **Soil treated with phosfon**

Fig. 7-25. *The growth retardant properties of phosphon.*

[Adapted from Agricultural Research Service 22–65, USDA, 1961.]

Substances that result in leaf abscission have had important uses in agriculture. The defoliation of cotton with Endothal (disodium 3,6-endoxohexohydrophthalate to facilitate mechanical harvesting is the best example. This compound has found horticultural application in the defoliation of rose plants prior to harvesting. The use of defoliants to facilitate grape harvesting is being tried experimentally.

Selected References

Audus, L. J. *Plant Growth Substances.* Leonard Hill, London. 1959. (The physiological action and practical application of growth regulators.)

Christopher, E. P. *The Pruning Manual.* Macmillan, New York. 1954. (A nontechnical but thorough treatment.)

Leopold, A. C. *Auxins and Plant Growth.* Univ. of Calif. Press, Berkeley. 1955. (The fundamentals of auxin action and their use in agriculture.)

Tukey, H. B. *Dwarfed Fruit Trees.* Macmillan, New York. 1964.

CHAPTER 8

Biological Competition

The earth is covered with a variety of life forms in competition for food, light, and elbow room. To a great extent man, the ascendant species, now directs this competition to his own advantage. The efficiency of this control is commonly thought of in terms of civilization or culture. The standard of living of a people is directly related to their ability to compete in the biological spectrum.

The two great professions that deal directly with man's control over his biological competitors are medicine and agriculture. Diseases of man, neglecting inborn errors of metabolism, are largely due to the competition by microorganisms for ascendancy in the human body. Agriculture, on the other hand, is concerned with man's efforts to control and exploit plant and animal life for food and fiber. The term horticulture, the intensive cultivation of "garden" crops, implies man's interference with the natural competition and interaction among living things. The forms of biological competition that we are concerned with in plant cultivation are plant pests (pathogens, predators, and weeds) and the crop plants themselves.

Plant pests take a heavy toll from world agriculture. In the United States the yearly loss in farm crops has been estimated at 5 billion dollars. Moreover, the annual cost of pesticides and related equipment amounts to almost 350 million dollars. The awesome destructive power of some pests could wipe out the crops in an entire section of the country. Others may not be spectacular but in the long run are equally insidious. These pests continually "peck away" at our abundance, but their damage tends to be unnoticed. To a particular grower or home owner a particular pest may mean the difference between feast or famine, sun or shade. All eventually share the cost of this waste.

COMPETITION BETWEEN CROP
AND PATHOGEN

Disease

The word disease means literally "not at ease." Broadly defined, a disease is any injurious abnormality. A distinction between these abnormalities—physiological or anatomical—is made on the basis of *cause*. Diseases caused by some biological agent are referred to as *pathogenic* diseases. *Nonpathogenic* diseases may include the adverse effects of abnormal physiological disorders, environment (extremes of heat, cold, fertility, water availability), graft incompatibilities, spray injury, or disorders due to unknown causes (Fig. 8-1).

The use of the word "disease" to refer to insect injury, much less to non-

Fig. 8-1. *The blank spots in this California pear orchard are a result of a serious "disease" known as pear decline. The cause of this malady is unknown but is related to the use of oriental rootstocks, mainly* Pyrus ussuriensis.
[Courtesy USDA.]

pathogenic disorders of plants, may be objectionable to some. Nevertheless, consideration of the term mental disease will indicate that the word disease is certainly not an exclusive one. The confusion arises from the use of the term in a restrictive sense to refer to the injurious effect caused by a taxonomically distinct organism in intimate association with the host plant for extended periods of time. This use of the term disease would apply to the detrimental effects that viruses, bacteria, and fungi have on plants. The detrimental effects of insects, mice, or birds would then be referred to as injury rather than disease, the term predator rather than pathogen being applied to these pests. The distinction between predator and pathogen, however, is not clear-cut. Many plant-attacking nematodes as well as insects (such as the peach tree borer) are in intimate contact with the plant for extended periods of time and would well be considered pathogens even in the sense of the restrictive definition. In the ensuing discussion, no special distinction will be made between pathogen and predator.

Pathogenic plant diseases may be discussed either in terms of the agent (pathogen) causing the disease or in terms of plant response. The specific responses of the plant are known as *symptoms*, which together with evidence of the pathogen, *signs,* permit the diagnosis of the disease; that is, the association of the disease with its cause. Care must be taken not to confuse the cause of the disease, the pathogen, with the disease itself.

Symptoms

Plants respond to the irritation of an external biological agent in a limited number of ways. The plant, or parts of it, may die—*necrosis.* This may be general, resulting in the complete death of the plant, or may be limited to specific organs, such as leaves, branches, flowers, or fruits. Death may be restricted to small areas resulting in spots or holes. Decline may be gradual and incomplete. For example, chloroplast breakdown appears as yellowing or mottling, but does not necessarily result in the immediate death of the plant. Another basic plant response is a reduced growth rate, which may affect the entire plant or certain of its parts, resulting in stunting, dwarfing, or incomplete differentiation. A third response is an increased growth of an abnormal and morbid type. This results in overgrowths—enlargements of organs, tissues, or cells—or tumor-like protuberances called galls. Although it is true that the basic plant responses are limited, the many variations involving different tissues often permit accurate diagnosis from the symptoms alone.

The Pathogen

The pathogen has been defined as the biological agent inciting the disease. One is constantly awed by the number and kinds of pathogens affecting horticultural plants. They include almost the whole biological spectrum. Their effect may be as transient as an insect bite or as persistent as a virus infection.

The pathogen's association with the plant provides it with nourishment, shelter, support, or some other advantage. Competition between plant and pathogen is part of the natural order of things. Disease is not evil, malicious, or a particularly unusual condition. Nor do plants escape disease by virtue of their being "healthy." Many pathogens attack only vigorous, thrifty plants.

The association of living organisms in which one organism derives nourishment from another, the host, is known as parasitism. The terms parasite and pathogen are not synonyms. Pathogens are injurious to the host at some stage of its life cycle, whereas parasites are not necessarily injurious. Most pathogens are, however, parasitic in nature. Many disease-causing organisms may be only incidentally pathogenic; their usual mode of life may consist in living on naturally dead or decayed tissue. They are known as *saprophytes*. Some pathogens have evolved with a specific host plant to such an extent as to be *obligately parasitic;* they can only survive on the living tissue of the host. The host range of some pathogens may be extremely large, or it may be specific enough to include only particular cultivars within a single species.

Viruses

Viruses are small infectious particles made up of a core of nucleic acid surrounded by a protein sheath. Their ultramicroscopic size is comparable to that of protein molecules (Fig. 8-2). Viruses are obligate parasites in that they reproduce only in the living cell. However, they may be removed from the organism and remain active; that is, capable of inciting infection. Some viruses remain active in extracted plant juices for many months; the tobacco mosaic virus remains active for years in dried plant material.

The question of whether viruses are living or nonliving has become meaningless in terms of modern knowledge. If the living system is defined in terms of a self-duplicating entity capable of reconstructing itself from different component parts, then the virus is indeed alive, despite its inability to "squirm" or "breathe." On the other hand, since viruses depend upon the metabolism of a living cell for replication, they cannot, by themselves, be considered a complete, living unit.

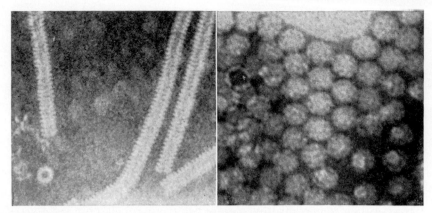

Fig. 8-2. *Plant viruses. (Left) Portions of tobacco mosaic virus particles. Even the spiral arrangement of the protein sheath is visible in this remarkable electron photomicrograph. The complete virus particle is about 150 × 3000 angstrom units (1Å = 10⁻⁸ centimeters). (Right) The protein subunits are visible in this photomicrograph of the turnip mosaic virus particles (300Å in diameter).*

[Courtesy R. W. Horne, Cambridge, England.]

The genetic structure of a particular virus that infects bacteria has been determined. These viruses show mutation and genetic recombination that is akin to sexual reproduction. Their genetic material is arranged in linear sequence, and linkage maps (see Chapter 10) can be constructed on the basis of the recombination of the characteristics that affect the expression of symptoms.

Diseases caused by viruses are common to most cellular organisms, and many viruses infect plants. Plant viruses have been classified into two main groups—*yellows* and *mosaic*—largely upon the basis of symptom expression, but also upon the basis of other factors. The symptoms of the yellows viruses include yellowing, leaf curling, dwarfing, excessive branching, shortening of internodes, and gall formation. These symptoms are probably brought about by hormonal unbalance and vascular disturbances. The symptoms of the mosaic viruses include a mosaic appearance and mottling, or spotting, which is due to chlorosis in small areas of the plant or to the death of tissues. The effect of viruses on the plant vary from slight to severe, depending upon the sensitivity of the host variety to the virus. Curly top, a virus disease that affects tomato, results in the quick death of the plant. A combination of viruses complicates the symptom picture; in general, multiple infection increases the complexity and severity of the symptoms. Some viruses produce no obvious symptoms yet considerable economic losses may occur.

Viruses are commonly transmitted by insects, generally leafhoppers (yellows group) or aphids (mosaic group). The yellows viruses persist in the agent of transmission, the *vector*, whereas the mosaic viruses do not. A few viruses are soil borne, and some of these are transmitted by nematodes. Some viruses are transmitted through the seed. But even when a virus is seed-transmitted, only a portion of the seedlings become infected. Mosaic viruses may be transmitted by rubbing infected leaves or, more commonly, by rubbing infectious sap on healthy leaves. Infection may also be transmitted through grafting, and some viruses can pass through the natural graft union created by dodder, a parasitic plant.

The asexual propagation of virus-infected plants will also propagate the virus. The only satisfactory way of maintaining virus-free stock of vegetatively propagated plants is by the perpetuation of plants that are found to be free of the pathogen. Maintenance of virus-free stock is difficult but is often achieved by isolation, roguing of infected plants, and control of insect vectors (Fig. 8-3). The certification of seed potatoes is based partly on freedom from virus. As a rule, once a plant contains virus, little can be done to free it. Inactivation of the virus in an infected plant by heat is effective for some viruses.

Bacteria

Bacteria, one-celled "plants" and the smallest of living "organisms," are responsible for many plant diseases. Seven genera of bacteria, none of which form spores, are plant pathogenic. Bacteria as a group are able to enter plants only through natural openings, such as the stomata and lenticels, or

Fig. 8-3. *A screenhouse for growing virus-free strawberry plants. The fine screen mesh keeps out aphids, which transmit the virus. These plants are maintained as a "nuclear" source of virus free-plants for nurserymen. A screenhouse for trees is in the background.*
[Courtesy Purdue University.]

through wounds. Insects are important in the transmission of bacterial diseases.

One of the most serious bacterial diseases, and the one in which bacteria were first shown to cause plant diseases, is fireblight—a disease of apple and pear caused by *Erwinia amylovora* (Fig. 8-4). Insects disseminate this bacteria, which penetrates the plant either through the nectar-producing glands in the flower, causing a blighting or death of the blossom (blossom blight), or through shoot terminals (shoot blight). The bacterial pathogen is also spread from infected parts to other parts of the tree by rain. The organism survives over winter in older bark lesions called cankers (Fig. 8-5). The disease is extremely serious on pear and has confined commercial production in the United States to the Pacific states and the Great Lakes area. Even in these locations, however, careful

Fig. 8-4. *Fireblight has almost completely destroyed this four-year-old pear.* [Courtesy of Purdue University.]

control measures must be used. This involves the constant removal of blighted wood, the use of antibiotic sprays, and the avoidance of rapid, succulent growth.

Symptoms of bacterial diseases include the death of tissues and the formation of galls. The soft rots common in storage diseases are associated with pectin-dissolving enzymes produced by the bacteria. Wilts produced by some bacterial diseases (Stewart's wilt of corn) are a result of vascular disturbances, specifically, a "plugging" of the vascular system by masses of the bacteria.

Fungi

Fungi, which cause the great majority of plant diseases, are multicelled plants. Except for some primitive types, they are characterized by a branching, thread-like (mycelial) growth. Fungi do not have chlorophyll and hence depend ultimately on green plants for their food. They may be saprophytic or parasitic, and many are both. Fungi reproduce by spores, which may be

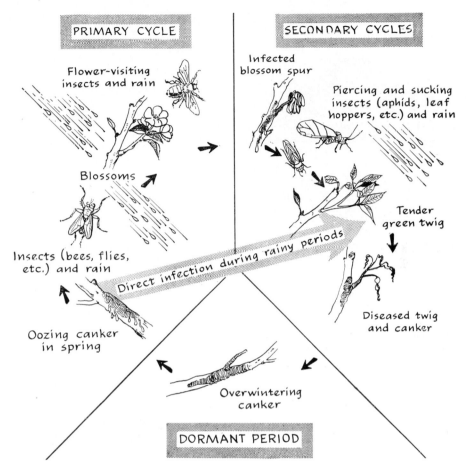

PRIMARY CYCLE

SECONDARY CYCLES

Flower-visiting
insects and rain

Infected
blossom spur

Piercing and sucking
insects (aphids, leaf
hoppers, etc.) and rain

Blossoms

Tender
green twig

Insects (bees, flies,
etc.) and rain

Direct infection during rainy periods

Oozing canker
in spring

Diseased twig
and canker

Overwintering
canker

DORMANT PERIOD

Fig. 8-5. *Life cycle of the bacterium* Erwinia amylovora, *which causes fireblight.*
[Adapted from Klos, Michigan State Univ., Extension Folder F-301, 1961.]

mitotically (asexually) or meiotically (sexually) produced. The life cycle of fungi is typically quite involved and comprises many different stages.

Fungi form three, large, well-defined groups, *Phycomycetes, Ascomycetes,* and *Basidiomycetes.* Those whose sexual stage is not known (and which presumably may never form a sexual stage) are lumped together in a more or less artificial group (the mycologist's "trash pile") as *Fungi Imperfecti.* The Phycomycetes are primitive fungi whose characteristic feature is the absence of cross walls in the mycelium. Examples of well-known horticultural plant diseases caused by species of Phycomycetes are downy mildew of grapes, seedling damping-off (caused by a number of species), and late blight of potatoes. Ascomycetes, which produce the largest number of plant diseases, are distinguished by their specialized sac (ascus) which contains the sexual spores (Fig. 8-6). Fungi of the Ascomycetes are responsible for the following diseases: apple scab, powdery mildews, brown rot of peaches and plums, and black spot of roses. The Basidiomycetes, the "higher fungi," produce a specialized sexual spore-forming structure called a *basidium*. Mushrooms, the culture of which is considered by some as part of the horticultural industry, belong to the Basidiomycetes. Diseases caused by Basidiomycetes are among the most destructive scourges of crop plants.

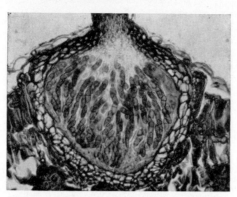

Fig. 8-6. *The fruiting body (perithicia) of* Venturia inaequalis, *which causes the apple scab disease. Eight two-celled ascospores are contained in each ascus.*
[Courtesy S. Maciejowska.]

They are popularly called *smuts* and *rusts* because of the appearance of masses of black or red colored spores on the host plant, as in onion smut, corn smut, asparagus rust, and cedar-apple rust. Some rusts require two unrelated plants for the completion of their life history. Thus, stages of the cedar-apple rust organism (*Gymnosporangium juniperi-virginianae*) infect both hosts.

Fungi are capable of entering the plant by themselves, although wounds and natural openings are utilized by many. Fungal disease is spread in a great number of ways. Spores are produced in enormous numbers and are spread by water or air currents. The pathogen that causes the apple scab disease is capable of forcibly discharging spores into the air. Mycelia growing saprophytically are a factor in the spread of soil-borne fungi. Some fungi are spread by insect vectors, as in the Dutch elm disease; others utilize insect wounds for access, as does the fungus responsible for brown rot of plums and peaches.

Symptoms of fungal diseases are extremely varied; all parts of the plant may be affected. Plant-pathogenic fungi generally cause localized injury, although some are responsible for vascular wilts. The presence of visible (to the unaided eye) forms of the fungus, as mycelial growth, masses of spores, or fruiting bodies, are often an integral part of symptom expression and help identify fungal diseases (Fig. 8-7).

Nematodes

Nematodes are nonsegmented worms (not to be confused with segmented "earth worms") of the phylum Nemeta (Fig. 8-8). Many species of nema-

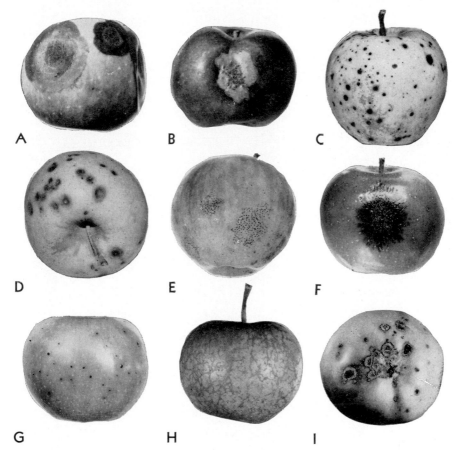

Fig. 8-7. *Fungal diseases of apple.* (*A*) *Bitter rot.* (*B*) *Cedar rust.* (*C*) *Botryosphaeria rot.* (*D*) *Black pox.* (*E*) *Fly speck and sooty blotch.* (*F*) *Blotch.* (*G*) *Blister spot.* (*H*) *Powdery mildew.* (*I*) *Scab.*
[Courtesy E. G. Sharvelle.]

todes are parasitic on plants and animals, including man; the major portion, however, are "free-living" in the soil and represent a large portion of the soil fauna. Although their size is macroscopic, they are small enough ($\frac{1}{8}$ – $\frac{1}{64}$ in.) to be generally inconspicuous. The importance of nematodes in causing plant disease is becoming increasingly apparent.

The majority of nematodes that attack plants are soil borne and generally feed on plant roots. They may feed superficially or may be partially or completely embedded in the root tissues. A few species of nematodes feed on the aerial portions of the plant (for example, the foliar nematode of chrysanthemum and the seed-gall nematode of bent grass). Some nematodes are

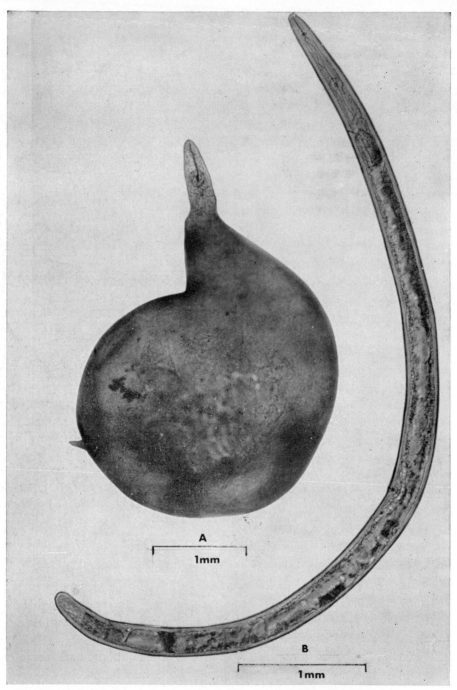

Fig. 8-8. *Nematodes of two genera, representing different morphological forms. (A) The swollen female of Meloidogyne (root knot nematode). (B) The worm-like female of Tylenchorhynchus (stunt nematode).*

[Courtesy W. F. Mai, photograph by H. H. Lyon.]

quite specialized parasites and attack only a few species of plants; others have a wide host range.

Symptoms of root injury are variable. There are two common types of nematodes. Those belonging to the genus *Meloidogyne* produce gall-like overgrowths on roots (Fig. 8-9) and are known as *root knot* nematodes. These readily observable symptoms allow positive identification of nematode injury and are used as a criteria in inspection of planting stock. The infected roots eventually deteriorate, and may afford access to other bacterial and fungal rots. The tissues, especially the vascular tissues, in the gall become disorganized; giant cells are often formed.

Fig. 8-9. *Root knot lesion on muskmelon as a result of nematode infection.*

Thus, the above-ground symptoms appear as drought injury (that is, excessive wilting and weak, yellow growth). Other plant-parasitic nematodes, such as those of the genus *Pratylenchus* (*meadow* nematodes), do not form galls. Both the root damage and the above-ground symptoms resemble those of other root rots. Owing to the difficulty of recognizing this pathogen, the meadow nematode may be easily transported in infected planting stock.

Arthropods

The phylum *Arthropoda* (literally, "jointed legged") include the invertebrate animals having an external skeleton; paired, jointed limbs; and a segmented, bilaterally symmetrical body. The *Arthropoda* is an enormous group, and contains about 75% of all known animal species, of which 90% belong to one order, *Hexapoda*, the true insects. Almost 700,000 species of true insects are known, and the estimated number of species actually existing in the world ranges from 2–10 million.

Species in two classes of the Arthropods, the *Arachnida* (e.g. mites) and the *Hexapoda*, the true insects, are the major plant pests. Species of the class *Arachnida* have four pairs of legs, are wingless and do not have a separate head. Hexapods have three pairs of legs, almost all are winged, although some are rudimentary or degenerate, and are typified by three body regions, including a separate head. A brief classification of the Arthropods showing the main orders of "true insects" attacking plants is shown in Table 8-1.

Table 8-1. *Partial classification of Arthropoda, including major orders of insects that attack plants.*

| | | TYPICAL MOUTHPARTS | |
CLASS	EXAMPLES	LARVAE	ADULTS
CHILOPODA	Centipedes		
DIPLOPODA	Millepedes		
CRUSTACEA	Crayfish, lobster		
ARACHNIDA	Scorpions, mites, ticks, spiders		
HEXAPODA (INSECTA)	True insects		
Orders with gradual metamorphosis			
Orthoptera	Grasshoppers, crickets		chewing
Thysanoptera	Thrips		rasping-sucking
Hemiptera	True bugs		piercing-sucking
Orders with complete metamorphosis			
Hymenoptera	Bees, ants, wasps	chewing	chewing-lapping
Coleoptera	Beetles	chewing	chewing
Lepidoptera	Butterflies, moths	chewing	syphoning
Diptera	Two-winged flies and mosquitos	chewing	piercing-sucking-sponging

The war between man and the six-legged creatures over crop plants is a continuous one. The battle lines are not clearly drawn. For example, we are aided by the intense competition between insect species; predatory insects must be regarded as beneficial. Furthermore, if man were to rid the earth of all insects, he would be the worse off, since he depends upon insect species for the pollination of many crop plants.

Our antagonists have many "built in" advantages. These include their small size, which makes them difficult to find; their power of flight, their extremely rapid rate of reproduction, and their specialized structural adaptations, which enable some species to exist in practically any location and to infest any plant species. In addition, the divisions of the life cycle of some insects into separate stages is an enormous advantage. This *complete metamorphosis* permits specialized structural adaptation for feeding and reproduction. The insect's life cycle consists of four stages: (1) *egg*, (2) *larva*, or feeding stage, (3) *pupa*, a quiescent stage in which the larva is transformed into the adult form and, (4) *adult*, or reproductive stage. Other insects, such as grasshoppers, have a *gradual* or *incomplete metamorphosis*, in which the physical changes from egg to adult are gradual. The intermediate stages are known as *nymphs*.

The larval stage of insects, which is often the most injurious to crop plants, often has no obvious resemblance to the adult stage (for example, the caterpillar and the butterfly). Thus, many of the descriptive names (tomato hornworm, apple maggot) given to insect pests refer to the larval form. The terms for the larval stages of the insect orders are not too specific. In general, the name *maggot* refers to the larval stage of Diptera (flies, mosquitos, gnats). *Miners* are Diptera larvae that tunnel within leaves. *Caterpillars* are the larval stages of the Lepidoptera (butterflies and moths). The term *grub* is used with reference to some of the soil-borne larvae of the Coleoptera (beetles), although the name is also applied to any other soil-borne larvae. The larvae of "click" beetles are known as *wireworms*. The larval and adult forms of beetles that infest grains and seeds are referred to as *weevils*. The name *slug* is applied to any slimy larvae, specifically to larvae of the Hymenoptera (bees, ants, and wasps). They should not be confused with the slimy body of snails, which belong to a completely different phylum, and which are also known as slugs. *Borers* are larvae, usually of moths or beetles, that tunnel within roots or stems. The term *worm* is also used to refer to insect larvae, but this is a misnomer.

Insects (and mites, which we shall also consider here) injure plants in their attempts to secure food. The damage caused directly and indirectly by insects is enormous and varied. It includes the destruction of plants by chewing insects, either in toto or in part; the spreading of other plant pathogens; and the contamination of plant products by the decomposed bodies or excreta of insects.

Insects feed on plants in two distinct ways. They either tear, bite, or "lap" portions of the plant (*chewing insects*) or pierce or rasp the plant and suck or sponge up the sap (*sucking insects*). Specialized mouth parts are involved in these two basic feeding patterns.

The chewing insects, adults or larvae, eat their way through the plant, riddling it with holes and tunnels (Fig. 8-10). Leaf-chewing insects that do not eat the tougher vascular portions may completely skeletonize the leaves; others less selective, devour the entire plant. Injury due to chewing insects that feed externally is seldom confused with anything else. Chewing insects that girdle the plant, and those that feed internally or on roots, are not as apparent. The internal feeders gain entrance to the plant from eggs deposited in the plant tissue or by eating their way in soon after being hatched on or near the surface of the plant. These internal feeders are almost impossible to control once they have entered the plant. Control consists in destroying them in their external stages. The symptoms of the peach tree borer, which may enter the tree soon after hatching, are typical of the symptoms caused by internal insect feeders, namely, a weakened, devitalized growth of the tree and a yellowing of the foliage. A gummy exudate may be observed where the borer has wounded the trunk. Peach or plum trees infested with borers often die in a few years.

Fig. 8-10.   *Insect damage. (Left) Cabbage looper on cabbage. (Right) Grasshopper on corn.*
[Photographs by J. C. Allen & Son.]

Injury by sucking insects (aphids, scale insects, leafhoppers, and plant bugs) results in a distinctly different type of symptom—the curling, stunting, and deforming of plant parts, usually the stem terminals. Spotting, yellowing, and a glazed appearance of the leaves are also common symptoms. The small size of red spider mites, which have sucking mouth parts, makes them difficult to see without a magnifying glass. They are often not diagnosed until they form webs by which time damage may be extremely severe.

Another symptom caused by both chewing and sucking insects are overgrowths called galls. These are formed from the abnormal growth of plant tissue in response to either the feeding reaction or merely the presence of the eggs deposited in the tissue. These galls, suggestive of cancerous growth, may be quite elaborate and structured. Some appear to do little damage to the plant; others obviously are quite injurious.

Birds, Rodents, Deer

Among the Chordates, or back-boned animals, birds, rodents, and deer are considered the greatest pests. Birds may become quite troublesome in such fruit crops as grapes, blueberries, and cherries. Birds may do severe damage to grapes; even a few pecked fruits permit the introduction of insects and rot, which in effect ruins the whole cluster.

Rodents (mice, ground moles, and rabbits) are among the most serious orchard pests. They feed in winter and early spring and often completely girdle fruit trees, especially apples. Unless prompt action is taken by bridge grafting, even large trees may be killed outright. The tunnels of ground moles can be a real nuisance in lawns or gardens.

In areas where they are naturally abundant or where their population is unchecked, deer may prove quite damaging to orchard and nursery stock. They are most troublesome during the winter, when their natural browse is in short supply, and when the horticulturist's vigilance is at its low ebb.

The Disease Cycle

The disease cycle includes all the series of sequential changes of the pathogen and the plant in relation to the disease. It involves the life cycle of both the pathogen and the plant.

Life Cycles

The *life history* of an organism includes all of the diverse forms and stages through which it passes. The life history of higher organisms, including that of man, is synonymous with the sexual cycle. Rather than the sequential steps from "womb to tomb" it is more correctly "gametes–fertilized egg–adult–gametes." The life history of lower organisms may be considerably more complex, and is often made up of a number of continuous stages of existence called *life cycles*. This may involve a number of asexual cycles within the sexual cycle. In addition, many lower organisms such as bacteria do not ordinarily pass through the sexual stage but exist as a single continuous form or utilize asexual spores exclusively, as in the Fungi Imperfecti.

In the temperate areas the life history must adjust to the seasonal cycle. Most pathogens pass through the winter in a stage of inactivity or dormancy. This overwintering stage, although usually specific for a particular organism, may be any stage in the life history. With the advent of spring the cycle resumes. The first cycle initiated at this time is known as the *primary cycle*. Subsequent cycles within the year are all known as *secondary cycles*. In areas where the change in seasons is not distinct—that is, where there is neither a sharp temperature differential nor a period of wet and dry—the pathogenic cycle may be a continuous secondary cycle. Greenhouse pests often fit into this class.

In reference to the disease, the cycle can be divided into two phases; a *pathogenic phase*, in which the organism remains associated with the living tissues of the particular plant; and an *independent phase* not associated with the living plant, in which the organism may be saprophytic, dormant, or pathogenic to another plant. The relative length of these two phases varies greatly. For example, the independent phase of plant viruses lasts only while they are being transported from plant to plant via insects. On the other hand, the independent stage of some pathogens may be very long. Mice injury to orchards, for instance, is usually confined to brief periods in late winter. Some fungi, such as *Verticillium*, live saprophytically as a natural part of the soil flora and become pathogenic only with the introduction of a suitable host plant.

Pathogenic Phase

The pathogenic phase may be divided into the stages of *inoculation, incubation,* and *infection.* Inoculation consists in the transference of some form of the pathogen (the *inoculum*) to the plant. The pathogen may be transferred under its own power, as are insects, or by some agent of inoculation. The important vectors are wind, water, insects, and man. In gall forming insects, the adult form would be the vector; the egg would be the inoculum. *Incubation* includes all phenomena involved with the pathogen from the time it actually enters the plant until the plant reacts to the pathogen—the *infection* stage. The important stages with respect to control are inoculation and incubation. By the time the plant reaches the infection stage, the damage has been done.

It is not possible to generalize on the relationship between the pathogenic stages and the life cycle. For example, the primary cycle of the fungus *Venturia inaequalis*, which causes apple scab, is formed when spores (ascospores) are produced from the sexual stage, which overwinters on leaves under the tree (the saprophytic stage). The secondary cycles are formed when asexual spores (conidia) are produced from primary infection. The life history of this pathogen unfolds in a single year and contains several asexual cycles (Fig. 8-11).

The codling moth, which infests apple, pear, and several other fruits, demonstrates a different type of pathogenic cycle. The life history may occur several times within a single year. The full grown larval stage overwinters in silken cocoons in trees or on the ground; the pupal stage is formed in midwinter. In the spring the grayish moths emerge and lay their eggs on the upper side of leaves, twigs, or spurs. The eggs hatch in 6–20 days, and the larvae chew their way into the young fruit. This is the primary

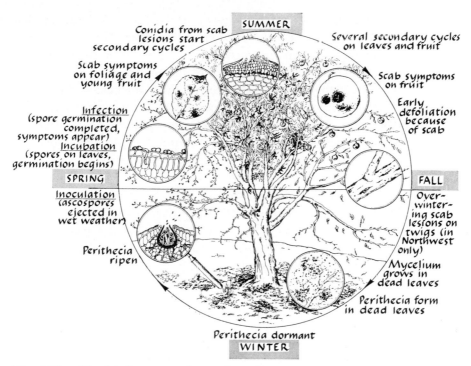

Fig. 8-11. *The life history of the apple scab fungus,* (*Venturia inaequalis*).
[From Pyenson, *Elements of Plant Protection,* Wiley, New York, 1951.]

cycle. After becoming full grown in 3–5 weeks, the larvae crawl out of the apple, drop to the ground, and spin cocoons. The moths may emerge to produce secondary cycles. There may be two or three generations, all of which may not be complete, depending upon the latitude.

Principles of Disease Control

"There's small choice in rotten apples."

SHAKESPEARE

The study of pathogenic plant diseases in the United States is divided between two disciplines: *plant pathology,* which deals with diseases of viral, bacterial, or fungal origin; and *entomology,* the study of Arthropods. (Nematodes are claimed by both, mice by neither.) The applied phase of these biological sciences is directed toward the *control* of these plant pests. This involves both alleviating the injury and preventing the spread of the pathogen.

There are two approaches to the control of pathogenic plant diseases.

One is directed at the pathogen and involves the use of techniques that prevent or restrict the pathogen's invasion of the plant. These techniques interfere at some point with the successful completion of some stage in the disease cycle. The other approach is directed toward the plant's ability to resist or at least tolerate the intrusion of the pathogen. It should be obvious that both methods of control depend upon an intimate knowledge of the disease cycle. To successfully control some diseases, many different methods must be utilized; effective control requires experience, vigilance, and persistence.

The economic value of pest control is the additional benefit obtained by the control measure less the cost of the control. Predicting the economic benefits of any control measure is particularly hazardous, because control, to be of value, must usually be applied in anticipation of the pest. Thus, many control measures can be thought of as a form of disaster insurance. In agriculture, expensive methods of pest control are only feasible with high-value crops. Consequently, horticulture bears a disproportionate share of the cost of pest control.

Legal Control

The separation of the pathogen and the plant may be accomplished by legal methods. For example, *quarantines*, which prohibit the importation of certain plants, may effectively eliminate or at least slow down the intro-duction of new pests harbored therein. Where this is not feasible or practical, subjecting plant shipments to inspection helps to prevent the spread of some pests.

Cultural Control

A number of techniques may be employed to reduce the effective population level of the pathogen. These include the elimination of diseased plants or seeds (*roguing*); the removal of infected parts of the plant (*surgery*); or the removal of plant debris, which may harbor some stage of the pathogen (*sanitation*). Cultural practices that alternate plants un-acceptable to the pathogen (*rotation*) may effectively starve out the patho-gen.

The effective population of the pathogen may be reduced by any method that renders the environment unfavorable to build up of the pathogen, such as draining land to discourage water-loving fungi, pruning to reduce foliage density and to increase the rate of drying, and varying temperature and humidity conditions in the greenhouse,

Physical Control

When individual plants are valuable enough to warrant the expense, physical barriers may be employed to protect the plant from larger pests. (Such barriers may also be effective in controlling microscopic pathogens, where insects are the important vectors.) Examples are screening to keep out insects or birds, guards to protect trunks of apple trees from mice injury, and the traditional garden fence to keep out rabbits. In Japan, developing pears are sometimes enclosed individually in silken bags to protect them from insect injury.

Physical methods may be used to selectively eliminate certain pathogens or to protect the plant against the intrusion of the pathogen. This requires the use of techniques that are differentially effective in destroying or repulsing the pathogen but will not damage the plant. An example of such a method is the use of heat. Hot water (110–122°F for 5–25 min) is used as a treatment for destroying seed- or bulb-borne pathogens. Hot water treatment is used to control some fungal diseases of grains, a bacterial disease (black rot) of crucifers, and has been used for nematode control with dormant strawberry plants. Heat treating strawberry plants has also been effective in inactivating some viruses. Steaming of potting soils is a common control for many soil pests.

The action of a strong stream of water (*syringing*) has some value in reducing the infestation of spider mites in home or greenhouse plantings. The use of firecrackers or noisemakers to discourage birds from small fruit plantations is successful to a limited extent, although often no more effective than the old-fashioned scarecrow. In many areas, however, these are subject to antinoise ordinances.

Traps may also be used to control the pathogen population. Substances to lure the pest (*attractants*) are incorporated in the trap. A recent example is the use of "blacklight" (light of wavelengths between 3400–3800 Å) to attract insects to the trap, where they are killed by some toxic solution or by rotating fan blades. The use of traps is generally not efficient for mice but has proved successful for rabbits in limited areas.

Chemical Control

The concentration of the horticultural industry has resulted in the concentration of plant pests. As a result the entire industry is now almost completely dependent upon the use of chemical control (Fig. 8-12). Commercial growers of practically all horticultural crops rely on complete "schedules" of chemical application and utilize many different compounds.

The agricultural chemical industry is a vigorous one and new materials are continually being released.

BIOLOGICAL ACTION OF CHEMICALS. *Pesticide* is the generic name for all chemicals that control plant pests. Pesticides, as the name infers, are usually toxic to some stage of the plant pest. (*Repellants* are compounds that may not be actively poisonous but make the crop plant unattractive to animal predators by virtue of their odor, taste, or other physical properties. They are included under the legal definition of pesticide.) Pesticides are classed according to the organism they control; for example, bactericide, fungicide, nematicide, miticide, insecticide, rodenticide. (Herbicides, chemicals which kill plants, will be discussed under weed control, later in this chapter.)

Fig. 8-12. *Control of summer diseases of apple with fungicide application. Fruits on right received no spray and show a number of summer diseases, including Brooks spot, black pox, and sooty blotch. Fruit on left received full season captan sprays.*
[Courtesy J. R. Shay.]

Pesticides are generally selective in their action. Thus, chemicals that are fungicidal are usually not insecticidal. But there are exceptions; for example, Bordeaux mixture (100 gal water; 10 lb hydrated lime; 6 lb copper sulfate), which is primarily fungicidal, has some value as an insect repellant. Pesticides that are toxic to a broad spectrum of organisms, including the crop, must be used in the absence of the plant, as in soil preplanting treatments.

It should be re-emphasized that pesticides are not necessarily toxic to all stages of a particular pathogen, nor is this necessary. Usually, a particular stage of the life cycle is especially vulnerable to chemical attack. This "weak link" may be a germinating fungal spore, the young larval stage of insects, or the insect vector of a virus disease. For example, it is much more difficult to kill fungi after they have extensively entered the plant. However, materials that will kill or prevent spores from germinating on the plant may prevent further inoculation and, in effect, control the disease.

Pesticides are classified as *systemics* or *nonsystemics*. *Systemics* are actually absorbed by the plant, and may be translocated within the plant, rendering the plant itself toxic to the pathogen. Systemics must of course be restricted in their use to nonedible plants unless they break down within the plant before consumption. Much more common are the *nonsystemics*, which merely coat the plant with a substance toxic to some stage of the pathogen. This distinction between *systemics* and *nonsystemics* is not clear-cut, however; many compounds whose main action is on the surface of the plant may be absorbed to some degree.

Insecticides are classified by their action as *stomach poisons* or *contact poisons*. Stomach poisons are usually used against chewing insect forms. The poison is ingested by the insect through the mouth into the stomach, where it causes the death of the insect. Since sucking insects are internal feeders, they are usually not affected by stomach poisons. They are controlled by *contact poisons* which kill by penetrating the insect body directly or through breathing or sensory pores.

A great number of compounds, both organic and inorganic, are used to kill plant pests. The inorganic materials are usually metallic salts of such metals as copper, mercury, lead, and arsenic. A few of the organic compounds occur naturally, such as nicotine, pyrethrum, and rotenone. However, most of the present-day organic compounds are now completely synthetic, as are DDT, the organic phosphates, the organic mercury compounds. A list of some of the important pesticides is presented in Table 8-2.

APPLICATION OF PESTICIDES. Chemicals are applied to plants in a number of formulations of the liquid, solid, or gaseous state, and consequently by a variety of methods. The aim is to obtain uniform coverage at a controlled rate. For highly active compounds the rate of application of the active ingredient may be extremely low, thus it is difficult to maintain adequate coverage without special equipment.

It is seldom practical to apply chemicals in their undiluted form. Consequently their distribution is carried out by the use of an inert carrier. The carrier may be a solid, such as talc, in which case the material is applied as a *dust*. Dusts have the advantage of lightness, but there is some question as to the persistence of the material. Moreover, some materials (for example, oils) cannot be applied in this manner.

The disadvantages of dusts are overcome by the use of a liquid carrier, usually water, in which the chemical is dissolved, suspended, or emulsified. The material is applied by pressure in droplets of various sizes (Fig. 8-13), but usually in the form of a spray (Fig. 8-14). The disadvantages of spraying lie in the bulk and weight of the water carrier. The trend in spraying is, therefore, to use high concentrations of the active material and achieve dispersion by a blast of air (Fig. 8-15).

Another difficulty found in using a water carrier is that plant surfaces,

Table 8-2. *Classification of some important pesticides (excluding herbicides) by chemical composition.*

CLASS OF MATERIAL	SPECIFIC EXAMPLE	MAJOR TYPE OF ACTION
Inorganic		
arsenic	lead arsenate	insecticide
copper	copper sulfate	fungicide, bactericide
mercury	mercuric chloride	fungicide, bactericide
sulfur	lime sulfur	fungicide
Organic		
Naturally occurring		
antibiotics	streptomycin	bactericide
nicotine	nicotine sulfate	insecticide
pyrethrum		insecticide
rotenone		insecticide
Synthetic		
carbamates	ferbam	fungicide
	Sevin	insecticide
chlorinated-hydrocarbons	DDT	insecticide
mercury compounds	Ceresan, Semesan	fungicide, bactericide
phosphates	malathion	insecticide, miticide
phthalimides	captan, phaltan	fungicide
pyrethrins		insecticide

since they are heavily cutinized, are "water repellant," causing the spray to form droplets instead of a continuous film. As a result, the deposited chemicals are irregularly dispersed. This may be overcome by the use of *wetting agents*—surface-active chemicals that break the surface tension. Other additives known as *stickers* improve the retention and persistence of the chemical application.

Fig. 8-13. *The drop-size spectrum.*

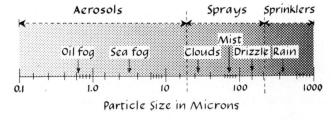

Fig. 8-14. *Applications of fungicides to tomatoes with a boom-type sprayer.*
[Photograph by J. C. Allen & Son.]

Volatile substances that are pesticidal in the gaseous state are known as *fumigants.* Some substances applied as sprays or dusts may also be used as fumigants; for example, nicotine sulfate may either be applied as a spray or volatilized and applied as a fumigant. Fumigants are, as a rule, extremely toxic to all life, and the problem in their use is to obtain selectivity. Thus, fumigants have been widely used in the absence of plants to control soil pests. The use of fumigants for edible horti cultural products is unacceptable, however, owing to the residue problem.

Fumigants may be stored under pressure as a liquid, or stored as a solid to be volatilized by heat. Such substances as paradichlorobenzene (mothballs) sublimate, and are applied as a solid. Soil fumigants are now being synthesized

Fig. 8-15. *Orchard speed sprayers use a blast of air as a carrier for high concentrate sprays.*
[Courtesy Farm Equipment Inst.]

that will volatilize when wet, and these may be applied to the soil in granular form. Increasing in importance for enclosed areas such as greenhouses are *aerosol bombs,* from which the toxic chemical is dispensed by means of a gaseous carrier. In *fogging,* the active ingredient is dispersed by heat volatilization in kerosene or some other petroleum oil.

PROBLEMS OF CHEMICAL CONTROL. Although chemicals have greatly diminished the problems of pest control, they have by no means solved them. Furthermore, the use of chemical control imposes many new problems.

1. *Residues on edible products.* Severe restrictions are imposed upon the use of chemicals in order to avoid health hazards. Risks cannot be tolerated. The quantitative determination of residue, and the determination of limits of safety for the operator, as well as for the consumer, must be established for each chemical by the manufacturer. The controversy over residues involves the question of potential health hazards by minute quantities of chemicals that are toxic at higher dose levels. The solution to the problem consists in choosing pesticides that break down before consumption or are metabolized harmlessly by the body, and in timing their application such that residues may be eliminated entirely. Some chemicals leave soil residues that may interfere with subsequent plant growth.

2. *The technical problems of application.* The timing of application must be extremely precise with regard to the effectiveness of treatment as well as the elimination of residues. Usually the pesticide must be applied before the trouble appears; once the symptoms are obvious, it is often too late for control. Thoroughness of application in tree crops often necessitates special pruning procedures. Due to chemical reactions that occur between certain chemicals, compatibilities must be taken into consideration when more than one pesticide is applied.

3. *Spray injury to the plant.* Care must be taken to insure that the cure is not more injurious than the disease. Spray injury can reduce yield as well as spoil the appearance or "finish" of the product. Some of the russetting injury on fruit can be traced to cuticle damage by pesticides.

4. *The development of genetic resistance by the pathogen.* The pathogen is not a static factor. Natural variation among pathogens produces types that may be resistant to the pesticide. Because of the enormous rate of reproduction of many pathogens, the pesticides act as a screening device for the selection of resistant types. When DDT was introduced in the 1940's many entomologists had hopes of victory in the war against insects. Within 10 years, however, mosquitos, house flies, and many other insects had developed a resistance to DDT.

5. *The disturbance of the biological balance.* When one pesticide is used in place of another, pests that formerly appeared to cause little damage may begin to assume major importance. Apparently, such pests were controlled by the former pesticide but not by the new one. For example, the older methods for controlling apple scab utilized lime sulfur, which was also effective against powdery mildew. But because of its adverse effect on fruit finish, lime sulfur was replaced by organic fungicides. Although these fungicides have proven very satisfactory for scab control, their use has re-

sulted in severe outbreaks of mildew, which have necessitated additional control measures.

Biological Control

Bugs have little bugs
    that bite 'em
And these have other bugs
    ad-infinitum.

Biological control utilizes direct competition between organisms. Certain insects feed on other insects (Fig. 8-16). In addition, there are bacterial diseases of insects, and there are virus diseases of bacteria. This competition between organisms may be directed toward the control of plant pests by the introduction of a natural parasite or predator of the pathogen. A recent example is the use of spores of *Bacillus thuringiensis*, a natural pathogen of caterpillars, as a spray material.

An example of successful biological control is the introduction of the vedalia beetle into California from Australia by Albert Koebele in 1888. This beetle feeds upon the eggs and larvae of the cottony-cushion scale, a serious insect pest of citrus. This beetle successfully controlled the scale until the use of DDT became prevalent in the late 1940's. The injury to the vedalia beetle, apparently caused by the DDT, upset the biological balance and resulted in the first outbreaks of cottony-cushion scale since 1890.

Fig. 8-16. *Insects parasitize other insects. (Above) Cocoons of the Braconid parasites emerging from the body of a tomato hornworm. The cocoons contain the pupal stage of a parasitic wasp that lays its eggs on the body of the hornworm. (Below) The potato beetle killer attacking larva of the Mexican bean beetle.*
[Photograph by J. C. Allen & Son.]

Biological control requires an organized attack on a pathogen. The use of biological control by individual growers by encouraging or importing insect predators, such as the "praying mantis," has at best only a very limited success.

The advantage of biological control is that, once put into effect, it appears to take place without the influence of man. However, the biological balance is often more apparent than real. The upsetting of this delicate balance, as by random environmental fluctuations, is a perfectly natural phenomenon. Commercial horticulture, which by its nature disturbs the natural biological pattern, cannot afford the risk inherent in biological control and at present depends upon chemical control as its main weapon against plant pests. Biological control, however, is an attractive measure, and one that is being given increasing attention.

The control of the screwworm, a severe pest of livestock, by utilizing artificially reared insects made sterile by being exposed to atomic radiation, has opened up a new approach to biologic control. Normal females are "monogamous" and mate only once. When mated to an irradiated male they will produce only sterile eggs. The basis of the control is the relatively low population of reproductive adults during the winter. If the number of irradiated sterile males released continually outnumber normal males the number of fertile eggs will continually decrease. (This will be the case regardless of the mating habits of the female.) The greater the proportion of irradiated males over normal males, the faster will be the control. The success of this program suggests its use as a method for controlling plant-attacking insects.

Physiological Alteration of the Host

Plants do not have an antibody mechanism that can be utilized to resist disease, as do animals. Thus, they cannot be made immune by vaccines. However, the physiology of the plant can be altered to affect the plant's ability to either resist invasion by the pathogen or to overcome the deleterious affects of the pathogen. For example, many vascular wilts caused by the fungus *Verticillum albo atrum* (for example, Verticillum wilt of maple) can be compensated for by vigorous growth of the plant. Applications of fertilizer to increase vigor causes the plant literally to outgrow the pathogen. The reverse technique is utilized in fireblight of pears. Infection and growth of the bacterium causing the disease is extremely rapid in fast-growing, succulent shoots. One method of control is achieved by slowing down rapid growth of the tree by eliminating excessive nitrogen fertilization or extensive pruning. The direct action of inorganic nutrients gives protection in some instances. For example, clubroot of cabbage appears to diminish in severity when the ratio of calcium to potassium in the soil is decreased. The affect of various levels of nutrients on disease resistance has not been intensively investigated.

Genetic Alteration of the Host

The innate ability of the plant to avoid the injurious effects of the pathogen is the ideal method of control (Fig. 8-17). This *genetic resistance* varies from complete absence of injury (*immunity*) through various degrees of partial resistance. The lack of re-sistance is referred to as *suscepti-bility*. *Tolerance* is a type of re-sistance in which the plant suffers infection and some injury, but is able to live with it.

Examples of plant resistance to viruses, bacteria, fungi, nematodes, and insects are known. The nature of plant resistance lies in the struc-tural alterations or biochemical effects that either prevent or dis-courage intrusion and persistence

Fig. 8-17. *Resistance of tomato to Fu-sarium wilt. The plot in the center is Indiana Baltimore, a susceptible variety. The plots on either side are wilt-resistant varieties.*

[Courtesy Purdue Univ.]

of the particular pathogen. Some plants have resistance to whole groups of pathogens; others have only a specific resistance to a particular species, or race, of pathogen. Where pathogen and plant are closely adapted to each other, a close relationship exist between the genetic resistance of the plant and the genetic ability of the organism to violate or overcome this resistance. The spontaneous origin of new races of the pathogen is one of the major problems the plant breeder faces in attempting to incorporate genetic resist-ance into an improvement program.

The combination of resistance and horticultural quality is one of the main objectives of the plant breeder (see Chapter 10). Resistance may be incorporated in the whole plant or, when the plant is composed of separate, grafted components, in part of the plant. Thus, resistance to root pests, such as the woolly aphis of apple, may be incorporated by the substitution of an aphis-resistant rootstock. Similarly, fireblight-susceptible varieties of pear are often grafted to a framework of the resistant Old Home variety. This prevents an infected limb from destroying the whole tree.

COMPETITION BETWEEN CROP AND WEED

Weeds as Pests

A weed may be defined as any plant that is undesirable. According to this definition, any crop plant that is out of place may be termed a weed.

More typically, however, the term refers to certain naturally occurring, aggressive plants that are injurious to man and his agriculture. The degree of "undesirability" of individual species varies greatly. Extremely noxious weeds, if left unchecked, may completely dominate crop plants. Crop losses are usually a result of competition for light, water, and mineral nutrients. Weeds are also indirectly responsible for crop losses in that they harbor other plant pests (for example, viruses, fungi, insects). In addition, weeds may lower the quality and economic value of crops. A horticultural example is the lowered quality of peppermint oil when the crop is contaminated with weeds. Because of their rank growth and unsightliness, weeds are a perpetual nuisance in turf. They represent a safety hazard on roadside and railroad right-of-ways, and they often clog irrigation ditches and streams. Finally, poisonous weeds (poison ivy, white snake root) directly affect the health and comfort of man and livestock; the pollen of plants such as ragweed is a source of misery to the millions who suffer from "hayfever." The annual cost of weed control in the United States exceeds the combined losses from all other types of plant pest. The fierce competition offered by certain weeds is due to a combination of their prolific reproductive capacity and vigorous, exuberant growth.

Reproductive Capacity of Weeds

In general, the destructive power of weeds is due to their sheer number. Some weeds produce seeds in enormous quantity. Weed species differ greatly, however, in terms of the number of seeds they produce; a single plant of the wild oat produces about 250 seeds, whereas a plant of the tumbling pigweed produces several million. One study of 181 perennial, biennial, and annual weed species reports an average of over 20,000 seeds per plant.

The seeds of certain weed species have become structurally adapted to dispersal by wind, water, or animals. For example, many weeds have hard seed coats and remain viable when passed through the digestive tract of animals. Man has become one of the chief disseminators of weeds through the shipment of crop seeds and plants. Most of the noxious weed species in North America are native to other parts of the world.

The large number of seeds and their efficient dispersal only partly explain the high reproductive capacity of weeds. (Many crop plants are also prolific seed producers, yet will not become weed-like.) The high reproductive capacity of weeds is particularly effective because of the extended seed viability coupled with delayed germination brought about by dormancy. The failure of a weed seed to germinate may be due to *natural* or *induced dormancy.* Natural dormancy was discussed in Chapter 5. Induced dormancy is brought about by environmental conditions that limit germination. Seeds buried deep in the soil by tillage may lack either sufficient oxygen or the light stimulus necessary for germination. The viability of weed seed buried in the soil may be extremely long in contrast to the relatively brief viability of most crop plants. In the eightieth year of an experiment on buried weed seeds—a study started in 1879 by Professor W. J. Beal at Michigan Agricultural College—three species, evening primrose (*Oenothera biennis*), curly dock (*Rumex crispus*), and moth mullein (*Verbascum blattaria*) had survivors as viable seed. Over half of the twenty weed species in the experiment had survivors after twenty-five years.

The combination of dormancy, extensive seed viability, and high seed production makes weed control exceedingly difficult. If weed seeds would all germinate at once, their control might be accomplished by a rigorous and intensive eradication program. The heavy weed seed population of agricultural soils makes weed control a continuing and integral part of crop culture.

Many weeds reproduce vegetatively as well as by seed. Some of the most pernicious weeds reproduce in this way: Johnson grass and quack grass, by rhizomes; wild morning glory, by roots; and wild garlic, by bulblets. Vegetative reproduction, by underground stem modifications or by roots, makes control by cultivation particularly difficult.

Weed Growth

The competition between weed and crop adversely affects both plants, but weeds usually win out over the crop plants. However, the exact physiological basis of the growth advantages that enable weeds to do this is not clear. Among the growth characteristics that explain the competitive ability of certain weeds are rapid germination, rapid seedling growth, and a root system that is deeply penetrating yet fibrous at the surface. Furthermore, weeds possess a natural resistance to many of the pests that crop plants are plagued by. Their resistance to heat and cold undoubtedly gives them an added advantage.

The luxuriant growth characteristic of weeds might appear to be a character that has been sacrificed during "domestication" of crop plants concomitant with the selection of horticultural attributes such as large fruit size. The loss of seed dormancy in most crop plants propagated by seed is an example of the loss of an adaptive trait. Another more reasonable explanation is that, to survive, weeds must be uniquely adapted to their surroundings, whereas crop plants may be grown in locations far removed from the conditions to which they are best adapted. The weed species change much more dramatically than do the crops across the United States. Thus, the study of weed control must be preceded by a knowledge of the natural history and ecology of the particular weed species involved.

Weed Control Methods

The many techniques utilized in the control of weeds may be grouped into physical, biological, and chemical methods. Weed control was given a new impetus with the discovery of 2,4-dichlorophenoxyacetic acid (2,4-D) as a selective weed killer in the mid 1940's. This proved to have far-reaching effects, not only on chemical weed control, but on weed research in general. So far, however, chemicals have not proved to be the ultimate solution to the weed problem. Weeds are well endowed in their struggle for space and survival. Successful control still involves the judicious combination of many methods.

Physical Techniques

Various controls involve the physical destruction of weeds. The pulling or grubbing of weeds is the simplest and most ancient form of weed control. The hoe, the basic hand tool, is still widely used. Various mechanical devices have been developed to automate this process (Fig. 8-18). The basic principle is to cut out, chop up, or cover the weeds and thereby destroy them. For maximum efficiency, cultivation should be carried out when weeds are very small. Weeds propagated by root are extremely difficult to control by cultivation and may actually be dispersed in this way.

Cultivation and tillage, the loosening or breaking up of the soil, are such widespread agricultural practices that many have come to believe that the loosening of the soil has beneficial functions other than the control of weeds. Yet a number of experiments have indicated that weed control is, indeed, the primary benefit of cultivation. The other advantages of cultivation, such as increased soil aeration or the conservation of soil moisture by the formation of a soil or dust mulch, may actually be counteracted by the destructive effects of inadvertent root pruning in the surface layer, the most productive portion of the soil. In addition, extensive cultivation with heavy machinery often leads to serious soil compaction problems. Although cultivation may conserve moisture by preventing runoff, it also contributes to considerable erosion of loose soil during heavy rains. Nevertheless, cultivation is still the major form of weed control for most crops, thus it should be timed in relation to weed-control efficiency.

Fig. 8-18. *Weed control by cultivation. (Above) A ten-row onion tillivator. (Below) A "power hoe" developed for strawberry cultivation. The operator steers with his feet and directs a movable hoe attachment.*

[Courtesy Purdue University, and Friday Tractor Co., Hartford, Michigan.]

The control of weed germination by mulching has been recommended from time to time. Recently, the use of black polyethylene plastic film has been encouraging in some trials. Mulching, however, is too expensive as a means of weed control in commercial plantings but is a valuable practice for home gardens.

The use of heat to control weeds is the "pasteurization" of greenhouse or cold-frame soils by steam (180°F for ½ hour) Weed seeds and certain "damping-off" organisms are controlled in this manner. Care must be taken to avoid sterilizing the soil, since this will adversely affect the bacteria involved in the nitrogen cycle. It is a good practice to avoid planting in freshly steamed soils; it is best to allow the balance of microorganisms to be restored.

Fire has been used to destroy weeds. Flame throwers have been adapted to control weeds in such places as railroad beds, and have been used in weeding cotton and onions. Similarly, burning of weed trash has been used, but this must be considered a poor practice. The burning over of muck soils to control weeds is a flagrant example of a resource waste.

Biological Techniques

The utilization of the natural competition between weeds and other organisms is the basis of biological control. The most spectacular example of biological control involves the introduction of insects that feed specifically on certain weeds. Prickly pear (*Opuntia* species), first introduced as an ornamental into Australia prior to 1839 by the early colonists, was brought under control by the importation of the moth borer *Cactoblastis cactorum* from Argentina. By 1925, the weed had infested 60 million acres, and the infested area was increasing at the rate of one million acres annually. Ten years after the introduction of the predator, control was almost complete. Although there were successive waves of regrowth, they were of diminishing proportions, owing to the successful establishment of the insect.

More recently the weed *Hypericum perforatum* (Saint-John's-wort, or Klamath weed) has been successfully controlled in California by the introduction of the beetle *Chrysolina gemellata*. This beetle, originating in France, had proved to be a satisfactory predator of this weed in Australia.

The use of insects to control weeds can be handled only on a large scale, and because of the inherent problems, must be placed under the control of some national agency. This form of control is usually used for introduced weeds that are not attacked by natural predators. In order for the introduction of insect predators to be successful, the insect must thrive in the new habitat and yet not become a pest to other agricultural crops. Thus, only those insects that are highly selective in their feeding habits can be imported. Care must be taken to avoid introducing parasites of the imported insect.

Crop competition is an important biological method of weed control. Weed populations can be reduced by proper rotation involving well-adapted crops that can compete with weeds, for example, silage corn, alfalfa. Often it is the kind of tillage used in the rotation that brings weeds under control. For example, cultivation in corn may reduce the grass weeds that become established in small grain crops. Similarly, horticultural practices that facilitate rapid growth and good crop stands will encourage crop competition.

The use of geese to control weeds has had limited success in some horticultural crops. Geese will selectively weed strawberries of grass, providing there is enough grass present, but they cannot be used in fruiting patches. Fields must be fenced, and careful management is required; for example, water must be rotated to keep the geese moving.

Chemical Techniques

> "Buildings and walls were razed to the ground; the plough passed over the site, and salt was sown in the furrows made. A solemn curse was pronounced that neither house nor crops should ever rise again."
> "The Fall of Carthage" (147 B.C.).
> From the *Cambridge Ancient History*, Vol. VIII

Substances such as common salt have been used for centuries to destroy vegetation. However, practical weed control in agriculture depends largely upon the selective destruction of weeds. In the early 1900's a number of compounds were shown to have selective action in destroying broad-leafed weeds in grain; for example, various copper salts, sulfuric acid, iron sulfate, sodium arsenite. But interest in these materials waned because of the unreliability of the results and the inadequacy of application equipment. The introduction of 2,4-D and other auxin-like herbicides in the 1940's rapidly transformed chemical weed control into a method of major importance. In rapid succession many other chemicals were introduced as weed killers. Herbicides have accounted for an increasing percentage of all pesticide sales. Chemical weed killers are widely used on lawns but are not advisable for home gardens because of the difficulty of applying them at the proper rate and the danger of injuring adjacent plants.

SELECTIVITY. *Nonselective herbicides* kill vegetation indiscriminately. A *selective herbicide* is one that under certain conditions will kill certain plants and not harm others. Selectivity in herbicides is a relative concept and depends to a large extent on the interaction of a number of factors: dosage, timing, method of application, chemical and physical properties of the herbicides, and the genetic and physiological state of the plants involved.

In order for a herbicide to cause death it must be absorbed by the plant and carry out some toxic reaction. Some kill only the area of the plant actually covered (*contact herbicides*), for example, dinitro-compounds, oils,

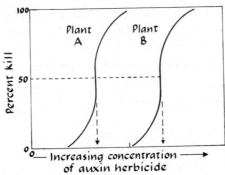

Fig. 8-19. *Selectivity to auxin-like herbicides is a function of dose. Arrows on mortality curves of two species indicate relative concentration of herbicide required to kill 50% of the plants.*

[From Leopold, *Auxin and Plant Growth*, University of Calif. Press, Berkeley, 1955.]

and arsenates; others are translocated within the plant (*noncontact* or *translocated* herbicides), for example, 2,4-D. Selectivity may be brought about by directing the herbicide away from the crop plant (*positional tolerance*) or by inherent morphological differences of the plant: amount and type of waxy cuticle, which results in differential wetting and absorption (for example, dinitro-compounds on peas versus weeds); the angle and shape of the leaves (for example, the differences between broad-leafed plants and grasses); or the location of the growing point (for example, protected in grasses, exposed in broad-leafed plants). Diuron is an effective weed killer on grapes because it does not reach their deeply growing roots readily. Selectivity may be achieved as a function of dose. An overdose of 2,4-D will seriously affect all plants, whereas in low doses it will effectively discriminate between certain plants (Fig. 8-19).

Physiological distinctions that result in selectivity exist between certain plants. This may be manifested in varieties of the same species. The precise mechanism of physiological selectivity is unknown, since the exact method by which many herbicides kill is obscure. Some interfere with enzyme systems; others disturb the metabolism of the plant in some manner. Physiological selectivity may be due to differences in the plant's ability to translocate herbicides. The tolerance of carrots to Stoddard solvent is apparently due to the inherent resistance of the cell membrane to penetration.

Plants may show differences in the intensity of the toxic reaction at different stages of growth. Thus, some herbicides may be effective only during a very early stage of plant development, such as seed germination; others may be effective only at some later stage, such as flowering. Combinations of different herbicides are often required to control the many weed species usually present.

TIME AND METHOD OF APPLICATION. *Preplanting* treatments are applied before the crop is planted. Fumigants and other nonselective herbicides achieve selectivity between weed and crop by the timing of application. If preplanting herbicides are nonselective and have residual effects, sufficient time must elapse before the crop can be planted. Selective preplanting herbicides that are now available discriminate between germinating weed seeds and crop seeds or between germinating weed seeds and transplants.

Fig. 8-20. *Pre-emergent application of herbicide to seed bed. Uniform and thorough coverage is essential.* [Courtesy Farm Equipment Inst.]

Pre-emergence treatments are applied after the crop is planted but before it has emerged from the soil (Fig. 8-20). To be effective the herbicide must have good coverage, remain on the surface of the soil, and be relatively unleached. Timing and soil moisture are very critical. Water is often required to activate the herbicide, but too much water may leach the herbicide. Because their action is restricted to the soil surface, the herbicides are applied after the crop is planted. Physiological selectivity is often utilized such that the crop will germinate but the weed will not. In addition, selectivity may be enhanced by time. The weed seeds germinate first, since the crop seeds have a slightly delayed germination owing to the time required to imbibe water or to their depth of planting.

Postemergence treatment is applied to the growing crop. Selectivity may be physiological, or it may be due to directed application away from the crop plant. Care must be taken to avoid drift of herbicides. Selectivity may be achieved as a result of plant age, for example, if the herbicide being used is toxic only to germinating seedlings at the dose being applied. When used in this way, herbicides are usually applied immediately after a thorough cultivation, since the ground must be free of germinated weeds.

Herbicides may be applied as a liquid, solid, or gas. Specialized equipment has been devised that accurately meters low dosages. This is essential because of the extremely low concentrations required for some highly active substances. The increased use of granular herbicides that are absorbed by roots eliminates the need for heavy, bulky, liquid carriers,

CLASSIFICATION OF HERBICIDES. The number of chemicals known to have herbicidal activity is large and is increasing at a rapid rate. Table 8-3 presents a classification of some important families of herbicides in terms of chemical composition. Although many compounds fit into well-defined groups on this basis, others do not appear to fit into any particular grouping. Lists of herbicides become outdated very quickly, since this technology is expanding at a rapid rate.

Table 8-3. *Classification of some important herbicides by chemical composition.*

CLASS OF MATERIAL	EXAMPLES
Inorganic	ammonium sulphamate
	potassium cyanate
	sodium arsenite
	sulfuric acid
Organic	
Oils	diesel oils, Stoddard solvent
Phenoxyacetic acids	2,4-D, 2,4,5-T, MCP, Sesone
Chlorinated acetic acids	TCA, dalapon
Amide-like compounds	
carbamates	IPC, CIPC, EPTC
acetamides	Solan, CDAA
ureas	monuron, diuron
triazines	simazine, atrazine
Substituted phenols	DNBP
Miscellaneous	Zytron, endothal, Dacthal, amino triazole

Oils such as diesel oil have long been used as contact, nonselective herbicides. Lighter fractions, such as stove oil and Stoddard solvent (used in dry cleaning), have proved to have selective herbicidal action. Stoddard solvent is widely used with carrots and cranberries. Heavy aromatic fractions were found to be superior to diesel oils as contact herbicides, and large numbers of these materials are used as nonselective herbicides.

Phenoxy or auxin-like materials are those substances that have a physiological action resembling indoleacetic acid (see Chapter 4). The most common of these are 2,4-D, 2,4,5-T and MCP. Note how similar their structural formulas are to one another and to that of indoleacetic acid (Fig. 8-21). Various derivatives of these compounds may be achieved by different substitutions and formulations. These affect the herbicidal as well as the physical properties of the molecule. For example, the amine formu-

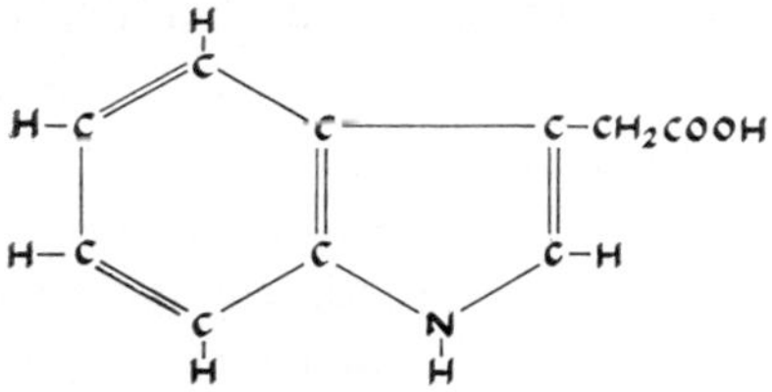

IAA
Indoleacetic acid

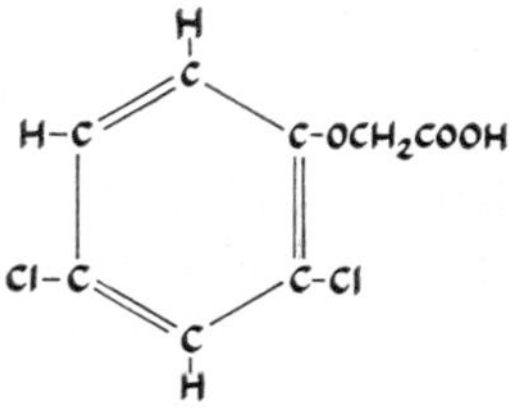

2,4-D

2,4 dichlorophenoxyacetic acid

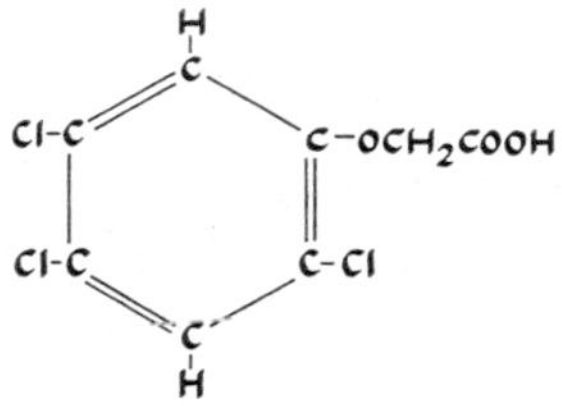

2,4,5-T

2,4,5 trichlorophenoxyacetic acid

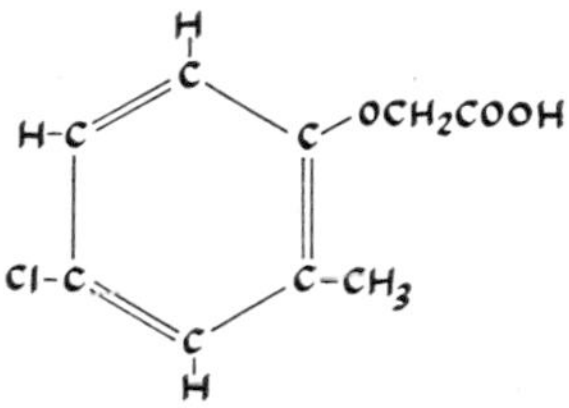

MCP

Methylchlorophenoxyacetic acid

Fig. 8-21. *Structure of auxin-like herbicides in comparison with that of indoleacetic acid.*

lation of 2,4-D is less volatile than the ester form. Volatile esters of 2,4-D are hazardous around sensitive crops such as grapes or tomatoes. The auxin herbicides are generally highly selective with respect to dose and are effective at extremely low concentrations. They have a short residual life in the soil and are of low toxicity to animals. Selectivity is achieved both by differential absorption and genetic differentiation to dose. At high enough concentrations auxin herbicides are toxic to all plants. The herbicide 2,4-D is used to control weeds in corn and strawberries, and is used as a broadleaf weed killer in turf.

Among the chlorinated acetic acids used in weed control are such compounds as TCA (trichloroacetic acid) and Dalapon (2,2-dichloropropionic acid). As a group they are more selective against monocots than dicots, and thus are used in the control of grassy weeds. Dalapon has the widest herbicidal use and is used for the control of both seedling and established perennial grasses.

Within their structural formula amide-like and related compounds contain the amide moiety N—C=O or the related groupings N—C=S or N—C=N. The physiological significance of their chemical structure is not known. Many important herbicides are included in this group, such as the triazines, carbamates, ureas, and acetamides. These are now some of the most important ones in horticulture.

FATE OF HERBICIDES. Herbicides, to be a successful agricultural tool, must dissipate in order that they will not interfere with future land use. Their eventual disappearance may result from vaporization, chemical breakdown, biological decomposition, leaching, or adsorption on soil colloids.

POPULATION COMPETITION

Population pressures markedly affect plant performance. As plant population increases per unit area, a point is reached at which each plant begins to compete for certain essential growth factors: nutrients, sunlight, and water. The effect of increasing competition is similar to decreasing the concentration of a growth factor.

Yield, whether it be of root, shoot, fruit flower, or seed, is usually expressed on a unit area basis rather than on a plant basis. One of the principal reasons is that "space" and the fixed costs associated with it are usually much more valuable than the costs of individual plants. Thus, the most important consideration is the effect that varying the plant population has on the yield per unit area rather than on the yield per plant. The optimum population, however, is the one which produces the greatest net return to the grower. It should be emphasized that yield must be interpreted in both quantitative and qualitative terms. The value of the total yield is not merely the total bulk, but is related to the quality of the yield (size per unit, color, appearance, culinary properties, and so on).

There are two horticultural phases to this problem. One is the effect of plant population per unit area (*interplant competition*), and the other is the effect of plant part number (*intraplant competition*).

Interplant Competition

Yield

The yield per unit area is equal to the yield per plant times the number of plants. When the population is below the level in which competition between plants occurs, increasing the population will have no effect on individual plant performance; the yield per unit area will increase in direct proportion to the population increase. As soon as competition between plants occurs, however, the yield per plant will decrease.

Once competition exists, the change in yield per unit area becomes a function of the change in yield per plant. There appear to be two fundamentally different relationships between yield per plant and population. For some crops, a plot of the logarithm of yield per plant versus arithmetic values for population describes a straight line (*semilog relationship*); for others (this is the most usual relationship) a plot of the logarithm of yield per plant versus the logarithm of population describes a straight line (*log relationship*). These relationships are shown in Fig. 8-22 and are discussed below.

In plants that show the semilog relationship, an increase in population that occurs after competition is reached will increase the yield per unit area at some particular population. If this population is exceeded, the yield per unit area will decrease. This type of relationship is found in corn and cabbage. In plants that exhibit the log relationship, the effect on yield per unit area of increasing population after competition is reached depends on the rate of change of yield per plant. This can be explained in terms of the slope of the straight line obtained in the log/log plot. If the slope is -1 (that is, if the slope is 45°, or curve B') an increase in population will have no effect on the yield per unit area. The yield contributed by each additional plant is compensated exactly by the decrease in yield of the other plants. Potatoes show this relationship.

If the slope of the log/log plot is greater than -1, then an increase in population will increase the yield per unit area, but at a decreasing rate. At some population, however, yields could conceivably decrease. In fruit yield this might occur if flower number decreased to less than one per plant, or if fruit size became too small to develop normally. Tomatoes and beans exhibit this type of relationship.

If the relationship between yield per plant and population produces a slope less than -1, then the yield per unit area will be a maximum just at the point where competition begins. Increasing the population will lower yield, but at a decreasing rate. A late single harvest of tomatoes exhibits this relationship.

Plant parts may respond to increased population pressures after competition begins by decreasing in size, number, or both. The decrease in the number of plant parts (for example, the response of potato tubers) may produce a very small corresponding decrease in the size of remaining parts. These compensating responses to competition may differ with various plant parts, even on the same plant. In corn, for example, an increase in popu-

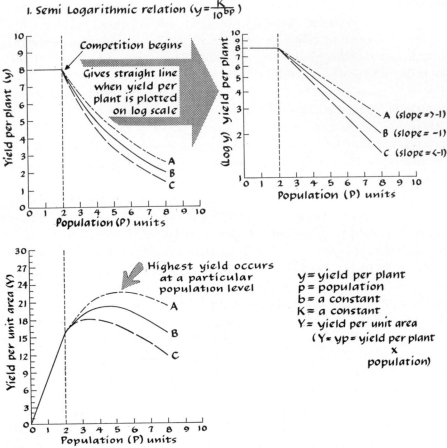

Fig. 8-22. (*Above and on facing page.*) *Relationship of yield to plant population.*

lation causes a decrease in ear number, ear size, and kernel number, but the kernel size remains relatively constant. The response of crops to crowding depends on which character is being measured (for example, yield of seed, or yield of some vegetative structure). In oats, for instance, the maximum yield of straw is obtained from a low seeding, whereas the maximum grain yield is obtained with the heaviest seeding.

The optimum size of plant parts (fruit, tuber, bulb, flower) is not necessarily the largest. (In pickling cucumbers it is the smallest.) Population competition may be utilized to produce a particular size of organ. For example, onion seed grown for "sets" to be replanted is sown at the rate of 70 lb/acre. The crowding produces a small bulb about $\frac{3}{4}$ in. in diameter for planting. When onion seed is planted for an edible crop and a larger

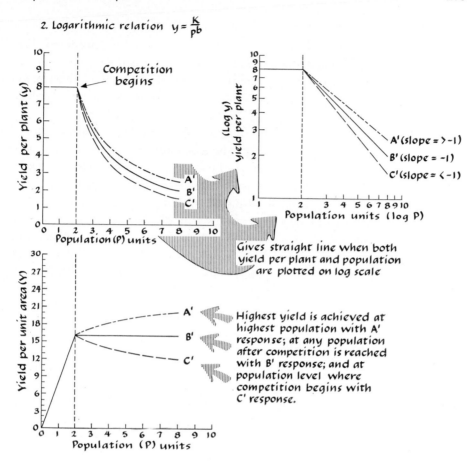

2. Logarithmic relation $y = \dfrac{K}{pb}$

Competition begins

A' (slope = > -1)
B' (slope = -1)
C' (slope = < -1)

Gives straight line when both yield per plant and population are plotted on log scale

Highest yield is achieved at highest population with A' response; at any population after competition is reached with B' response; and at population level where competition begins with C' response.

bulb size is desired, the planting rate is 2–4 lb/acre. Similarly, large increases in pineapple yields have been obtained by close spacing of large-fruited varieties.

Environmental factors such as nutrition or moisture levels may drastically change the level at which the response to crowding occurs. Thus, in tomatoes, varietal response differs with the season. Of particular interest is the different type of response that may occur with different genetic types of the same plant. The dwarf corn produced with the *compact* gene appears to demonstrate a different response to competition than normal corn, which means that yields may be constantly increased in proportion to population. The rearrangement of a plant population by rows increases competition in comparison to equidistant plant spacing, but this may be necessary for cultural considerations such as cultivation for weed control and access for spraying and harvesting equipment.

Quality of Yield

Population pressures affect quality factors that must be considered. For example, crowding of tomatoes increases the foliage canopy, which tends to protect the fruit from being burned by the sun. On the other hand, excessive crowding of potted chrysanthemums produces an undesirable, spindly growth.

A high population level has an adverse effect on disease control. Plants grown exceptionally close together produce a dense cover that discourages rapid drying and produces conditions favorable for the growth of many fungi. In addition, the dense cover is impenetrable to spray application and limits chemical disease control. Sometimes dense foliage facilitates the actual spread of diseases by contact, as is true of tobacco mosaic virus in tomato. High population may be utilized as a method of weed control. The increased shade produced by a dense cover of vigorous plants may permit the crop plant to outcompete weeds. This is utilized in turf management.

Intraplant Competition

The interrelationship between parts of the same plant is an important component of population competition. This almost invariably involves fruit and flower size. Size per unit is an important component of value in practically all horticultural crops. For example, high yields of extremely small fruit may be economically worthless.

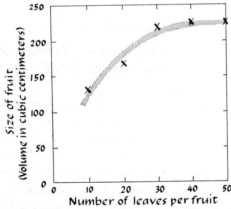

Fig. 8-23. *Relationship between the number of leaves per fruit and fruit size in the Delicious apple.*

[Adapted from data of Magness, Overly, and Luce, Washington Agr. Expt. Sta. Bull. 249, 1931.]

Fruit Size

An important factor in fruit size is the leaf to fruit ratio. Since leaves are the carbohydrate source nourishing the fruit, fruit size will be related in any given genotype to the amount of leaf area per fruit. (Fig. 8-23). The seeds get first call on the carbohydrates produced by the leaves. When the seed requirements are satisfied, the extra carbohydrates become available to the fruit. Only then do the extra carbohydrates become available for the vegetative organs.

Leaf area may not be a constant value. Indeterminate plants (plants in which the main axis remains vegetative) have a constantly increasing leaf area as the plant grows. Under a heavy load of maturing fruit, however, many indeterminate plants stop vegetative growth. The result is a constant leaf to fruit ratio. In mature, bearing fruit trees the amount of leaves produced in any one season is relatively constant because the amount of new growth tends to be small.

There are two ways to compensate for fruit competition. One is to increase the number or efficiency of the leaves. The other is to reduce the fruit load by blossom or fruit removal, that is, by *thinning* (Fig. 8-24). Increasing leaf growth and efficiency is accomplished by various cultural practices involving plant nutrition (see Chapter 6). This may be self defeating when higher nutrition increases fruit number. Thinning, on the

Fig. 8-24. *The effect of thinning on fruit size. The left side of tree was thinned; the right side of the tree was not.*
[Courtesy Purdue Univ.]

other hand, is an expensive practice and is confined largely to high-priced fruit crops whose value is largely dependent on size per unit (apples, pears, peaches, plums).

Yield and Fruit Size

Below the levels of intraplant competition, yield is directly related to the number of fruit. Under competition, however, the increase in yield levels off. The practical level for thinning popular peach and apple varieties occurs at levels where total yield is practically unaffected. This is because these varieties are potentially large fruited. The timing of thinning, however, must be early to be effective. The general relationship between the number of fruit, fruit size, and yield in apples and peaches is plotted in Fig. 8-25.

Other Considerations

In addition to size, other important considerations are involved in fruit competition. In apples, for instance, a relationship exists between quality and fruit load. With an unusually light crop, apples of some varieties may get too large (over $3\frac{1}{2}$ in.), and storage quality decreases. On the other hand, with fewer leaves per fruit, there is a decrease in fruit sugars (mainly sucrose), which affects edible quality. A corresponding decrease in anthocyanin pigments per fruit decreases red color, although this effect is relatively slight.

Competition between fruit and vegetative parts may result in severe damage to the plant; for example, with grapes excessive fruit load renders the plant susceptible to winter injury as a consequence of low sugar accumulation by the vegetative organs. In periods of stress, such as drought, fruit is removed from young trees in order to prevent desiccation and

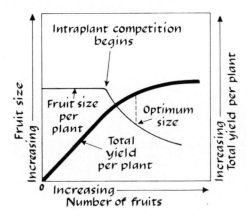

Fig. 8-25. *Idealized relationship between fruit size and yield. The total yield per tree is only slightly reduced by thinning popular large-fruited varieties of apples and peaches. However, the value of unthinned fruit may be economically worthless. Some reduction in total yield is desireable in order to keep alternate bearing varieties producing on an annual basis.*

subsequent winter injury. Heavy fruiting in tomatoes will increase susceptibility to foliage diseases.

In fruit crops that produce flower buds in the year previous to fruiting (especially apples and pears), fruit competition may be responsible for *biennial bearing*. The competition for nutrients between a large number of developing fruit apparently prevents the development of fruit buds for next year's crop. Once this pattern has started it is difficult to stop, for in the off-bearing year an extra abundance of flower buds will form in the absence of fruit competition.

Flower Size

In plants grown for individual flowers rather than for clusters, unit size is an important component of value, just as it is in fruit. For this reason, flower size is commonly increased by reducing the number of developing flowers per shoot. This is accomplished by *disbudding*, the removal of all buds but one per shoot. Disbudding is a standard practice in the culture of roses, carnations, chrysanthemums, and peonies.

Economics of Population Control

If we grant that the goal of the commercial producer of plants is profit, then the optimum population will be the one in which profits are greatest. With respect to populations of plants or of plant parts a number of factors must be considered. For example, all costs must be taken into consideration. This involves the costs of plants and planting (or thinning), as well as the costs of cultivation, disease control, and harvesting. From these figures the actual costs of production for each level of population can be determined. Similarly, the returns at each population level can be determined if the yield responses are known. This will be the value of each unit, determined from its size and quality multiplied by the total number of units of that value. The profit (or loss) at each population level may be determined by subtracting total costs from total returns.

If we could predict all plant responses, costs, and returns, it would be relatively easy to "program" the problem, that is, substitute values into a mathematical formula and solve (with an electronic computer if necessary) the equation. Although this degree of control is not yet possible, it is being approached, as has been illustrated by the cling peach predictions made in California. However, empirical solutions to these problems have been obtained by trial and error through the years. It will be interesting to compare these empirical answers with the mathematically determined solutions when they become available. The obvious advantage of the mathematical approach is its "instantaneous" utilization of changing information concerning prices, costs, and yield responses. It should be pointed out that the same type of analysis is available to "noncommercial" growers. Although monetary values are usually not placed on pride or satisfaction they might well be for purposes of analysis.

Selected References

Anderson, H. W. *Diseases of Fruit Crops*. McGraw-Hill, New York. 1956. (The important, deciduous, temperate fruits are treated. Insects are not covered.)

Christie, J. R. *Plant Nematodes*. Florida Agr. Exp. Station, Gainsville, Fla. 1959. (The biology and control of plant nematodes.)

Crafts, A. S., and Robbins, W. W. *Weed Control*. McGraw-Hill, New York, 1962. (A comprehensive text and manual on the principles of weed control.)

Duncan, W. G. Effects of plant population and of fertilizer placement upon plant growth and development. PhD thesis, Purdue University. 1958. (A brilliant analysis of the effects of plant population pressures on yield.)

Insects. USDA Yearbook. 1952. (A popular but broad treatment.)

Pfadt, R. E. (editor). *Fundamentals of Applied Entomology*. Macmillan, New York. 1962. (Each chapter is contributed by a specialist.)

Pirone, P. P., Dodge, B. O., and Rickett, H. W. *Diseases and Pests of Ornamental Plants*. 3rd ed. Ronald, New York. 1960. (A thorough treatment.)

Plant Diseases, USDA Yearbook. 1953. (Good coverage of horticultural crops.)

Walker, J. C. *Diseases of Vegetable Crops*. McGraw-Hill, New York. 1952. (A useful manual. Insect pests are not discussed.)

CHAPTER 9

Mechanisms of Propagation

Propagation refers to the controlled perpetuation of plants. The basic objective of plant propagation is twofold: to achieve an increase in number and to preserve the essential characteristics of the plant. There are two essentially different types of propagation: *sexual* and *asexual*. *Sexual propagation* involves the increase of plants through seeds formed from the union of gametes. *Asexual* propagation involves the increase of plants through ordinary cell division and differentiation. The essential feature of asexual propagation is that plants are capable of regenerating missing parts. Thus, a stem cutting initiates roots, a root cutting develops shoot buds, and a leaf cutting initiates both roots and shoots.

CELL DIVISION

The basic difference between sexual and asexual propagation involves the distinction between the two types of cell division—*mitosis* and *meiosis*—in which the chromosomes are distributed. Chromosomes are linear structures in the nucleus that contain the *genes*, the carriers of genetic information.

Mitosis

In mitosis a synchronized division takes place in which both the chromosomes and the cell divide (Fig. 9-1). The chromosomes duplicate themselves longitudinally, each half moving to alternate ends of the cell. The two resulting daughter cells thus receive exactly the same number and kind of chromosomes. The division of the cell distributes equally the other constituents of the cell.

This increase in cell number, in plants as well as in animals, is called

281

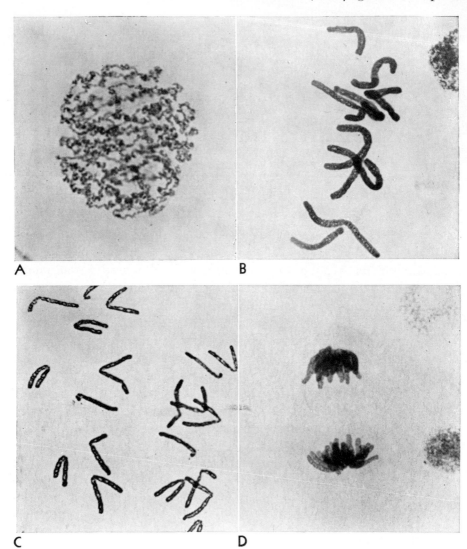

Fig. 9-1. *Mitosis in the California coastal peony. The vegetative cells of this species have 10 chromosomes (2n = 10). Although mitosis is continuous, the process is broken down into a number of stages for descriptive purposes. (A) Prophase. The nucleus of a cell in the process of division. During this stage the nucleus becomes less granular and the linear structure of the chromosomes can be readily followed. Note the chromosome coils. (B) Metaphase. The 10 chromosomes line up in the equatorial plate, which appear as an "equatorial line" due to the smearing process. The chromosomes have reduplicated, and each appears visibly doubled. (C) Anaphase. The chromosomes have separated, and approach the poles of the cell. It is possible to pick out the pairs in each group and to match the daughter chromosomes,*

mitotic division. The differentiation of the cells into tissues and organs ordinarily is not related to any chromosomal difference. The fact that each cell contains all the necessary genetic material implies that any cell potentially can give rise to the entire organism. The production of an entire plant from a single carrot parenchyma cell has been achieved. The formation of shoot buds from roots, or roots from leaves, is common in plants. The genetic continuity of mitosis insures that a bud on the potato tuber will, under the right conditions, produce an entire potato plant.

Meiosis

In meiosis—a sequence of cell divisions that occurs in the formation of gametes—the number of chromosomes is reduced by half (Fig. 9-2). The chromosomes in the ordinary vegetative cells of higher plants normally occur in pairs, making up the somatic number. The two chromosomes of a pair (homologues) are morphologically similar and contain the same kind of genes, although each member of the gene pair may not be identical as a result of some alteration (mutation). The combination of different genes is responsible for the genetic variability between living things. The sexual process is one mechanism that provides for the reassortment and recombination of genetic factors so that organisms may be able to survive through time in an ever changing environment. The reassortment of genetic factors taking place between and within chromosomes is accomplished by meiosis; the recombination is accomplished by fertilization (see Chapter 10).

Meiosis is basically a series of two divisions in which the cells divide twice but the chromosomes only once. This results in four cells, each having the haploid number; that is, half the number of chromosomes possessed by the vegetative cells. Each of these four cells is potentially a gamete. Fertilization, the fusion of two gametes, subsequently restores the diploid number.

The most obvious effect of meiosis is the reduction in chromosome number from the diploid to the haploid number. This is necessary to provide a constant chromosome level when gametes recombine at fertilization. The

---

which have just separated from each other. (D) Telophase. During this stage the contracted chromosomes are pressed close together at each end of the cell. A wall is subsequently formed across the cell, forming two "daughter" cells with the same number and kind of chromosomes as exist in the original cell.

[Courtesy M. S. Walters and S. W. Brown.]

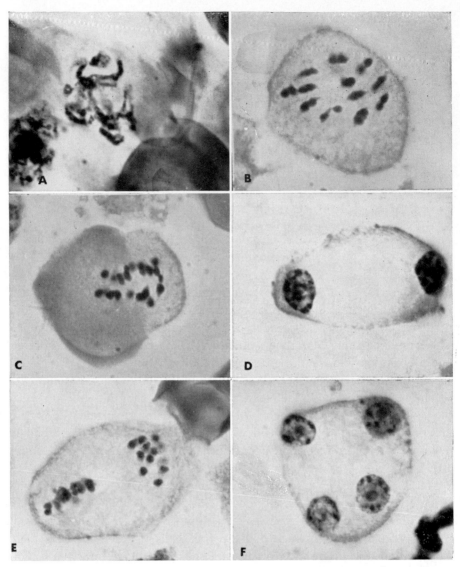

Fig. 9-2. *Meiosis in pepper. This species has 24 chromosomes in the vegetative cells (2n = 24). Note that there are 2 divisions in meiosis. (A) In the prophase of the first division, the 24 chromosomes pair up along their length at the same time that they appear doubled. This can be seen clearly in the bottom of the picture. (B) At metaphase of the first division, 12 pairs of chromosomes are visible on the equatorial plate (face view). Each chromosome pair consists of 2 doubled chromosomes (4 chromatids). (C) Anaphase of the first division. (D) Telophase of the first division. (E) Metaphase of the second division: one plate is a face view; the other is a side view. (F) Telophase of the second division. Walls will be formed across the cell to form 4 pollen grains, each containing 12 chromosomes. Each grain will contain half as many chromosomes as the original cell.*

less obvious but most important effect of meiosis is the reassortment of chromosomes, which are distributed to the gametes.

The basic difference between mitosis and meiosis occurs at the first division. In meiotic division the chromosomes become visibly double, as they do in mitosis, but this is the last time the chromosomes divide, although the cells will divide once more. Unlike mitosis, the two homologous chromosomes, now visibly doubled, pair up (*synapse*) along their length. The attraction between the doubled chromosomes changes to repulsion, and each doubled chromosome of a pair moves to opposite poles of the cell. As a result the cell has half as many "whole" chromosomes at each end.

Apparently, when the chromosomes pair at the first division an actual exchange of segments (*crossovers*) occurs between homologous chromosomes. (This exchange involves the *chromatids*, the half chromosomes.) The precise mechanism by which the exchange of chromosome material takes place is still not fully understood. The net result of the first division is thus not only a reduction in chromosome number but a rearrangement of segments between homologous chromosomes. In the second division, which immediately follows the first, the division of doubled chromosomes is similar to that of mitosis. However, owing to the previous crossovers these two daughter nuclei may not be duplicates of each other.

Consequences of Sexual Reproduction

The genetic consequences of sexual propagation are more fully discussed in Chapter 10, but a brief discussion will be given here. Plants that are continually self-pollinated, such as the tomato or pea, contain essentially similar pairs of genes on homologous chromosomes (that is, they are homozygous). Homozygous plants will reduplicate themselves exactly by sexual reproduction, or *breed true*. Plants that tend to cross-pollinate, such as the petunia or cucumber, will have many dissimilar pairs of genes on homologous chromosomes (that is, they are *heterozygous*). Sexual reproduction constantly rearranges these genetic factors. Cross-pollinated plants *do not* breed true, but *segregate*.

The problem of reproducing a particular plant exactly thus depends on its natural method of pollination. Seed propagation will duplicate naturally any plant that is highly self-pollinated because such plants tend to be homozygous. A particular cross-pollinated plant can only be duplicated exactly by asexual methods because it is heterozygous. However, a high degree of uniformity in some character may be achieved in the seed propagation of cross-pollinated plants as a result of constant selection. For example, in well-selected petunia varieties each plant may have the same flower color, although it can be demonstrated that the plants are not identical for all characters.

SEED PROPAGATION

Seed is the most common means of propagation for self-pollinated plants, and is extensively used for many cross-pollinated plants. It is often the only possible or practical method of propagation. There are many advantages in propagating by seed. It is usually the cheapest method of plant propagation. Seeds also offer a convenient method for storing plants over time. When kept dry and cool seeds remain viable from harvest to the following planting season, and some seeds, such as Indian lotus (*Nelumbo nucifera*), remain viable for as long as 1000 years. Another advantage to seed propagation is that it provides a method for starting "disease-free" plants. This is especially important with respect to virus diseases, since it is almost impossible to free infected plants. Most virus diseases are usually not seed transmitted. The major disadvantages to seed propagation, besides the already discussed genetic segregation in heterozygous plants, is the long time required in some plants from seed to maturity. For example, eight years are often required for pears to fruit from seed. Potatoes do not produce large tubers the first year when grown from seed. Here asexual propagation not only provides trueness to type but in many plants saves several years.

Seed Origin and Development

The seed is the result of complex growth and developmental events. These include the development of the pollen and embryo sac (male and female gametophyte), pollination, fertilization, and maturation processes.

Pollen Formation

In the anther, *pollen mother cells* undergo meioses to produce microspores —haploid male spores that, when developed, are known as pollen. The pollen grain can be thought of as a separate plant, the *male gametophyte* (Fig. 9-3). This haploid "plant" producing the male gametes is the remnant of the gametophytic generation, which may be well developed in more primitive plants, such as ferns and mosses. In seed plants this stage is very much reduced. The haploid nucleus of the microspore divides mitotically

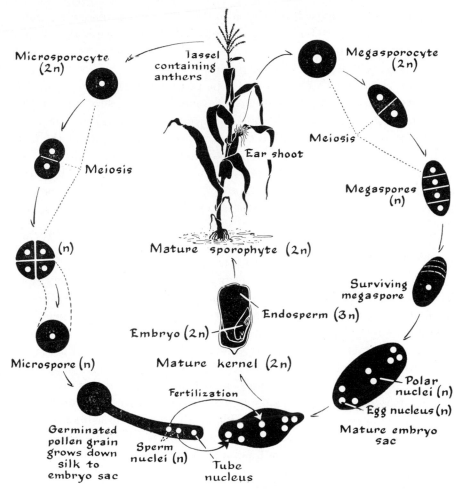

Fig. 9-3. *The life cycle of corn* (Zea mays), *illustrating pollen and embryo sac formation.*

[Adapted from Srb and Owen, *General Genetics*, Freeman, San Francisco, 1952.]

to form the generative nucleus and the tube nucleus. The generative nucleus often appears to have cytoplasm associated with it, resembling a cell within a cell. The generative nucleus is destined to divide mitotically, either in the grain or in the pollen tube, to form two nuclei—the *male gametes.*

Embryo Sac Formation

There is no common term, unless it be "embryo sac," that corresponds to the word "pollen." This is probably because the embryo sac is inconspicuously located inside the enlarged base of the pistil. The *megaspore mother*

cell, borne inside a specialized region in the ovary called the ovule, undergoes meiosis to produce four haploid cells. Of the four haploid cells produced, three disintegrate. The remaining cell, the *megaspore,* or female
spore, divides mitotically and when mature develops into the *female gametophyte,* or *embryo sac.* This development proceeds in various ways. Most
commonly, however, the haploid nucleus undergoes three successive mitotic
divisions. The eight resulting nuclei form a cell membrane around them and
arrange into three groups within the embryo sac. The middle of the three
cells at the micropylar end develops into the female gamete, the *egg cell.*
The two *polar* cells at the center of the embryo sac will eventually be part of
the endosperm. The function of the two cells (*synergids*) that accompany
the egg cell or the three cells (*antipodals*) at the other end of the embryo
sac is obscure.

Pollination

Pollination refers to the transfer of pollen from the anther to the stigma.
The transfer of pollen to any flower on the same plant or clone is *self-
pollination,* (or *selfing*); the transfer of pollen to a flower on a different plant
is *cross-pollination.* Self-pollination is usually accomplished by gravity or by
the actual contact of the shedding anther with the sticky stigmatic surface.
In cross-pollination wind and insects are the important agents of pollen
transfer. Most plants both self- and cross-pollinate naturally, with the proportion varying depending upon functional or structural features of the
flower or on genetic incompatibility. Plants are referred to as *naturally self-
pollinated* when the amount of cross-pollination is less than about 4%; as
often cross-pollinated when self pollination is more frequent than cross-
pollination; and as *naturally cross-pollinated* when cross-pollination is predominant.

Natural self-pollination is achieved through functional and structural features of the flower. Flowers that lend themselves to this mode of pollination
are perfect; that is, they contain both stamens and pistils. In some plants,
such as the violet, the shedding of pollen before the flower is open (*cleis-
togamous flower*) insures self-pollination. A common structural feature of
self-pollinating plants consists of a pistil growing through a sheath or ring
of anthers, as in the tomato.

Cross-pollination, typical of many horticultural plants, is brought about
in many different ways. The most basic is the separation of stamens and
pistils into separate flowers (*monoecism*) as in corn and cucumbers. The
extreme form of this is the separation of staminate and pistillate flowers in
different plants (*dioecism*), as in spinach, asparagus, and holly. However,

many perfect flowered plants cross-pollinate. This is achieved by anatomical or physiological features of the flower which prevent self-pollination. For example, the differential maturation of stamens or pistils will prevent natural selfing. The structural features of the flower that insure cross-pollination are often related to pollen transfer by insects. Among the special adaptations that aid in insect pollination are petal color, odor, and presence of nectar. In some plants an intimate interdependence exists between the plant and the insect. For example, pollination of the Smyrna fig, which produces only female flowers, is carried out by the *Blastophoga* fig wasp. This wasp develops only in the wild, inedible caprifig, which produces only male flowers, hence the name caprification for this process. The winged female wasp escapes from the caprifig covered with pollen and will enter Smyrna figs and in the process effect pollination. The Smyrna fig, not suitable for the development of the wasp, requires the presence of the caprifig for development.

Incompatibility (self-sterility) is a physiological mechanism that prevents self-fertilization. A genetic factor (or factors) serves to prevent pollen tubes produced by the plant from growing in the style of the same plant. Incompatibility factors prevent self-pollination in such crops as cabbage, tobacco, petunia, and apple.

Fertilization

The pollen grain, after landing on the stigmatic surface of the pistil, absorbs water and other substances such as sugars, and forms a tube. The tube literally grows down the style to the embryo sac. The pollen tube penetrates the embryo sac, where one male gamete unites with the egg to form the *zygote*. After mitotic division the zygote becomes the *embryo* of the resultant seed. The other male gamete fuses with the two polar nuclei and forms the *endosperm*. This complete process is referred to as *double fertilization*.

Seed Maturation

Fertilization initiates rapid growth of the ovary and subsequent development of the seed. Usually the ovary will not develop unless it contains viable and growing seed. Common exceptions (*parthenocarpy*) are seedless grapes and oranges. In these the developing seed breaks down at an early point in its development. The growth of the fruit has been discussed in Chapter 5.

The growth pattern of a developing lettuce seed is presented in Fig. 9-4. Note that the development of the embryo is preceded by endosperm growth. When rapid growth of the embryo begins, it does so at the expense of the endosperm. The amount of endosperm at maturity varies with different

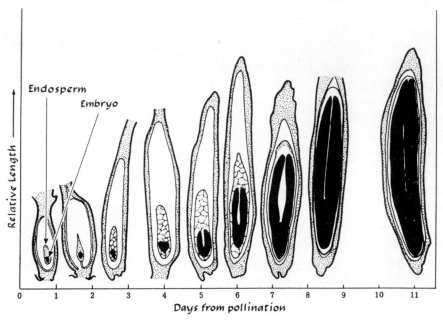

Fig. 9-4. *Growth of one-seeded fruit of lettuce. Note that the early growth of endosperm precedes that of the embryo.*

[Adapted from Hartmann and Kester, *Plant Propagation,* Prentice-Hall, Englewood Cliffs, 1959; After Jones.]

plants. The endosperm may be completely absorbed at seed maturity, in which case stored food may be in the embryo itself, as in the cotyledons of bean seeds.

Seed Production and Handling

Although the area of seed production of some flowers and vegetables (for example, tomato, watermelon) is the same as the area of crop production, most seed crops are grown in specialized locations. (The principal horticultural seed-producing areas of the United States are in the western states, principally Idaho and California.) The limitation may be imposed by specific flowering requirements, such as cold induction or photoperiod. In addition, there are specialized requirements of seed production: low moisture at harvest to permit proper maturation of the seed and to reduce the incidence of fungal and bacterial disease; and isolation, which is required to prevent contamination in cross pollinating species. For example, sweet corn seed cannot be produced in the Midwest because the abundance of pollen from field corn or popcorn would result in undesirable hybrids. Very little tree and shrub seed is grown commercially. This seed is collected from natural stands, from nurseries and arboreta. Seed from fruit trees, the seedlings of which are often used as root stocks, is obtained as a by-product of the fruit-processing industry.

A considerable amount of hand labor is required in the harvesting of flower and vegetable seed. This is particularly true of species in which the seed head, or pods, shatter easily or of plants on which the seed matures gradually, such that at any one time there may be mature seed pods, flowers, and flower buds. Examples are aquilegia, delphinium, salvia, petunia, and pansy. One great advantage of hand picking is that the cleaning operations are greatly simplified. With other crops the entire plant is cut and placed on sheets of canvas or in windrows to dry and is then threshed. This procedure is used with carnation, centaurea, daisy, gypsophila, hollyhock, larkspur, French marigold, lychnis, phlox, scabiosa, snapdragon, verbena, sweetpea, nasturtium, and morning glory.

In many crops the seed must be extracted or milled from the fruits and then cleaned. The separation of the seed from fleshy fruits such as the tomato is accomplished through fermentation of the macerated pulp. Seed is removed from dried pods or seed heads by milling. Cleaning is facilitated by differences in size, density, and shape of the seed in comparison with the plant debris or other seeds which are harvested incidentally. Screens may be used to separate large particles from the seed. Small light fragments are blown from the seed by passing an air stream through the seed as it passes from one screen to another or as it is passed across a porous bench or against an inclined plane. The heavier seed remains at the base while lighter material moves up the plane. Seeds or particles that are of the same density as the crop seed but of a different shape can be removed on an "indent machine." A wheel covered with indentations is passed through a mass of seed, and each "indent" picks up a seed. The size and shape of the indentation is determined by the crop being cleaned. Some seeds, particularly beans and peas can be separated on the basis of color. Single seeds are picked up by suction through perforations on a hollow wheel and then are passed through a photoelectric cell. If the cell detects a seed of the wrong color, a device releases the vacuum and ejects the seed. Throughout the milling and cleaning operations, extreme care must be taken in the adjustment of the machinery. Seeds which are chipped or damaged may be reduced in viability or may produce abnormal seedlings.

Seed Storage

The storage life of seeds varies greatly with species. With any species the longevity is greatly affected by storage conditions. Most seeds retain the highest viability in a relative humidity of 4–6%, although some species (for example, silver maple, citrus) lose viability under low moisture. The best temperatures for storing many seeds have been shown to be between 0° and 32°F. Actual storage conditions required for seed depends ultimately on the species and on the length of storage time desired. For most seeds, temperatures of 32–50°F and a relative humidity of 50–65% is adequate to maintain full viability for at least one year.

Germination

Germination, the series of events from dormant seed to growing seedling, is dependent upon seed viability, the breaking of dormancy, and suitable environmental conditions. The germinating seed and young seedlings are

Fig. 9-5. *Germination of corn seed is being tested by the "rolled towel" technique. One hundred seeds are placed on moist paper towling, which is sealed in wax paper, rolled, and stored under standardized temperature conditions. After seven days, the percentage germination is evaluated.*
[Photograph by J. C. Allen & Son.]

vulnerable to certain diseases (for example, damping-off), thus protection must be provided.

Viability

Seed viability refers to the percentage of seed that will complete germination, the speed of germination, and the resulting vigor of seedlings. The viability of seed lots can be determined by standardized testing procedures. Probably the most significant measure of viability is the *germination percentage,* the percentage of seed of the species tested that produces normal seedlings under optimum germinating conditions (Fig. 9-5). Germinating tests are usually performed on moistened absorbent paper under rigidly controlled environmental conditions (Fig. 9-6). The length of the test varies, for some species are notoriously slow to germinate. Perhaps the greatest problem is in distinguishing between dormant and nonviable seed. Seed dormancy must be overcome to obtain a reliable test. A rapid chemical test involving tetrazolium (2,3,5-triphenyltetrazolium chloride) makes it possible to evaluate viability in nongerminating dormant seed. Living cells color red, whereas nonliving cells show no color.

Fig. 9-6. *Seed germinator with complete environmental control including light. This germinator was designed for the Indiana State Seed Laboratory.*
[Photograph by J. C. Allen & Son.]

Breaking Dormancy

The breaking of dormancy and the creation of a suitable environment are necessary to initiate the germination process. The treatments depend on the type of dormancy involved (see Chapter 5). They include scarification, stratification, embryo culture, or various combinations of these treatments, with suitable environment control.

SCARIFICATION. The germination of seed that contains an impervious seed coat may be promoted by *scarification*—the alteration of the seed coat to render it permeable to gaseous and water exchange. This is accomplished by a number of techniques, mechanical methods involving abrasive action being the most common. The action of hot water (170–212°F) is effective in honey locust seed. Seed can be scarified by the corrosive chemical action of sulfuric acid.

DRY STORAGE AND STRATIFICATION. Seed that will not germinate immediately after harvest requires *dry storage* for a period of days or months. The physiological basis of this type of dormancy is not clear but has been associated with the evolution of volatile inhibitors. The afterripening of some seeds requires a period of moist storage known as *stratification*.

Cold-stratification—the afterripening of dormant embryos by storing them at high moisture and low temperature—is a prerequisite for the uniform germination of many temperate zone species, such as apple, pear, redbud. The cold-stratification of apple and pear seed involves storing the moist aerated seed at around 32°F. The germination percentage increases with time until the third month of treatment. The stratification media consists of moist soil, sand, and peat or such synthetic substances as vermiculite. An effective means of preventing the loss of moisture and of providing an adequate exchange of oxygen and carbon dioxide consists in sealing the seed in polyethylene bags containing a moist blotting paper.

Warm-stratification—moist storage above approximately 45°F—promotes germination in some species as a result of microbial decomposition of the seed covering. Seed such as viburnum, which possesses different types of dormancy (*double dormancy*), are first *warm-* and then *cold*-stratified. In seeds such as redbud a combination of scarification and cold-stratification is used.

Environmental Factors Affecting Germination

The germination of seed that does not require afterripening, or of seed that has had this requirement satisfied, depends upon external environmental factors, namely, water, favorable temperature, oxygen, and, sometimes, light.

The amount of water required for germination varies somewhat with different species. For example, celery requires that soil moisture be near field capacity, whereas tomato will germinate with soil moisture just above the permanent wilting point. For most seed, overwet conditions are harmful, since they prevent aeration and promote disease. However, moisture must be maintained during germination lest the germinating seedling dry out. Shading to conserve moisture is recommended until germination is complete. The use of glass over seed flats conserves moisture, but care should be used to prevent the seeds from getting too hot.

Table 9-1. *Soil temperatures for vegetable seed germination.*
[From Hartmann and Kester, *Plant Propagation*, Prentice-Hall, New Jersey, 1959; after Harrington and Minges.]

MINIMUM

32°F	40°F		50°F	60°F	
Endive	Beet	Parsley	Asparagus	Bean, Lima	Okra
Lettuce	Broccoli	Pea	Sweet Corn	Bean, Snap	Pepper
Onion	Cabbage	Radish	Tomato	Cucumber	Pumpkin
Parsnip	Carrot	Swiss Chard		Eggplant	Squash
Spinach	Cauliflower	Turnip		Muskmelon	Watermelon
	Celery				

OPTIMUM

70°F	75°F	80°F	85°F		95°F
Celery	Asparagus	Bean, Lima	Bean, Snap	Pepper	Cucumber
Parsnip	Endive	Carrot	Beet	Radish	Muskmelon
Spinach	Lettuce	Cauliflower	Broccoli	Sweet Corn	Okra
	Pea	Onion	Cabbage	Swiss Chard	Pumpkin
		Parsley	Eggplant	Tomato	Squash
				Turnip	Watermelon

MAXIMUM

75°F	85°F	95°F		105°F	
Celery	Beans, Lima	Asparagus	Eggplant	Cucumber	Squash
Endive	Parsnip	Bean, Snap	Onion	Muskmelon	Sweet Corn
Lettuce	Pea	Beet	Parsley	Okra	Turnip
Spinach		Broccoli	Pepper	Pumpkin	Watermelon
		Cabbage	Radish		
		Carrot	Swiss Chard		
		Cauliflower	Tomato		

The effect of temperature upon germination varies with the species involved and is related somewhat to the temperature requirement for optimum growth of the mature plant (Table 9-1). In general, the germination rate increases as temperature increases, although the highest germination percentage may be at a relatively low temperature. An alternating temperature is usually more favorable than a constant temperature. Because of its critical role in respiration, oxygen is necessary for seed germination in all plants except some water-loving species (for example, rice, cattails). The use of proper drainage and tilth in seed beds promotes rapid germination, largely as a result of good aeration (Fig. 9-7).

The effect of light in stimulating or inhibiting the germination of some seed, discussed in Chapter 5, is a reversible red-far red phenomenon. To produce good stocky plants ample light must be supplied during early seedling growth.

Fig. 9-7. *Good seedbed preparation promotes rapid seed germination.*

[Courtesy Ford Motor Co., Tractor and Implement Div.]

The action of certain salts has been shown to influence germination. At concentrations of 0.1–0.2%, potassium nitrate will increase germination in a number of plants, and is used in seed testing. In general, high salt concentrations brought about by overfertilization inhibit germination.

Embryo Culture

The artificial culture of the embryo is used to facilitate seed germination in certain species. For example, the embryo in many early-ripening peaches (for example, the Mayflower) is not sufficiently mature to germinate when the fruit is ripe. This problem, a serious impediment to the breeding of early ripening peaches, can be overcome, however, by excising the embryo from the pit and culturing it under aseptic conditions in media providing certain nutrients.

Tukey's Solution for Culturing Mature and Relatively Immature Embryos

Stock Chemical	Relative amounts
KCl	5
$CaSO_4$	1.25
$MgSO_4$	1.25
$Ca_3(PO_4)_2$	1.25
$Fe_3(PO_4)_2$	1.25
KNO_3	1

Use 1.5 g of mixture/liter of water.

This technique is also used in viburnum to escape dormancy. The routine germination of orchid seed involves culture in artificial media. These seeds, which are almost microscopic in size, consist of a simple, undifferentiated embryo and contain no reserve food.

Knudson's Solution B for Growing Orchid Seedlings
(mg/liter)

$Ca(NO_3)_2 \cdot 4H_2O$	1000	agar	17.5 g
$(NH_4)_2SO_4$	500	sucrose	20.0 g
KH_2PO_4	250		
$MgSO_4 \cdot 7H_2O$	250		
$FePO_4 \cdot 4H_2O$	50		

Disease Control

Disease is a critical factor in the germination process. This is especially true for seed that must be stratified or which requires an extensive period of time to germinate. The control of these diseases is an integral part of the technology of seed propagation.

The major diseases of germinating seeds are grouped under the single name *"damping-off."* It is caused by a number of separate fungi, mainly species of *Pythium, Rhizoctonia* and *Phytophthora.* The disease is expressed either by the failure of the seedling to emerge or by the death of the seedling shortly after emergence. A common symptom is the girdling of young seedling stems at the soil surface. Damping-off usually occurs only in young, succulent seedlings during or shortly after germination, but older plants may be affected in severe cases. Damping-off can be severe in both greenhouse and field soils and often is a limiting factor in the success of seed propagation. Protection from this and other seedling diseases involves both the direct control of the organism and the regulation of environmental conditions such that they favor the rapid growth of the plant rather than the growth of the pathogens.

SEED AND SOIL TREATMENT. A number of seed treatments are available to either eliminate the organisms from the seed or to provide protection to the seedling when planted in infested soil. These consist in coating the seed with a suitable fungicide, such as mercuric chloride, cuprous oxide, calcium hypochlorite. A common seed treatment involves a 5-minute dip in a 10% solution of Chlorox (which is a 5.25% solution of sodium hypochlorite). A number of commercial compounds prepared for seed treatment are available. The treatment of seeds in hot water (122°F for 15–30 min) has been used for seed-borne diseases of vegetables (for example, Alternaria of onion). Such treatment must be precise, however, or the seed may be seriously injured.

Soil may be treated by applying fungicides to the upper surface or by applying heat. Raising the soil temperature to 180°F for 30 min ("pasteurization") is always recommended for potting soils to control weeds and nematodes, as well as damping-off organisms. Complete sterilization of soil interferes with nutrient availability and should be avoided. Sphagnum moss has proved satisfactory as a germination and stratification media for some seeds because inhibitors and low pH prevent the growth of many of the damping-off organisms. The use of sterile media such as sand, vermiculite, or perlite may be desirable for seed germination. However, care must be taken to avoid recontamination of sterilized soil. The low population of natural predators (bacteria and other fungi) may result in great damage if this soil becomes reinfested with the pathogen.

CONTROL OF THE ENVIRONMENT. Any environmental effect that encourages more rapid plant growth as compared to the buildup of pathogens is effective in the control of seedling diseases such as damping off, because older seedlings appear to resist attack. The temperatures most favorable to damping-off fungi lie between approximately 70° and 85°F. Thus, damping-off tends to be severe when cool-season crops are germinated at temperatures that are too high, and vice versa. For best control germinating temperatures should be optimum for the crop. This principle can be utilized in the control of damping-off in the field by regulating planting dates. Good viable seed and rapid seedling growth are important. Many of the fungi responsible for damping-off are water-loving,* and are encouraged in wet soils. Cloudy weather and periods of poor drying encourage the damping-off complex; consequently, frequent and shallow watering should be avoided after planting.

Sanitation to reduce the buildup of organisms responsible for damping-off should be practiced in the greenhouse, where this trouble is a perpetual problem. This involves eliminating plant refuse, disinfecting the walks and the potting area, keeping unsterilized soil out of the potting area, and general cleanliness.

Planting

Seed may be either sown in a permanent location (*direct seeding*) or planted first in some container from which the young plants can be transplanted once or many times before permanent planting. The growing of *transplants* makes it possible to provide precise environmental control during the critical stages of germination and early seedling growth. Many ornamentals and vegetables for early production are grown from transplants.

Direct Seeding

Plants that are difficult to transplant, or for which the individual value of the plant does not justify the trouble and expense that transplanting entails, are grown by direct seeding. Many of the common vegetables are always direct seeded (for example, beans, sweet corn, radishes) (Fig. 9-8). Although direct seeding requires much less labor and trouble than transplanting, one of its limitations is weed control. However, the recent advances

---

* The class Phycomycetes, in which both *Pythium* and *Phytophthora* belong, are often referred to as "water molds."

Fig. 9-8.   *Direct seeding in an eight-row planter.*
[Photograph by J. C. Allen & Son.]

in chemical weed control have made the direct seeding of some crops, such as tomato, economically feasible.

Precision spacing is important in direct seeding to prevent the need for extensive plant thinning or replanting. This is difficult to accomplish with small seeds, however, thus attempts have been made to "pelletize" the seed by coating it with some suitable material, usually clay with additives. The increased size of the seed facilitates planting, and the coating material may be treated with fertilizer to encourage rapid seedling growth. Pelleting has been somewhat successful with lettuce, but with present materials it is of doubtful value for most crops, since the pelletizing materials can reduce or retard germination. But this is an area of seed technology that can be expected to change dramatically.

Transplants

The growth of transplants is a specialized part of seed propagation. Seed may be germinated first in "seedling flats" containing specially prepared media, and the seedlings transplanted in some suitable container. If the seedlings transplant with difficulty (as do curcurbits) the seed may be planted directly into individual containers, such as 3 × 3 in. veneer plant bands. The germination media in the seedling flats is usually sand or a sand-soil mixture. Sand has the advantage of being well drained and relatively easy to maintain free of disease-producing fungi. Germination media are lacking in nutrients, but this is not important as long as the seeds are transplanted soon after emergence. Supplemental feeding with nutrient solution can be provided. The depth of planting in seedling flats depends on the size of the seed. As a rough approximation, the depth of planting should be 1–2 times the largest seed diameter. Very fine seed may be sprinkled over the surface of the soil.

Seedlings grown in flats should be transplanted as soon as they are large enough to handle. The transplanting operation must be done carefully to prevent injury. In many plants, however, the destruction of the tap root results in a more fibrous root system, which may be advantageous. The transplanting operation is best made with the soil media just wet enough to be impressionable, but not wet enough to be sticky. A "dibbler" is useful for making the planting hole.

A number of containers, made of various materials, are available for transplanting, for example, flats, pots, and bands. Containers made of a decomposible organic material such as peat are proving of value, especially for retail flower transplants. In their manufacture, peat pots are treated with a fungicide to prevent decomposition by mold growth and with nitrogenous fertilizer to overcome nitrogen deficiencies commonly associated with the use of organic materials. Wooden plant bands are best soaked in nitrogenous fertilizer for the same reason.

Field transplanting is a part of both seed and vegetative propagation. Transplants may be planted along with soil or "bare-rooted." The transplanting of bare-rooted plants of many crops (tomato, strawberry, nursery stock) is well adapted to mechanization (Fig. 9-9). Transplanting machines are

Fig. 9-9. *A tomato transplanting operation. Starter solution is being added to the transplanter.*

[Photograph by J. C. Allen & Son.]

often equipped to apply water and starter solution. Bare-root nursery plants are usually covered with mud before transplanting to prevent drying.

VEGETATIVE PROPAGATION

Vegetative propagation involves nonsexual reproduction through the regeneration of tissues and plant parts. In many cases this process is a completely natural one; in others it is more or less artificial, depending on the interference and regulation by man. The many methods of vegetative propagation depend on the plant and the objectives of the propagator. The advantages of vegetative propagation are readily apparent. Heterozygous material may be perpetuated without alteration. In addition, vegetative propagation may be easier and faster than seed propagation, as seed dormancy problems may be completely eliminated and the juvenile stage reduced. Vegetative propagation also makes it possible to perpetuate clones that do not produce viable seed or do not produce seed at all, e.g. Washington Navel orange, Gros Michel banana, Thompson Seedless grape.

The following summary lists the various methods of vegetative propagation.

1. Utilization of apomictic seed; citrus.
2. Utilization of specialized vegetative structures.
   Runner; strawberry
   Bulb; tulip
   Corm; gladiolus
   Rhizome; iris
   Offshoot; day lily
   Stem tuber; white potato
   Tuberous root; sweet potato
3. Induction of adventitious roots or shoots.
   (a) Layering: regeneration from vegetative part while still attached to the plant.
   (b) Cutting: regeneration from vegetative part detached from the plant.
4. Grafting: the joining of plant parts by means of tissue regeneration.

Utilization of Apomictic Seed

Apomixis refers to the development of seeds without the complete sexual process. It is therefore a form of nonsexual or vegetative reproduction. The most significant type of apomixis is that in which the complete meiotic cycle is eliminated. The seed is formed directly from a diploid cell, which may either be the nonreduced megaspore mother cell or some cell from the maternal ovular tissue. As a result of apomixis, a heterozygous cross-pollinating plant will appear to *breed true*.

Although apomixis is widespread within the plant kingdom, it is not a common means of asexual propagation. It is utilized in the propagation of Kentucky bluegrass, citrus, and the mango. These species, however, are only partially apomictic, and seed will be derived from both the sexual and apomictic process.

Utilization of Specialized Vegetative Structures

The natural increase of many plants is achieved through specialized vegetative structures. These modified roots or stems are often also food storage organs (bulbs, corms, tubers), although in some plants they function primarily for natural vegetative increases, as do runners. These organs enable the plant to survive adverse conditions, such as the cold period in temperate climates or the dry period in tropical climates, and give the plant a means of spreading. These specialized structures renew the plant and themselves through adventitious roots and shoots and are commonly utilized by man as a means of propagation. When these structures subdivide naturally, the process is called *separation;* when they must be cut, the process is called *division.*

Stem Modifications

BULBS. Bulbs are shortened stems with thick, fleshy leaf scales (Fig. 9-10). In addition to their development at the central growing point, buds develop at the axils of the leaf scales. These buds form miniature bulbs (*bulblets*) that, when grown to full size, are known as *offsets*.

The development of bulbs from initiation to flowering size takes a single season in the onion, but most bulbs, such as the daffodil and hyacinth, continue to grow from the center, becoming larger each year while continually producing new offsets. The asexual propagation of bulb-forming plants is commonly achieved through the development of scale buds. Various stages of development may be utilized from the individual scales, offsets, or the enlarging mature bulb itself. In hyacinth propagation the bulb is commonly wounded to encourage adventitious bulblet formation. The bulblets develop into usable size in 2–4 years.

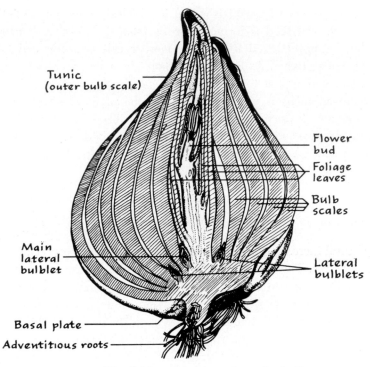

Tunic
(outer bulb scale)

Flower
bud

Foliage
leaves

Bulb
scales

Main
lateral
bulblet

Lateral
bulblets

Basal plate

Adventitious roots

Fig. 9-10.   *Structure of a tulip bulb.*

[Adapted from Hartmann and Kestner, *Plant Propagation*, Prentice-Hall, Englewood Cliffs, 1959; after Mulder and Luyten.]

CORMS. Corms, although they resemble bulbs, do not contain fleshy leaves, but are a solid-stem structure containing nodes and internodes. The gladiolus, crocus, and water chestnut (*Eleocharis tuberosa*) are examples of corm-forming plants. In large, mature corms, one or more of the upper buds develop into flowering shoots. The corm is expended in flower production, and the base of the shoot forms a new corm above the old. At season's end, one or more new corms may develop in this manner. *Cormels*, or miniature corms, are fleshy buds that develop between the old and new corms. Cormels do not increase in size when planted, but produce larger corms from the base of the new stem axis. These require 1–2 years to reach flowering size. This is the usual method of propagating corm-producing plants. Corms may also be increased by division, but this is not commonly practiced because of disease problems.

RUNNERS. *Runners* are specialized aerial stems that develop from the leaf axils at the base or crown of plants having rosette stems (Fig. 9-11). They

Fig. 9-11. *Runnering in the strawberry geranium* (Saxifraga sarmentosa).

[Courtesy E. R. Honeywell.]

provide a means of natural increase and spread. Among the plants propagated by runners are the strawberry, strawberry geranium (*Saxifraga sarmentosa*), and bugle weed (*Ajuga*). The commercial propagation of strawberries is done through runner-plant production. Leaf clusters, which root easily, are formed at the second node of the runner. These rooted plants may in turn produce new runners. Runnering is photoperiod sensitive, being commonly initiated under a day length of 12 hours or longer. Dormant plants are dug by machine in the fall or in the spring. The yield in plants per mother plant varies with the variety, but under optimum conditions may be as high as 200:1. A field increase of 20–30:1 is common. Some species of strawberries are nonrunnering, and many of the everbearing varieties usually form relatively few runners. These plants may be vegetatively propagated by crown divisions, but the increase in plants is much lower than in those with runners.

RHIZOMES. Horizontally orientated cylindrical stems growing underground are called rhizomes (Fig. 9-12). Rhizomes contain nodes and internodes of various length, and readily produce adventitious roots. Rhizomes may be thick and fleshy (iris) or slender and elongated (Kentucky bluegrass). Growth proceeds from the terminal bud or through lateral shoots. In many plants the older portion of the rhizome dies out. If new growth proceeds

proceeds from branching, then the new plants eventually become separated. Rhizomatous plants are easily propagated by cutting the rhizome into several pieces, each containing a vegetative bud.

TUBERS. Tubers are fleshy portions of underground rhizomes. The white potato is the best known example. The potato is propagated by planting either the whole tuber or pieces containing at least one "eye." If the whole tuber is planted the terminal eye commonly inhibits the other buds, but this apical dominance is destroyed when the tuber

Fig. 9-12.   *Root system and rhizomes of the tawny day lily,* Hemerocallis fulva. [Courtesy G. M. Fosler.]

is cut. Commonly the "seed pieces" are kept at 1–2 ounces to provide sufficient food for the young plant. The seed pieces may be cured to effectively heal the cut surface (see Chapter 11). Chemical treatments are used to prevent disease.

OFFSHOOTS. In many plants lateral shoots develop from the stem, which when rooted serves to reduplicate the plant (Fig. 9-13). These have been referred to in horticultural terminology as *offsets, suckers, crown divisions, ratoons,* or *slips,* depending on the species. Lateral shoots may be referred to collectively as *offshoots.* The increase of bulbs and corms by offsets is a similar type of phenomena. Propagation of plants that produce offshoots is easily made by division. In

Fig. 9-13.   *Pineapple may be propagated from slips—leafy shoots originating from axillary buds borne on the base of the fruit stalk. They may also be grown from the crown that issues from the top of the pineapple or from suckers that grow lower down on the stem.*

[Courtesy Dole Corp.]

temperate climates, rooted offshoots of outdoor perennials may be divided either in the fall or spring.

Root Modification

TUBEROUS ROOTS. Roots as well as stems may be structurally modified to propagative and food storage organs. Fleshy, swollen roots that store food materials are known as *tuberous roots* (Fig. 9-14). Shoot buds are readily formed adventitiously. Tuberous roots of some species may contain shoot buds at the "stem end" as part of their structure.

The sweet potato is commonly propagated from the formation of rooted adventitious shoots called slips. In the dahlia, the roots are divided, but each tuberous root must incorporate a bud from the crown. In the tuberous

Fig. 9-14. *Tuberous roots of (A) sweet potato, (B) dahlia, and (C) tuberous begonia. The tuberous root of the sweet potato and dahlia disintegrate in the production of the new plant. The tuberous begonia root enlarges each year.*

[From Hartmann and Kestner, *Plant Propagation*, Prentice-Hall, Englewood Cliffs, 1959.]

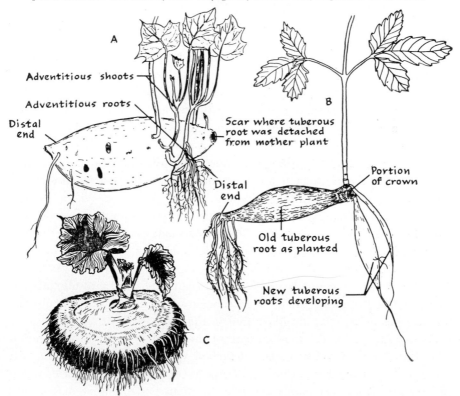

Adventitious shoots

Adventitious roots

Distal end

A

Scar where tuberous root was detached from mother plant

B

Distal end

Old tuberous root as planted

Portion of crown

New tuberous roots developing

C

begonia, the primary tap root develops into an enlarged tuberous root with buds forming at the "stem end." This root can be propagated by division, but each section must contain a bud.

SUCKERS. Shoots which arise adventitiously from roots are called suckers, although the term has been commonly used (less precisely perhaps) to refer to shoots originating from stem tissue. The red raspberry, for example, is propagated by suckers abundantly produced from horizontal roots. In the red raspberry, suckering may be stimulated by extensive pruning. The rooted suckers are usually dug during the period of plant dormancy.

Induction of Adventitious Roots and Shoots

The regeneration of structural parts in the propagation of many plants is accomplished by the artificial induction of adventitious roots and shoots. When the regenerated vegetative part is attached to the plant, the process is called *layerage;* when the regenerated vegetative part is detached from the plant of origin, the process is called *cuttage*. These two processes, although technically different, are part of the same phenomenon, namely, the ability of vegetative plant parts to develop into a complete plant.

Layerage is often a natural process. In the black raspberry, the drooping stem tips tend to root when in contact with the soil; in strawberries, the runners form natural layers. Because the regenerated stem is still attached and nourished by the parent plant, the timing and techniques of layerage are not as critical as in cuttage, in which the vegetative part to be regenerated is severed from the parent plant. Rooting may be facilitated by such practices as wounding, girdling, etiolation, and disorientation of the stem, which affects the movement and accumulation of the carbohydrates and auxin needed to stimulate root initiation.

Layerage is a simple and effective means of propagation that can be practiced in the field. It is especially suited to the amateur because of the high degree of success possible with only a minimum of specialized facilities. Layerage is not adaptable to large scale nursery practices, however, and for this reason it is normally used only for plants that are naturally adapted to this method of propagation, or if propagation by cuttings is difficult. Different types of layering are illustrated in Fig. 9-15.

Cuttage is one of the most important means of vegetative propagation. The term "cutting" refers to any detached vegetative plant part that can be expected to regenerate the missing part (or parts) to form a complete plant. Cuttings are commonly classified by plant part (root, stem, leaf, leaf

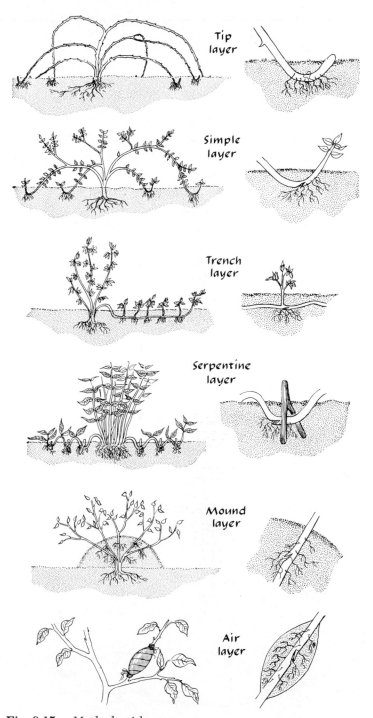

Fig. 9-15. *Methods of layerage.*

[Adapted with permission of the publisher from *Principles of Horticulture* by Denisen, copyright 1958 by The Macmillan Company.]

bud). In *stem cuttings* or *leaf bud cuttings* a new root system must be initiated; in *root cuttings* a new shoot must be initiated; and in *leaf cuttings* both roots and shoots must be initiated.

Anatomical Basis of Adventitious Roots and Shoots

The formation of adventitious roots can be divided into two phases. One is initiation, which is characterized by cell division and the differentiation of certain cells into a root initial. The second phase is growth, in which the root initial expands by a combination of cell division and elongation. Although the two processes usually occur in sequence, in some plants, such as the willow, the time between initiation and development is well separated.

Root initials are formed adjacent to vascular tissue. In herbaceous plants, which lack a cambium, the root initials are formed near the vascular bundles close to the phloem. Thus, roots will appear in rows along the stem, corresponding to the major vascular bundles. In woody plants, initiation commonly occurs in the phloem tissue, usually at a point corresponding to the entrance of a vascular ray.

The production of both adventitious roots and shoots from leaf cuttings commonly originates in secondary meristematic tissues—cells which have differentiated but later resume meristematic activity. In *Kalanchoë* (*Byrophyllum*) new plantlets form during leaf development from meristematic regions on the leaf edges (Fig. 9-16).

Fig. 9-16. *In* Kalanchoë, *new plants arise from meristem located in notches at the leaf edge. Shoot and root primordia are present in adult leaves.*

[From Mahlstede and Haber, *Plant Propagation*, Wiley, New York, 1957.]

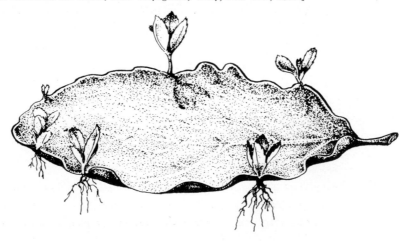

Adventitious roots and shoots may be derived from different kinds of tis-sue; for example, in African violet leaf cuttings the roots are initiated from cells between the vascular bundles, whereas shoots are initiated from cells of the epidermis or cortex. In the sweet potato, on the other hand, roots and shoots may be derived from callus tissue formed on the cut surface.

The formation of complete plants from pieces of root is dependent upon both the initiation of adventitious shoots and the extension of new root growth. Adventitious shoot buds develop from cells of the phloem paren-chyma and from rays. New roots originate from older tissues through latent root initials, although new root initials may arise adventitiously from the vascular cambial region.

Physiological Basis of Rooting

The ability of a stem to root is a variable character, depending on the plant and subsequent treatment. Some insight into the physiological basis of rooting has been developed from studies on *easy* and *difficult-to-root* plants. The ability of a stem to root has been shown to be due to an interaction of inherent factors present in the stem cells as well as to transportable sub-stances produced in leaves and buds. Some of these transportable substances are auxin, carbohydrates, nitrogenous compounds, vitamins, and other unidentified compounds. Substances that interact with auxin to affect root-ing may be referred to as *rooting cofactors*. In addition, such environmental factors as light, temperature, humidity, and oxygen play an important role in the process. The physiological factors involved in rooting are only begin-ning to be understood; it is still not possible to effect rooting in many plants, for example, in blue spruce, rubber tree, and oak.

Auxin level is closely associated with adventitious rooting of stem cut-tings, although the precise relationship is not clear. The normal rooting of stems appears to be triggered by the accumulation of auxin at the base of a cutting. The increase in rooting by the application of indoleacetic acid or auxin derivatives supports this concept (see Chapter 7). However, it is cer-tain that auxin is only part of the stimulus, for rooting of many difficult-to-root cuttings is not improved by auxin alone. Other specific factors that either stimulate (as does catechol) or inhibit rooting have been isolated. More such factors can be expected to be found.

The presence of leaves and buds exerts a powerful influence on the root-ing of stem cuttings. In many plants the effect of buds is due primarily to their role as a source of auxin production, whereas the rooting stimulation provided by leaves is related in part to carbohydrate production. But in many plants the affect of leaves and buds can be shown to be due to

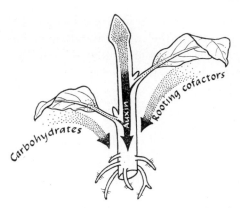

Fig. 9-17. *The rooting of a cutting is dependant cn auxin, carbohydrates, and the presence of rooting cofactors. The cofactors interact with auxin to trigger rooting.*

additional transportable cofactors, which complement both carbohydrate and auxin application (Fig. 9-17).

An important component of the ability of a stem to root is the nutritional status of the plant. In general, high carbohydrate levels are associated with vigorous root growth. On the other hand, high nitrogen levels affect the number of roots produced. Although low nitrogen levels increase the number of roots produced, a deficiency will inhibit rooting.

The accumulation of auxin as well as the accumulation of carbohydrates explains in part the effectiveness of ringing and wounding in stimulating rooting. In addition, wounding stimulates root initiation by some other unknown process. Callousing of the wounded surface also increases the efficiency of water absorption. This wounding effect is utilized to increase the absorption of applied auxin.

The effectiveness of stem rooting varies with the stage of development and the age of the plant, the type and location of stem, and the time of year. Owing to the great variation between species, precise conclusions concerning the relationship of these factors to rooting cannot be made. In general, rooting ability is associated with the juvenile stage of growth. Such plants as English Ivy, apple, and many conifers become very difficult to root when they reach the mature stage. Mature, difficult-to-root plants may be made easy to root by a reversion to the juvenile stage. Generally, adventitious shoots from the base of mature plants tend to assume juvenile characteristics. In mature plants that become difficult to root, these adventitious shoots may be induced by severe pruning. Thus, a form of layering called stooling maintains the juvenile stage of growth by continued pruning at the base of the plant. The stem bases are mounded with soil to facilitate rooting.

The ability of a stem to root is also affected by its position on the plant; lateral shoots tend to root better than terminal shoots. Vegetative shoots also tend to root better than flowering shoots. These differences may be related in part to auxin level and amounts of stored food.

Cuttings vary in their ability to root, depending upon the type of stem tissue from which they are derived. Cuttings may be made from succulent nonlignified growth (*softwood cuttings*)* or from wood up to several years old (*hardwood cuttings*). Although almost all types of cuttings of easy-to-root plants root readily, softwood cuttings of deciduous, woody plants taken in the spring or summer generally root more easily than hardwood cuttings obtained in the winter. However, dormant hardwood cuttings are used when possible because of the ease of shipment and handling. Dormant cuttings must be stored until the shoot's rest period is broken, although rooting is less affected by dormancy. The time that softwood cuttings are taken varies greatly with different plant species. In the azalea, softwood cuttings root best in the early spring; in other broadleafed evergreens, the optimum time for rooting may be from spring to late fall.

Environmental Factors Affecting Rooting

HUMIDITY. The death of the stem as a result of desiccation before rooting is achieved is one of the primary causes of failures in propagation by cutting. The lack of roots prevents sufficient water intake, although the intact leaves and new shoot growth continue to lose water by transpiration. Leaves or portions of the leaf are removed to prevent excessive transpiration. However, this practice is not desirable because the presence of leaves encourages rooting. The use of mist (Fig. 9-18) maintains high humidity and also reduces leaf temperature by maintaining a water film on the leaf. This enables high light to be employed in order that photosynthesis need not be reduced. The use of automatic controls to produce an intermittent mist is desirable because excess water may be harmful to many plants and because higher temperatures of the rooting media can be maintained.

TEMPERATURE. The use of bottom heat to maintain the temperature of the rooting medium at about 75°F facilitates rooting by stimulating cell division in the rooting area. The aerial portion may be kept cool to reduce transpiration and respiration. Daytime air temperatures of 70–80°F and night temperatures of 60–70°F are optimum for the rooting of most species.

LIGHT. Light in itself appears to inhibit root initiation (or conversely, the lack of light encourages it). Softwood and herbaceous cuttings indirectly respond to light because of its role in the synthesis of carbohydrates. However, deciduous hardwood cuttings that contain sufficient stored food, and

---

* Softwood cuttings of plants that are normally nonwoody are sometimes referred to as *herbaceous cuttings*, whereas those of woody plants prior to lignification are known as *greenwood cuttings*.

to which artificial auxin can be supplied, root best in the dark. The role of light in inducing rooting thus varies with the plant and with the method of propagation. The reason the absence of light favors root initiation in stem tissues is not clear. Root promotion may be achieved by the use of opaque coverings that etiolate the stem. Etiolation probably affects the accumulation of auxins and other substances that are unstable in light.

ROOTING MEDIA. The rooting media must provide sufficient moisture and oxygen and must be relatively disease free. It is not necessary that the rooting media be a source of nutrients until a root system is established. The rooting medium may have an effect on the percentage of cuttings rooted and on the type of roots formed. Various mixes containing soil, sand, peat, and artificial inorganic substances such as vermiculite (expanded mica) and perlite (expanded volcanic lava) have been widely used. Perlite used alone or in combination with peat moss has proven especially effective

Fig. 9-18. *An in-bench mist installation. The supply pipe runs along the bottom of the bench. The polyethylene wind barrier eliminates the problem of drift. The deflection-type nozzle produces a mist by directing a fine stream of water against a flat surface. An intermittent mist, commonly 4 seconds on and 56 seconds off, is controlled by a time clock.*
[Courtesy Purdue Univ.]

Fig. 9-19. *Rooted cuttings of woody ornamentals planted in a mixture of perlite and peat. Fertilizer must be added. They will be marketed as container-grown stock.*
[Courtesy Perlite Inst.]

because of its good water-holding properties, drainage, and freedom from root rotting diseases (Fig. 9-19). Sand or water alone may be satisfactory for some easy-to-root cuttings (Fig. 9-20). When water is used alone improved results are achieved with aeration.

Grafting

Grafting involves the joining together of plant parts by means of tissue regeneration, in which the resulting combination of parts achieves physical union to grow as a single plant. The part of the combination that provides the root is called the *stock;* the added piece is called the *scion.* The stock may be a piece of root or an entire plant. When the scion consists of a single bud only, the process is referred to as *budding.* (Budding and cuttings represent the most important methods of asexual propagation.) When the graft combination is made up of more than two parts, the middle piece is referred to as an interstock, body stock, or interpiece.

There are two basic kinds of grafts: *approach* and *detached scion.* In the approach graft the "scion" and "stock" are both connected to a growing root system. In the detached scion graft, the most common method, only the

Fig. 9-20. (*Left*) *A home propagator made up of a large pot filled with sand. The hole of the smaller inner pot is plugged with cork and kept filled with water. Uniform moisture is maintained by seepage from the small pot's porous sides.* (*Right*) *Cuttings that are easy to root, such as coleus, may be propagated in water.*
[Courtesy E. R. Honeywell.]

stock supplies roots, since the scion is severed from any root connection. Approach grafting is used when it is difficult to obtain a union by the ordinary procedures. The root connection to the scion acts as a "nurse" to the scion until union is achieved, at which time the scion is severed from its own roots. The general "carpentry" or "art" involved in both these methods of grafting are similar, although the method used in obtaining a union might appear to vary.

The Graft Union

The *graft union* is the basis of graftage. It is formed from the intermingling and interlocking of callus tissue produced from the stock and scion cambium in response to wounding. The cambium, the meristematic tissue between the xylem (wood) and phloem (bark), is continuous in perennial woody dicots. Monocotyledonous plants with a diffused cambium cannot be grafted. Callus tissue is composed of parenchymatous cells. Under the influence of the existing cambium, the callus tissue differentiates new cambial tissue. This new cambium re-differentiates xylem and phloem to form a living, growing connection between stock and scion (Fig. 9-21). The basic technique of grafting consists in placing the cambial tissue of stock and scion in intimate association such that the resulting callus tissue produced from stock and scion interlocks to form a continuous connection. A snug fit is often obtained by utilizing the tension of the stock and/or scion. Tape, rubber, or nailing is also used to facilitate contact. Various types of budding and grafting are shown in Fig. 9-22. Natural grafts may be formed as a result of the close intertwining of roots or stems.

Although there is usually no actual interchange of cells through the graft union, the connection is such that many viruses and hormones pass through unheeded. This principle is utilized in virus identification. Plants containing a suspected virus, but which may not show obvious morphological symptoms, are grafted to a plant that is sensitive and will show the symptoms of the virus. This process is known as *indexing* (Fig. 9-23).

Incompatibility

Owing to the lack of any antibody mechanism, plants have a greater tolerance to grafting than do animals. The ability of two plants to form a successful graft combination is related in large part to their natural relationship.

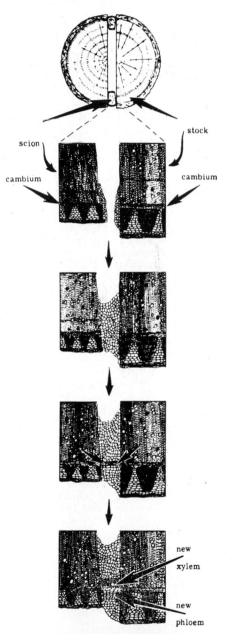

Fig. 9-21. *Developmental sequence during the healing of a cleft graft union. The graft union is formed from the redifferentiation of the callus tissue under the influence of the stock cambium.*

[From Hartmann and Kestner, *Plant Propagation*, Prentice-Hall, Englewood Cliffs, 1959.]

GRAFTING

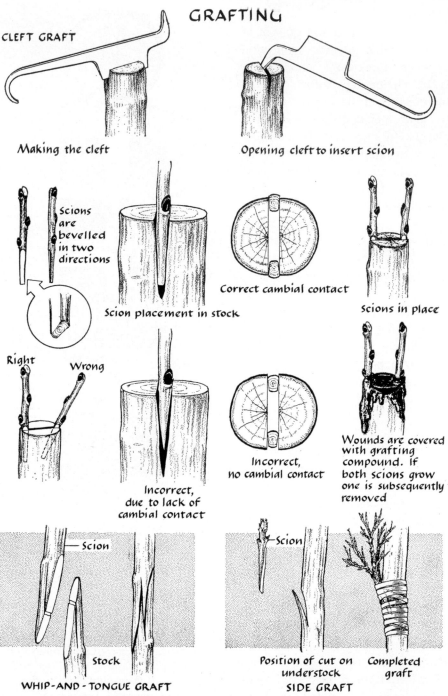

CLEFT GRAFT

Making the cleft

Opening cleft to insert scion

Scions are bevelled in two directions

Scion placement in stock

Correct cambial contact

Scions in place

Right　　Wrong

Incorrect, due to lack of cambial contact

Incorrect, no cambial contact

Wounds are covered with grafting compound. If both scions grow one is subsequently removed

Scion

Stock

WHIP-AND-TONGUE GRAFT

Scion

Position of cut on understock

Completed graft

SIDE GRAFT

Fig. 9-22. *(Above and facing page) Techniques of budding and grafting.*

BUDDING

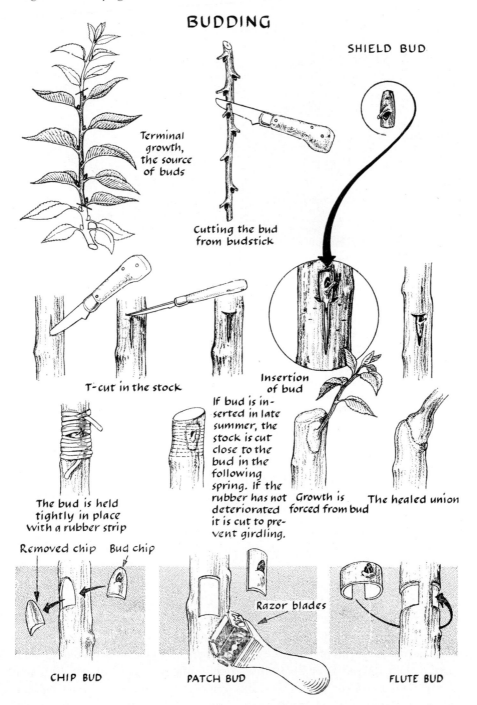

SHIELD BUD

Terminal growth, the source of buds

Cutting the bud from budstick

T-cut in the stock

Insertion of bud

If bud is inserted in late summer, the stock is cut close to the bud in the following spring. if the rubber has not deteriorated it is cut to prevent girdling.

The bud is held tightly in place with a rubber strip

Growth is forced from bud

The healed union

Removed chip   Bud chip

CHIP BUD

Razor blades

PATCH BUD

FLUTE BUD

Fig. 9-23. *Indexing strawberries by means of the leaf graft. Left. The middle blade of the trifoliate leaf of strawberry is cut to a wedge and inserted into the split petiole in place of the removed blade of the sensitive indicator,* Fragaria vesca. *The exised leaf is usually held in place with a self-sticking latex tape. Right. After two months the grafted leaf from each of two different plants is still alive. The older leaves have been removed to show the new growth. The normal regrowth on the left indicates that the inserted leaf was free of any virus affecting the indicator plant. The stunted, deformed growth on the plant at the right indicates transmission of a virus from the excised leaf to the indicator plant.*
[Courtesy Purdue Univ.]

The inherent failure of two plants to form a successful union—*graft incompatibility*—may be due to both structural and physiological effects. Incompatibility may be expressed in a high percentage of grafting failures; poor, weak, or abnormal growth of the scion; overgrowths at the graft union; or poor mechanical strength of the union, which in extreme cases results in a clean break at the graft. Incompatibility may be manifested immediately or be delayed for several years. In some cases incompatibility has been traced to a virus contributed by one of the graft components, which was itself virus tolerant. In such cases incompatibility is due to the virus sensitivity of the other component. If the sensitive component is the root stock, the entire tree may be adversely affected.

In general, grafting within a species results in compatible unions. Grafts made between species of the same genera or species of closely related genera vary in their degree of compatibility. For example, many but not all pears (*Pyrus* species) may be successfully grafted on quince stock (*Cydonia oblonga*), but the reverse combination, quince scions on pear stock, is not successful. Incompatibility may be bridged by an interpiece composed of a variety compatible to both components. A few exceptional graft combinations involving species of different families have been experimentally produced in herbaceous plants.

Factors Influencing Grafting Success

In addition to the inherent compatibility of the plant there are a number of factors that affect successful "take" in grafting. Skillful grafting or budding techniques are, of course, necessary. Success is then dependent upon environmental factors, which promote callus formation. In general, callus formation is optimum at about 80–85°F. After the grafting of dormant material (bench grafting), the completed graft is best stored under warm and moist conditions for a week or two to stimulate callus formation.

It is very important that high moisture conditions be maintained to prevent the scion from drying out. Waxing the tissue after grafting serves to prevent desiccation of the delicate callus tissue. Special waxes are available that consist of various formulations of resins, beeswax, paraffin, and linseed oil. Bench grafts should be plunged in moist peat to prevent desiccation during the period of healing at warm temperature. The use of plastic films has proved successful in conserving moisture. Oxygen has been shown to be required for callus formation in some plants (for example, the grape). Waxing should not be used with such plants because of its effect in limiting the oxygen supply.

The percentage of "take" in grafting is often improved if the stock is in a vigorous state of growth. The scion, however, should be dormant to prevent premature growth and subsequent desiccation. Growing trees are often grafted with dormant scions from refrigerated storage. In summer budding, irrigation should be supplied before budding in order to invigorate the stock. The leaf buds of most temperate woody plants, when inserted in late summer, remain naturally dormant until the following spring.

Grafting of Established Trees

In addition to its role as a method of propagation, grafting is useful in many instances for variety change, repair, or invigoration of older established trees. Grafting to effect growth is discussed in Chapter 7.

TOPWORKING. Owing to the long time required for growth of many fruit or nut crops, it is often desirable to utilize the existing framework and root system of a larger, established tree. It becomes possible to rework a tree and rapidly bring an improved variety into production. The regrafting of scions onto a large growing tree to utilize an existing framework is called *top-working*. The cleft graft is usually used.

In topworking, the length of the scion inserted may have an effect on subsequent growth. The few buds from short scions all tend to produce vigorous vegetative growth. Bud break on long scions is confined to the terminal buds; the basal buds often grow into fruiting spurs. This technique is utilized to bring new varieties into early bearing for observation.

INARCHING, BRIDGING, AND BRACING. Inarching is a form of "repair" grafting that involves reinforcing the existing root system of an already growing tree. It is used when the current root system is weak and must be replaced to save the tree. A number of seedlings or rooted cuttings are planted around the tree and are then approach grafted onto the stem. The graft is usually held in place by nailing.

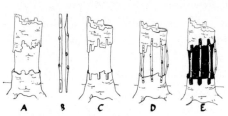

Fig. 9-24. *Bridge grafting.*
[From Eaton, Publication 439, Ontario Dept. of Agriculture, 1961.]

Bridge grafting, as the name infers, is a means of "bridging" an intact root and stem when the connection between them has been damaged. Bridge grafting can save a tree from death when the stem has been girdled by mice (Fig. 9-24).

Bracing the framework of a tree can be accomplished by means of grafting. The technique involves the twisting of young branches around each other to encourage the formation of a natural graft.

Selected References

Hartmann, H. T. and Kester, D. E. *Plant Propagation.* Prentice-Hall, New Jersey. 1959. (The most valuable and comprehensive book on the subject.)

Hawthorn, L. R. and Pollard, L. H. *Vegetable and Flower Seed Production.* Blakiston, New York. 1954. (The technology of seed production.)

Seeds. USDA Yearbook. 1961. (The story of seeds.)

Woody Plant Seed Manual. USDA Miscellaneous Publication 654. 1948. (A manual on all phases of seed handling of woody plants.)

CHAPTER 10

Plant Improvement

Almost all of the edible plants in use today were domesticated before the advent of written history. Ornamentals such as the rose and lily have been in cultivation for thousands of years. Plant improvement has been continuous during this time as a result of man's deliberate differential reproduction of certain plants. This process of *selection* over the years has been extremely effective; most of our cultivated plants no longer even remotely resemble their wild ancestors. *Plant breeding*, the systematic improvement of plants, is an innovation of the last century. In the past 50 years, the study of the mechanisms of heredity—*genetics*—has placed plant breeding on a firm theoretical basis. Plant breeding has become a specialized technology and is responsible for a large part of the current progress in horticulture.

Since the needs and standards of man change, the job of the plant breeder is a continuous one. For example, mechanical harvesting becomes possible only with plants that bear the bulk of their crop at a given time. It demands that plants be structurally adapted to the machine. The raw material for these and other changes may be found in the tremendous variation that exists in cultivated plants and in related wild species. The incorporation of these alterations into plants adapted to specific geographical areas demands not only a knowledge of the theoretical basis of heredity but the art and skill necessary for the discovery and perpetuation of small but fundamental differences in plant material.

THE GENETIC BASIS OF PLANT IMPROVEMENT

Variety is more than the spice of life; it is the very essence of it. Differences between horticultural plants range from the obvious (water lilies versus watermelons) to the almost imperceptible variation that might exist between two apple trees of the same clonal variety growing side by side.

323

Variation can be partitioned into two types, *environmental* and *genetic*. Genetic differences are due to the hereditary makeup of the organisms. This variation can be traced to differences in *genes*, the fundamental units that determine heredity. Environmental variation can be demonstrated by comparing organisms of identical genetic makeup grown under different environments. Similarly, differences between plants grown under identical environments must be due to genetic differences. The range of environmental variation is enormous, but its boundaries are determined by genetic makeup. (It is difficult to conceive of any environmental condition that will transform water lilies to watermelons.) The genetic makeup of an organism is referred to as its *genotype*. The net outward appearance of the organism is the *phenotype*. In a stricter sense, the phenotype is the interaction product of a genotype with its internal and external environment.

The question of which type of variation, genetic or environmental, is more important is meaningless. The pertinent question is *which genotype is best suited to a particular set of environmental conditions;* and, given a particular genotype, *which environmental conditions will permit the optimum phenotypic expression of that genotype.*

The fundamental discovery that the genotype is inherited as discrete units was first published in 1865 by Gregor Mendel, and Austrian abbot, from experimental work carried out with the garden pea. Environmental variation, however, is not transmitted in this manner. This was first firmly established by the Danish geneticist and breeder Johannsen in 1903, from research on seed size in the common bean. Johannsen demonstrated that inheritance of phenotypic variation is only possible when it is a result of genetic differences.

Genes and Gene Action

The chromosomes contain the code-controlling mechanism that coordinates the physiological activities of the cell and consequently the organism. The study of many organisms has indicated that the information provided by the chromosomes involves the formation of enzymes that affect biochemical reactions. The unit of the chromosome conferring a single enzymatic effect is called the *gene*. Structurally, the gene appears to be a portion of the desoxyribose nucleic acid (DNA) molecule, the nonprotein portion of the chromosome. How the genetic code inherent in the DNA molecule works to effect enzyme synthesis is not known. However, considerable information is accumulating concerning gene-mediated biochemical pathways.

Gene action can be demonstrated with flower pigmentation. Two anthocyanin pigments distinguished by differing degrees of red color have been shown to be chemically differentiated by a single hydroxyl group. The synthesis of these pigments proceeds in a stepwise fashion, as shown in Fig. 10-1. The addition of a single hydroxyl group changes the color of the plant's petals from bright red to bluish red. This biochemical step is gene controlled. Thus, the petals of a plant that contains a gene (C) controlling the transformation of pelargonidin to cyanidin will be bluish red. A plant having only an altered version of this gene (c) incapable of adding the hydroxyl group will have bright red petals. Alternate forms of a particular gene are referred to as *alleles* (C and c are alleles). The change in the gene's internal structure, which gives rise to new alleles, is known as *mutation*. Mutations are changes in the genetic information and are ultimately responsible for the inherent variation in all living things.

Each plant species contains a characteristic number of chromosomes known as the $2n$, or somatic, number ($2n = 12$ in spinach, 14 in pea, 16 in onion, 18 in cabbage, 20 in corn, 22 in watermelon, 24 in tomato, and so on). The reproductive cells, or *gametes*, contain the haploid number (n) of chromosomes. Each chromosome occurs in pairs in the vegetative cells making up the somatic number. In meiosis one chromosome of each pair is distributed to the gametes, reducing the diploid number by one-half. Fertilization subsequently restores the diploid number to the zygote, the fertilized egg. Thus, in somatic cells of diploid plants, each gene is present twice. A particular gene (for example, C and its allele c) may be present in any one of three combinations, CC, Cc, or cc. A plant containing two identical genes, CC or cc, is homozygous for that allele. When the alleles are different, as with Cc, the plant is heterozygous.

What is the difference in outward expression (phenotype) when the genetic constitution (genotype) is CC, Cc, or cc? With reference to our example of petal color, the assumption can be made that if the allele c is completely nonfunctional, as regards hydroxylation of pelargonidin, two

Fig. 10-1. *The conversion of pelargonadin to cyanidin involves the addition of a singly hydroxyl group and is controlled by a single gene.*

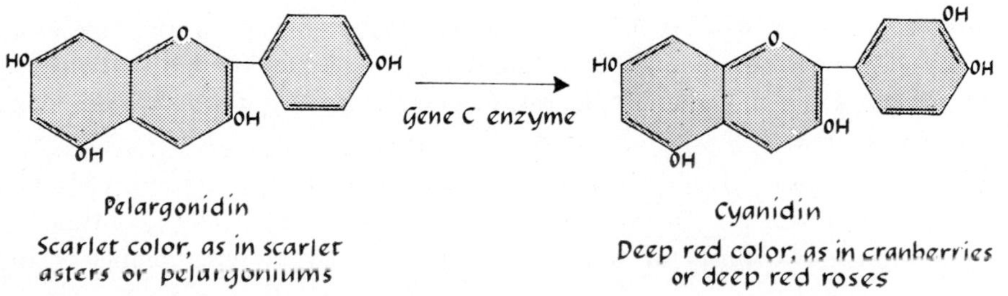

Pelargonidin
Scarlet color, as in scarlet asters or pelargoniums

Gene C enzyme

Cyanidin
Deep red color, as in cranberries or deep red roses

alleles *cc* should not be any more efficient. This can be shown experimentally, for flowers of *cc* plants are bright red, and chemical analysis of their petals yields no cyanidin. The

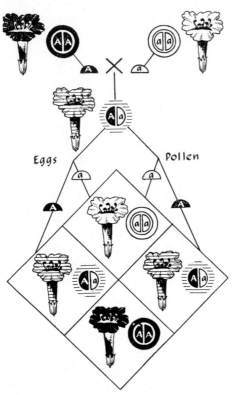

difference between plants that are homozygous (*CC*) and those that are heterozygous (*Cc*) cannot be predicted. The allele may be efficient enough to produce sufficient enzyme such that plants with only one functioning allele (*Cc*) cannot be distinguished phenotypically from those having two functioning alleles (*CC*). When this is the case it would appear that the allele *C* dominates *c*. The condition in which heterozygous plants *Cc* are indistinguishable from homozygous *CC* plants is termed *dominance*. If the heterozygote *Cc* is intermediate in phenotype between the two homozygous types *CC* and *cc*, dominance is said to be incomplete.

Fig. 10-2. *Mendelian segregation illustrating incomplete dominance in the four o'clock* (Mirabilis jalapa). *Note that the phenotypic ratio of 1 red:2 pink:1 white is also 3 colored:1 noncolored.*
[Adapted from Dobzhansky.]

Assume a complete dominant gene *A* with a recessive allele *a*. A heterozygous plant *Aa* will produce two kinds of gametes (*A* and *a*) in equal proportions. A cross, designated with respect to these alleles as *Aa* × *Aa*, will produce three kinds of progeny in a predictable ratio if all gametic and zygotic types are equally viable. It can readily be seen that the possible types of zygotes resulting from all combinations of the two kinds of gametes *A* and *a* will be *AA*, *Aa*, *aA*, and *aa* or 1*AA*, 2*Aa*, and 1*aa* (Fig. 10-2). If we assume dominance, then *AA* plants are indistinguishable from *Aa* plants. Thus the phenotypic ratio becomes 3*A*— (whatever the effect may be) to 1*aa*.

The genotypes *AA* and *Aa* may be distinguished by a genetic test. The genotype *AA* will produce a single type of gamete (*A*). The genotype *Aa* will produce two kinds of gametes (*A* and *a*). By crossing plants of the phenotype *A* with themselves, or with the double recessive *aa*, these two genotypes may be separated on the basis of their progeny:

AA selfed (*AA* × *AA*) ⟶ all *AA* (*AA* plants "breed true")
in contrast with
Aa selfed (*Aa* × *Aa*) ⟶ 3*A__*:1*aa* (*Aa* plants segregate),
or
AA × *aa* ⟶ all *Aa*
in contrast with
Aa × *aa* ⟶ 1*Aa*:1*aa*.

Generations are designated by specialized terminology. The first cross (usually referring to homozygous genotypes that differ with respect to a particular character) is the P_1, or the *parental generation*. The progeny of such a cross is the first filial generation (always referred to in writing and speaking as the F_1). If the parents are homozygous for all genes concerned, the F_1 is heterozygous and nonsegregating. The F_2 (second filial generation) results from intercrossing or selfing F_1 plants:

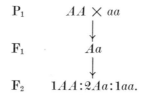

$$P_1 \qquad AA \times aa$$

$$F_1 \qquad Aa$$

$$F_2 \qquad 1AA:2Aa:1aa.$$

The F_2 is typically the segregating generation, which, if large enough could theoretically include every possible genotype. Further generations are known as F_3, F_4, F_5, and so on. A cross of the F_1 with one of its parents is known as a *backcross*.

Multigenic Inheritance

The inheritance of a single gene difference can be expanded for examples involving two or more genes. The assortment of one pair of chromosomes at meiosis has no effect on the assortment of the other pairs; consequently, genes on separate chromosomes segregate independently of each other. Thus, a plant heterozygous for two gene pairs (*Aa* and *Bb*) will produce four different types of gametes (*AB*, *Ab*, *aB*, and *ab*) in equal proportions. The self progeny of the *AaBb* plant will segregate into phenotypic ratios of 3:1 for each factor, if we assume complete dominance. The combined phenotypic ratio will be 9*A__B__*:3*A__bb*:3*aaB__*:1*aabb*. This cross is diagrammed in Fig. 10-3.

When two genes affect the same biochemical pathway the phenotypic

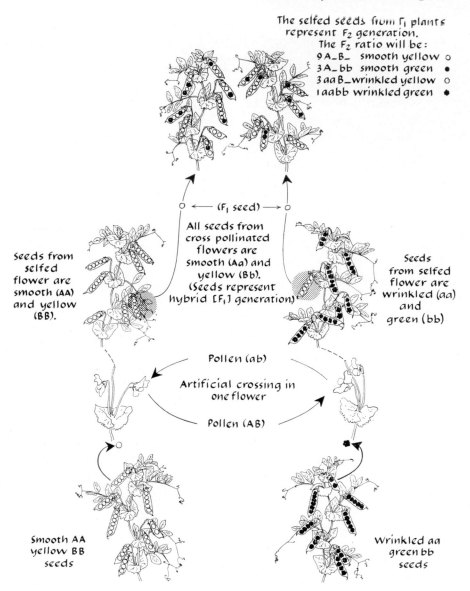

The selfed seeds from F₁ plants
represent F₂ generation.
The F₂ ratio will be:
9 A_B_ smooth yellow o
3 A_ bb smooth green ●
3 aa B_ wrinkled yellow o
1 aabb wrinkled green ●

o ← (F₁ seed) → o

All seeds from
cross pollinated
flowers are
smooth (Aa) and
yellow (Bb).
(Seeds represent
hybrid [F₁] generation)

Seeds from
selfed
flower are
smooth (AA)
and yellow
(BB).

Seeds
from selfed
flower are
wrinkled (aa)
and
green (bb)

Pollen (ab)

Artificial crossing in
one flower

Pollen (AB)

Smooth AA
yellow BB
seeds

Wrinkled aa
green bb
seeds

Fig. 10-3.   *The independent assortment of two genes in peas.*
[Adapted from Horowitz.]

ratio gives some idea of the gene action involved. For example, two genes, both of which show complete dominance, and both of which interact to effect a single character, will transform the 9:3:3:1 ratio into a ratio of 9:7. Either gene, when homozygous recessive, will block some essential step, as shown in Fig. 10-4. This phenomenon of gene interaction is called *epistasis*.

Different types of gene action produce various F_2 ratios as a result of the consolidation of various genotypic classes having similar phenotypes.

Quantitative Inheritance

Characters that are continuous from one extreme to the other, such as size, yield, or quality, are of utmost significance in plant improvement. The inheritance of continuous or quantitative characters is an extension of the genetic principles briefly discussed for non-continuous or *qualitative* traits. It can usually be shown that there are many genes that will each contribute a small increment of effect to ꞌmodify the character. The individual effects of quantitative genes (also known as multiple factors, polygenes, modifiers) are extremely difficult to ascertain because of the large environmental effects present in relation to the small contribution of the individual gene. As a result it is not possible to determine the precise pattern of gene action. The special techniques used to analyze the inheritance of quantitative characters involve mathematical and statistical analysis of the variation through many generations. These techniques make it possible to predict the number of genes differing in a particular cross, as well as their average contribution and average dominance. These methods rely, however, on particular assumptions (for example, no epistasis) that are difficult to prove precisely.

An example of the pattern of quantitative inheritance is shown in Fig.

In the tomato, dominant genes R and A^t (apricot) are both required to synthesize lycopene, the red pigment in the fruit.

rr — Depletes all pigment
a^{t}a^t — Depletes lycopene

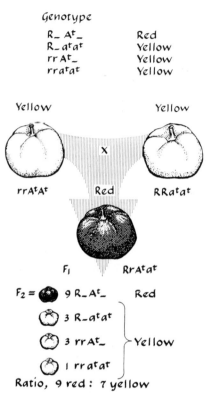

Genotype

R_ A^t_   Red
R_ a^{t}a^t Yellow
rr A^t_   Yellow
rr a^{t}a^t Yellow

Yellow   Yellow

X

rrA^{t}A^t Red   RRa^{t}a^t

F$_1$ RrA^{t}a^t

F$_2$ =   9 R_A^t_   Red

3 R_a^{t}a^t
3 rrA^t_   Yellow
1 rr a^{t}a^t

Ratio, 9 red : 7 yellow

(Because of differences in amount of β carotene, which produces yellow color, yellow genotypes can be differentiated by chemical analysis.)

Fig. 10-4. *Epistasis in the tomato.*

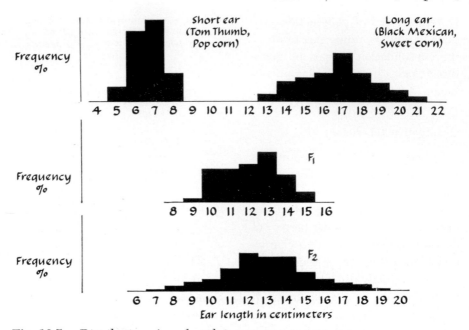

Fig. 10-5. *Distribution of ear length in a popcorn-sweet corn cross.*

[Adapted from Srb and Owen, *General Genetics*, Freeman, San Francisco, 1953; after Emerson and East.]

10-5. A cross between two homozygous lines of corn, one short-eared, and the other long-eared, produced an F_1 population whose mean ear length was between the parental lines. The parental and F_1 variation is presumably all environmental. The distribution of the F_2 population includes the homozygous parental types. The F_2 can be shown mathematically to have more variation than either the F_1 or the lines of the parental generation. This increased variation in the F_2 is a result of genetic segregation.

Except for a deficiency of parental types, the data as presented are similar to the data that would be expected from a single partially dominant gene if we assume enough environmental variation to obscure the differences between the three F_2 classes (AA, Aa, aa). However, the major differences between a single gene and a many-gene difference can be shown by selfing F_2 plants to produce F_3 lines. If we assume a single gene difference, there will be only three genotypes in the F_2 (the genotypic ratio being $1AA:2Aa:1aa$). Two of these would be true breeding genotypes (AA and aa), duplicating the parental types. The other genotype (Aa) would segregate to produce an F_3 distribution identical to the F_2. Note that each parental type would be duplicated in $\frac{1}{4}$ of the F_2 population.

It turns out that there are many more than three F_2 genotypes in this F_2!

As the number of genes differentiating the parents with respect to ear length increases from one to n, the number of F_2 genotypes increase from 3 to 3^n. On the other hand, the number of genotypes resembling the parental types decrease from $2(\frac{1}{4})$ of the F_2 population to $2(\frac{1}{4})^n$. If we assume that only 10 genes differentiate ear length, there are 3^{10} or 59,049 different genotypes in the F_2. To recover every genotype, a minimum population of 4^{10}, or 1,048,576 plants, would have to be grown. In this population there would be only one plant duplicating each of the parental genotypes.

The genetic value of a seed-propagated plant is the average performance of its progeny. Thus, the basic problem in the improvement of quantitatively inherited characters lies in distinguishing genetic from environmental effects. The plants that have the best appearance may not be the most desirable genotypically. The great economic importance of quantitative characters demands that the breeder of horticultural plants be familiar with the basic principles governing their inheritance.

Linkage

Since plants contain thousands of genes but only a limited number of chromosomes, it is apparent that each chromosome must contain many genes. Genes located on the same chromosome are not randomly assorted but tend to be inherited together. This condition is referred to as linkage. There is a relation-

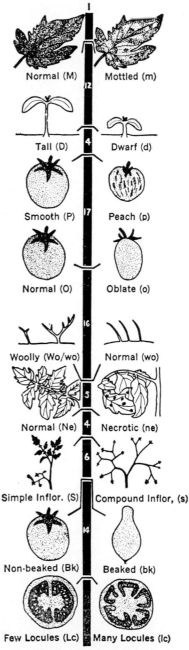

Fig. 10-6. *Map of chromosome 2 (linkage group I) of tomato.*
[From Butler, *J. Heredity*, **43**:25–35, 1952.]

ship between the physical closeness of genes and the intensity or strength of their linkage. The assortment of genes on the same chromosome is related to an actual exchange of chromosome material in meiosis.

By special techniques it is possible to locate genes on their respective chromosomes. Since the genes occur in a linear sequence on the chromosomes, it is possible to determine their relationship to each other by their linkage strengths. In this way the topology of the chromosomes may be mapped, as shown in Fig. 10-6 for the tomato. The linkage map may be constructed only for genes for which mutant forms are known.

Linkage may occur between genes controlling qualitative and quantitative characters. In the peach there is a particularly undesirable association between small fruit size (a quantitative character controlled by many genes) and the smooth-skin character producing the nectarine, which is controlled by a single gene. The breaking of this apparent linkage is a prerequisite for the breeding of large nectarines. Large populations are needed to obtain the rare but desirable combination that produces large nectarines from crosses between large peaches and small nectarines. The smooth-skin gene also appears to be related to brown rot susceptibility. Another interesting association in the peach involves rubbery flesh (versus melting flesh) and clingstone (versus the freestone) character. Similarly, the glandless varieties of peaches and nectarines are highly susceptible to mildew. Unless recombinant types are obtained, it is difficult to prove whether such associations are actually genetic linkages or whether they are due to some physiological relationship.

Hybrid Vigor

Hybrid vigor, or heterosis, refers to the increase in vigor shown by certain crosses as compared to that of either parent. The classic example of hybrid vigor is the mule, an interspecific cross of a mare and a jackass. The effect in plants has been described as similar to that caused by the addition of a balanced fertilizer. Hybrid vigor is often associated with an increased number of parts in *indeterminate* plants (whose main axis remains vegetative and in which flowers form on axillary buds, for example, cucumber), and with increased size of parts in *determinate* plants (whose main axis terminates in a floral bud, for example, sweet corn). In perennial plants the vigor persists year after year.

The term hybrid is applied loosely; any organism resulting from genetically dissimilar gametes is technically a hybrid. Thus, a plant that is heterozygous for a single-factor pair is a genetic hybrid. In horticultural and botanical terms the word hybrid is often incorrectly used to refer specifically to the result of crosses made between species. The word in the expression "hybrid corn" refers to a particular combination of inbred lines.

Genetic Consequences of Inbreeding

The phenomenon of heterosis is intimately associated with the decline in vigor brought about in some plants by continued crossing of closely related individuals (*inbreeding*). The genetic consequences of inbreeding are best explained with *selfing* (crossing a bisexual plant with itself), an extreme example of inbreeding.

Selfing has no effect on homozygous loci:

$$AA \times AA \longrightarrow AA,$$
$$aa \times aa \longrightarrow aa.$$

As shown previously, however, the selfing of a plant that is heterozygous for a single gene (*Aa*) produces progeny of which half are homozygous (*AA* and *aa*). This phenomenon may be generalized for any number of genes. With each generation of selfing, fifty percent of the heterozygous genes become homozygous (Fig. 10-7). Continued selfing will ultimately produce plants that are homozygous for all genes. Such plants are known as *inbred*, or *pure*, lines. Inbreeding can now be defined as any breeding system that increases the homozygous state.

The effect of inbreeding depends on the degree of heterozygosity and on the method of pollination of the plant. Homozygous plants (naturally cross- or self-pollinated) are unaffected by inbreeding. Nevertheless, heterozygous cross-pollinated plants tend to show a loss of vigor upon inbreeding that closely parallels the increase in homozygosity. There are, however, great differences between species and lines. Heterozygous individuals of self-

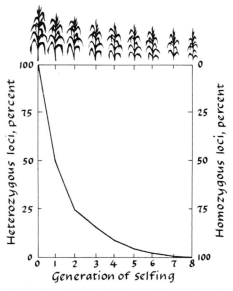

Fig. 10-7. *Selfing reduces the number of heterozygous genes by half in each generation. By the sixth generation, over 95% of these genes are expected to be homozygous. Most cross-pollinated plants show a decrease in vigor as homozygosity is reached.*

pollinated plants can be obtained by artificial crosses between different homozygous lines. When these heterozygous lines are selfed, the characteristic decline in vigor commonly found in cross-pollinated plants is usually not found.

Fig. 10-8. *Hybrid vigor in the onion from crossing two inbred lines.*
[Courtesy K. W. Johnson.]

The crossing of unrelated inbred lines of cross-pollinated crops restores the vigor lost by inbreeding (Fig. 10-8). The progeny of these crosses are referred to as F_1 hybrids. In maize some F_1 hybrids have shown as high as 15–25% increases in yield over the original open-pollinated varieties from which the inbred lines were derived. This increased vigor is apparently due to the genotypic control, which is made possible by the selection of inbreds. A vigorous F_1 hybrid line being uniform assures an increased performance of the F_1 over the segregating open-pollinated varieties. This lack of variation in F_1 hybrids, although disadvantageous under certain conditions, is usually desirable in this age of mechanization and pre-packaging.

Crossing various varieties of self-pollinated crops (which in reality are also inbred lines) increases vigor in isolated cases, but the magnitude is very much less than in cross-pollinated plants.

Genetic Explanation of Heterosis

Although the incorporation of heterosis is a most significant feature in plant improvement, its genetic basis is not completely established. The genetic explanation must reconcile both inbreeding depression and the apparent stimulation of vigor associated with heterozygosity. The two major theories proposed are now referred to as the *dominance* and *overdominance* hypotheses.

The dominance hypothesis, first proposed by Jones in 1917, is based on the assumption that cross-pollinated plants contain a large number of recessive genes concealed in the heterozygous condition. As the recessive condition is largely due to an absence of some essential gene function, these concealed recessives are largely deleterious. Upon inbreeding they become homozygous, resulting in a decline in vigor. Crossing inbred lines from diverse sources restores vigor. The recessives of each inbred are "covered up" by their dominant or partially dominant alleles, carried by the other inbred, much as the wearing of two moth eaten bathing suits might cover the modesty of a bather. In successful combinations the in-breds mutually complement each others' deficiencies. In its simplest case this situation may be expressed by the cross

$$aaBB \times AAbb \longrightarrow AaBb.$$

The hybrid *AaBb* is more vigorous than either of its homozygous parents because it contains both dominant alleles, whereas each parent is deficient in either gene *A* or *B*.

According to the dominance hypothesis, the vigor of a hybrid is due to the large number of dominant genes it contains. The high heterozygosity is merely a concomitant and nonessential part of hybrid vigor. The theory assumes that, were it possible to obtain each heterozygous gene in the homozygous dominant condition, the vigor of this genotype would be as great or greater than that of the heterozygous type. The failure to obtain true-breeding homozygous lines that are as vigorous as F_1 hybrids is due to the great number of genes involved and perhaps to linkages between deleterious and beneficial alleles.

The concept of inbreeding depression lies in the quantitative level of deleterious genes in the population, a direct function of the natural method of pollination and the phenomenon of dominance. The lack of a significant inbreeding depression and of heterosis in naturally self-pollinating crops is due to the absence of any deleterious "hidden" recessives. Any deleterious recessives become quickly exposed by the natural inbreeding mechanism of self-pollinating crops and are eliminated by the forces of natural selection.

The dominance hypothesis has not been an entirely satisfactory explanation to some geneticists. This is due largely to the high estimates of recessive alleles in the open-pollinated population required for the phenomenon and to other mathematical considerations. The overdominance hypothesis assumes that heterozygosity *by itself* may be advantageous. The reduction of vigor upon inbreeding is a direct result of the attainment of homozygosity. This theory assumes that the heterozygous condition *Aa* is superior to either homozygote (*AA* or *aa*). This has been termed *over-dominance*. There are two interpretations of overdominance at the gene level. One assumes that both alleles are physiologically active. The combined activity of both alleles in the heterozygous condition produces the heterotic effect. The alternative explanation assumes that the recessive allele is inactive but that dominance is incomplete. However, the reduced amount of essential gene product is optimum; the amount produced by the homozygous types is either deficient or inhibitory. There are experimental verifications, although rare, of both types of gene action.

It is difficult to distinguish between the dominance and overdominance hypotheses. The essential features of the hybrid effect are explained by both. The correct explanation lies in determining primary action of individual quantitative genes. In general, however, the dominance hypothesis is thought to be the most likely explanation of hybrid vigor.

Polyploidy

Variation in chromosome number is referred to as *polyploidy*. Although many plants normally have only two complete sets of chromosomes (the diploid number), other multiples of chromosome sets may occur. Plants containing various numbers of sets are referred to as follows.

NO. OF CHROMOSOME SETS	NAME OF TYPE
1	monoploid
2	diploid
3	triploid
4	tetraploid
5	pentaploid
6	hexaploid
7	septaploid
8	octoploid

In addition to the variation of whole sets of chromosomes (*euploidy*) there is variation involving chromosomes within a set (*aneuploidy*). An example of aneuploid variation is shown in Fig. 10-9.

Many plants can be shown to be naturally polyploid. Some varieties of apple and pear are triploid; tart cherries are tetraploid; cultivated strawberries are octoploid. In this regard the English convention of referring to the basic number of chromosomes in a set as the x number avoids much confusion. Thus, the basic number of chromosomes in the genus *Fragaria*, to which the strawberry belongs, is 7 ($x = 7$). The chromosome number in the vegetative cells of the cultivated strawberry is 56 (8 sets of 7 chromosomes), or $2n = 56 = 8x$. The chromosome numbers in the gametes, the haploid or n number is $n = 28 = 4x$. The concept of n is halfness, whereas the concept of x is oneness.

Polyploids may occur spontaneously or may be artificially induced by

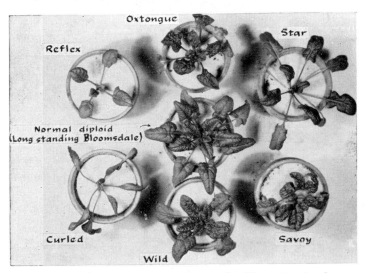

Fig. 10-9. *The six trisomics of spinach. The spinach plant in the center is a diploid having 12 chromosomes (6 pairs) in the vegetative cells. The six plants surrounding it all have 13 chromosomes. Each trisomic has a different extra chromosome, which confers a characteristic appearance.*

special treatment. For example, the formation of callus tissue by wounding is effective in inducing tetraploidy in the tomato. An alkaloid called *colchicine,* derived from the autumn crocus, has the remarkable property of doubling the chromosome number in a wide variety of plants when applied in concentrations of 0.1–0.3%. This drug interferes with spindle formation in mitosis; the chromosomes divide, but the cell does not. Tetraploids are produced routinely with the use of colchicine. Seed treatment (usually 24 hours) produces tetraploidy in about 5% of the surviving seedlings. The drug may also be applied to the growing points of seedlings or large plants by a variety of methods.

An artificially induced tetraploid may usually be distinguished from

Fig. 10-10. *Increased cluster size as a result of colchicine-induced polyploidy in the Portland grape. (Left) Diploid. (Right) Tetraploid.*
[Courtesy H. Dermen.]

Fig. 10-11. *Diploid, triploid, and tetraploid spinach. In spinach and sugar beets the triploid condition appears to be the most vigorous.*

a normal diploid by its larger, thicker leaves and organs (Fig. 10-10), and somewhat slower, coarser growth. Cell size is larger, and fertility is often reduced. Larger pollen size is usually a reliable indicator of tetraploids. Actual chromosome counts are necessary, however, for positive identification. The morphological changes associated with chromosome doubling vary within and between species. The promiscuous induction of tetraploidy seldom leads to anything of immediate value. Ploidy manipulations, however, have become a valuable tool in breeding. In some plants the large size associated with higher ploidy is of value; for example, there are now a number of tetraploid snapdragon varieties. Ploidy manipulation has proved of importance in increasing fertility in hybrids derived from wide crosses. In some crops the triploid condition is desirable because of increased vigor (Fig. 10-11) and fruit size (pears, apples) or to take advantage of reduced fertility, such as in the banana or in the seedless watermelon (Fig. 10-12).

Chromosome Behavior of Polyploids

Tetraploids, unlike diploids, have four chromosomes of each type. The chromosome behavior of tetraploids depends on their pairing relationships at meiosis. If they pair two by two (bivalent pairing) they will separate normally. However, if all four chromosomes pair together (quadrivalent pairing) there is a possibility of a 3–1 distribution leading to gametes with unbalanced chromosome numbers. This type of

Fig. 10-12. *The seedless watermelon is the result of a cross between a tetraploid and a diploid. The triploid fruit matures, although as a result of sterility, most of the seed does not develop normally. The small underdeveloped seeds are similar in texture to seeds of cucumber in the edible stage.*

[Courtesy Purdue Univ.]

chromosome separation is largely responsible for the reduced fertility of tetraploids.

The cross of a tetraploid with a diploid produces a triploid:

$$2n \text{ gamete} + n \text{ gamete} = 3n \text{ zygote.}$$

Chromosome pairing commonly involves the three chromosomes of each type (trivalent pairing). When the chromosomes separate at the first division of meiosis, two chromosomes go to one end of the cell, and the other chromosome goes to the other. Since the assortment of each trivalent is independent, gametes with chromosome numbers from n to $2n$ may be formed. Consider spinach, for example, in which $n = 6$. In a triploid ($3n = 18$) the possible types of chromosome assortment at anaphase 1 of meiosis is 6–12, 7–11, 8–10, and 9–9. The seven types of gametes in terms of chromosome number (6,7,8,9,10,11,12) are produced in a binomial distribution and occur in the frequency of 1:6:15:20:15:6:1. Only $\frac{2}{64}$ of the gametes are n or $2n$. As the chromosome number of plants increases, the frequency of n and $2n$ gametes in triploids becomes very small. Gametophytes having unbalanced numbers of chromosomes are either nonviable or are at a great selective disadvantage. Consequently, triploids are commonly quite sterile. They may be propagated asexually (as in apple and pear) or produced anew each year from tetraploid-diploid crosses (as in seedless watermelons).

Genetics of Polyploids

The single-gene ratios in diploid organisms are based on the assortment of two alleles per gene. In tetraploids, however, four alleles are present at each locus. There are two types of homozygous genotypes (*AAAA* and *aaaa*) and three kinds of heterozygous genotypes (*AAAa*, *AAaa*, and *Aaaa*). The genetic ratios from crosses involving these types differ from those of diploids. The *AAaa* heterozygote will produce gametes in a ratio of 1*AA*: 4*Aa*:1*aa*. If *A* is completely dominant and produces the *A*__ phenotype even with three doses of *a* (*Aaaa*), the progeny of *AAaa* selfed will produce a phenotypic ratio of 35*A*__:1*aa*. This ratio, however, is affected by the location of the gene on the chromosome. Thus, tetraploidy tends to muddle the genetic picture. Recessive genes appear hidden, for they occur less frequently. As a result of this, genetic analysis of polyploid species is exceedingly complex.

BREEDING METHODS

Sources of Variation

Genetic variability is the raw material of the plant breeder. For many cultivated plants a wealth of material is available from varieties already under cultivation. A complete collection of such widely grown plants as the apple, tomato, or rose must be worldwide in scope (Fig. 10-13). The new Crops Research Branch of the Agricultural Research Service (USDA) facilitates the exploration and introduction of genetic variability for the improvement of plants and the establishment of new crops. Societies have been organized around many plants (especially ornamentals), and often assist in the dissemination of plant material. Examples in the United States are the African Violet Society and the Tomato Breeders Cooperative. Breeders are often good sources of plant material.

The richest source of genetic variability for a particular species has been shown to be its geographical area of origin. In this *center of diversity*

Fig. 10-13. *A collection of English varieties of tomatoes selected for greenhouse production.*
[Courtesy Purdue Univ.]

a pool of genes exists for exploitation by the plant breeder. The incorporation of this genetic variability, when in the form of closely related species, may involve such special techniques as the manipulation of chromosome numbers or the artificial culture of embryos. In the tomato valuable genes for resistance to Fusarium wilt, tomato leaf mold, and gray leaf spot have come from a related species that grows wild in Peru, *Lycopersicon pimpinellifolium.*

Sports

Mutations of spontaneous origin, although rare, contribute to genetic variability. These changes are referred to in horticultural terminology as *sports.* Desirable mutations occurring in adapted, asexually propagated plants may result in an immediate improvement such as the color sports in many apple varieties and tree types in coffee plants.

Mutations occurring somatically may involve only a sector of tissues, resulting in a *chimera* (Fig. 10-14). (A chimera is named after a mythical beast having the head of a lion, the body of a goat, and the tail of a dragon.) Such chimeras, when vegetatively propagated, tend to be unstable. This is because buds may be formed from tissues with or without the

Fig. 10-14. *Plant chimeras contain genetically different tissues. Various types may be derived from buds arising from a sectored chimeral stem.*
[Adapted from Jones, *Botan. Rev.,* 3:545–562, 1937.]

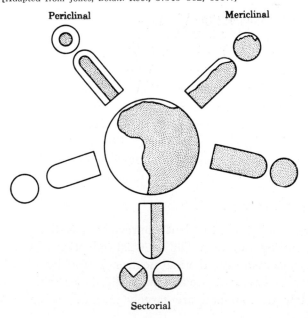

Periclinal   Mericlinal

Sectorial

mutation. For example, the White Sim carnation, a sport of the Red Sim variety, is a chimera. Buds which form from internal tissues will produce red flowers. Upon close inspection, the normal White Sim blooms also show small islands of red tissue. Before extensive propagation from a sported plant, it is important to have evidence that it is stable.

From a study of the performance of various types of natural variants, under different environmental conditions, it may be possible to make an immediate improvement by merely selecting the best individuals. However, with established crops it becomes more and more difficult to make improvements in this manner. Usually, the individual desirable characters are present in many plants, no one of which contains all the desirable attributes, in which case it becomes necessary to attempt to recombine the characters by hybridization (sexual crossing) in the hope of obtaining plants having as many of the desirable features as possible. When these characters are spread over many varieties the process necessitates making many crosses.

The desired characters are too often found only in plants that may be horticulturally unsatisfactory from other standpoints. Resistance to the apple scab disease is found in species with almost inedible fruit less than 1 in. in diameter. In addition, there are a great many characters to be considered. For example, a successful strawberry variety must satisfy (1) the growers with respect to yielding ability, season of ripening, and disease resistance; (2) the consumer's preferences for appearance and quality; (3) the nurseryman producing the plants; and (4) the shippers, handlers, and processors.

The incorporation of these various characteristics, most of which are quantitatively determined, involves many series of crosses carried over many generations. With each generation the amount of plant material tends to pyramid into unmanageable proportions unless rigid selection is maintained. Breeding becomes a problem in biological engineering. The main effort of the plant breeder is involved with the recombination of desired characters in as efficient a manner as possible in terms of land, time, and labor.

Artificial Creation of Variability

One of the limitations to plant improvement is the dependence upon naturally occurring variation. The artificial induction of mutation by radiation (X-rays, gamma rays, thermal neutrons) provides a method for creating changes that have not occured naturally. Since such induced changes are completely random and are largely harmful, refined techniques for screening are needed. For example, large populations of plants could easily be screened in the seedling stage for resistance to a disease if the susceptible plants died soon after inoculation. A promising application of irradiation may lie in its use in obtaining beneficial changes in asexually propagated material. In this way, otherwise adapted material may be screened in the search for a single desirable change in the hope of eliminating further generations of breeding and extensive testing.

Genetic Structure of Crop Varieties

The method of pollination has a profound effect on the genetic constitution of the plant. The amount of cross-pollination varies from essentially none in plants such as the garden pea to 100% in dioecious and self-incompatible plants. Two main groups are recognized; naturally *self-pollinated* plants, in which cross pollination is less than 4%, and naturally *cross-pollinated* plants, in which cross pollination exceeds 40%. The intermediate types are usually considered along with the cross-pollinated group.

Self-pollinated plants are ordinarily homozygous for practically all genes. The exceptions are a result of chance cross-pollination and mutation. However, any heterozygosity is quickly eliminated as a consequence of natural inbreeding. Thus, although a hybrid between two divergent types will be heterozygous for many genes, by the F_6 to F_{10} generations of natural selfing, the population will consist of many different individuals, each of which are for all practical purposes completely homozygous. The basic problem in the improvement of self-pollinated plants lies in selecting the best genotype from the unlimited number of different genotypes. Once a satisfactory homozygous plant is selected the problem of genetic maintenance is small as compared to that of cross-pollinated plants.

The genes in naturally cross-pollinated, seed-propagated plants are recombined constantly from generation to generation. A cross-pollinated variety is typified not on the basis of any one plant but by a population of plants. The problem of improving cross-pollinated plants consists in somehow maintaining visible uniformity while avoiding the decline in vigor associated with homozygosity. In general, procedures that result in severe inbreeding cause a loss of vigor. Once a desirable population is achieved there is still the perpetual problem of maintenance. A unique method of producing uniformity and at the same time maintaining heterozygosity has been the process of producing F_1 hybrids. At present, however, technical difficulties prevent this breeding method from being used with all cross-pollinated crops.

A large number of cross-pollinated crops (apple, rose, gladiolus) are normally vegetatively propagated. Here improvement depends on the selection of a single desirable genotype. The problem of genetic maintenance is solved by the elimination of the sexual process. In improving these plants by recombination, inbreeding must also be avoided. Hybridization between unrelated plants is usually made in order to obtain a vigorous population within which selection may be practiced.

Selection

The problem of the breeder confronted with a population containing many diverse genotypes is to recognize and save only the most desirable types. This process of selection differs depending on the method of reproduction of the plant.

Selection in Self-pollinated Crops

Two fundamentally different types of populations of self-pollinated crops exist. One is a mixture of different homozygous lines as found in a collection of varieties. Here selection consists of determining the best genotype by testing. As each variety is homozygous, the problem of genetic maintenance is eliminated. The best genotype can be expected to be duplicated from its selfed seed. The other type of population is a mixture of different heterozygous genotypes, as found in the F_2 population of a cross between different homozygous varieties. As discussed previously, some completely homozygous types are theoretically expected, but their number greatly decreases as the number of genes differentiating the original cross increases. The problem of improvement is now twofold: to select the best genotype and to transform this genotype as closely as possible into a homozygous line.

The genetic value of a self-pollinated, seed-propagated plant is the average performance of its progeny. The task of selecting the best genotype from an F_2 population is difficult because of the problem of distinguishing between genetic and environmental variation. Selection of the most desirable genotypes is accomplished on the basis of progeny performance. This process, which is known as pedigree selection, is based on the assumption that the best homozygous genotype will be derived from the heterozygous plant that produces the most desirable progeny.

Assume that selfed seed from a number of F_2 plants are planted out to produce F_3 lines. Since each selfing brings about homozygosity in a 50% increase each generation, the variability within F_3 lines will be half as great as the variability between F_2 plants. That is, the plants within a particular F_3 line will resemble each other more so than will the aggregate of all F_3 lines. For example, some lines will be uniformly large and some uniformly small. By choosing between a number of lines rather than choosing a single F_2 plant there is less chance of confusing genetic and environmental effects.

The selection process may then be repeated. The best appearing plants in the best F_3 lines are planted out, and selection is made again on a "pedigree" basis between F_4 lines. By the sixth to tenth generation the lines derived from single plant selections will be homozygous for over 95% of their genes. Such lines are, for practical purposes, considered to be true breeding. If one of these lines are of superior type, it may be "named," and is then considered a new horticultural variety.

The problem of straight pedigree selection is the extreme expense it entails. Fairly extensive records must be maintained, and unless rigid selection is maintained the program soon "mushrooms" to extremely unwieldy proportions.

An alternate method of selection is known as *mass selection*. In this technique the best appearing plants are selected and maintained in bulk without testing the progenies separately. This may be accomplished by eliminating (*roguing out*) the undesirable plants in each generation and harvesting the remaining plants. This can be done mechanically for some crops, such as by screening for seed size or harvesting at a particular date to select for a particular season of ripening. After 6–10 generations, the population will consist of a heterogeneous mixture of "somewhat selected" homozygous genotypes. The progeny of any plant can be expected to form the basis of a new variety. The problem now is to determine the best genotype by testing. This method will be successful if the better genotypes are retained in the mass selection process either by judicious selection or merely by virtue of large numbers.

The processes of mass selection and pedigree selection can be combined. For example, F_2 plants can be "pedigree selected" on the basis of F_3 line performance. Thus the greatest genetic differences are exploited early, and the obviously undersirable types are eliminated. The best F_3 lines may then be bulked and carried on by mass selection until homozygosity is reached, at which time "pedigree selection" is resumed.

Selection in Cross-pollinated Crops

Pedigree selection depends on genotype evaluation by inbreeding. Straight pedigree selection is undesirable as a method of improving cross-pollinated plants, in which inbreeding leads to loss of vigor, unless some procedure is set up to combine inbred lines and restore vigor. Mass selection enables a cross-breeding population to become relatively uniform for certain visible characters and to conserve enough variability to maintain vigor. Inbreeding is avoided by natural interpollination.

Mass selection often leads to a rapid improvement of cross-pollinated plants. However, it sometimes becomes difficult to increase this "genetic gain" after a certain point. To obtain more control of the genotypes making up the cross-pollinating population, pedigree and mass selection may be combined. This is accomplished by selfing individual plants and "pedigree selecting" them on the basis of their progeny. The selected lines are then allowed to interpollinate to restore "heterozygosity." The process may be repeated for a number of cycles. There are several variations of this procedure. When the character evaluated is a fruit or a seed, selection must be made after pollination. In this case the "female" parent is pedigree selected, and the "male" parent is mass selected.

In a very real sense, F_1 hybrids are an extreme form of this method. Here the inbreeding process is carried on to homozygosity, and vigor is restored by combining two (or four in a double cross) inbreds. The selection of the inbred combination results in uniform, genetically controlled hybrids.

Selection of Asexually Propagated Crops

In asexually propagated plants, selection is straightforward, since any genotype may be perpetuated intact. The problem is one of testing, that is, of determining the best genotype. If the most desirable selection is still unsatisfactory and further improvement is necessary, the selection of the best genotype to be used for further crossing is more difficult because the best performing selection does not always make the best parent. A sample of genotypes must be selected and tested as parents on the basis of their progeny performance.

Utilization of Hybrid Vigor

The production of F_1 hybrids as a breeding method for seed-propagated, cross-pollinated plants depends upon a number of factors. The first requirement is that it must be possible to obtain inbred lines. This may be difficult with self-incompatible plants. In addition, some inbred lines become so weak that they are exceedingly difficult to maintain. The second requirement is that it must be possible to make an efficient cross between the inbred lines. This may be exceedingly difficult in perfect-flowered plants, unless each hand pollination yields a great number of seeds. One method used in overcoming this is the incorporation of male sterility, which transforms one line into a "female" variety (Fig. 10 15). If this method is used special breeding techniques are required to perpetuate the male-sterile line. The third requirement is an economic one. The improvement must be great enough to warrant the extra expense of hybrid seed.

The process of producing F_1 hybrids by the inbreeding process has not proved practical in cross-pollinated plants that are vegetatively propagated, although it is often suggested as a breeding method. Each clonal variety is essentially a hybrid, which, if duplicated asexually, need not be duplicated by crossing two unique inbred lines. The great advantage of F_1 hybrids in cross-pollinated plants is their *uniformly* high vigor. However, the process of vegetative propagation assures absolute genetic uniformity.

Fig. 10-15 *Controlled hybridization in the onion. Genetically determined male sterility transforms one inbred to a female line. Male sterility in onions results from interaction between a cytoplasmic factor* $\boxed{S}$ *and a doubly recessive nuclear gene ms. Plants with* $\boxed{N}$ *(normal) cytoplasm or with gene Ms, either homozygous or heterozygous produce viable pollen.*

[Adapted from Srb and Owen, *General Genetics*, Freeman, San Francisco, 1953.]

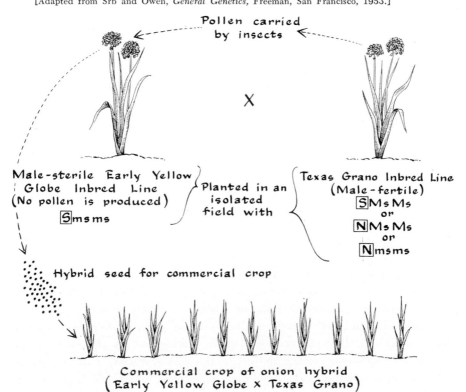

Pollen carried
by insects

X

Male-sterile Early Yellow
Globe Inbred Line
(No pollen is produced)
$\boxed{S}$ms ms

Planted in an
isolated
field with

Texas Grano Inbred Line
(Male-fertile)
$\boxed{S}$Ms Ms
or
$\boxed{N}$Ms Ms
or
$\boxed{N}$ms ms

Hybrid seed for commercial crop

Commercial crop of onion hybrid
(Early Yellow Globe × Texas Grano)

Vigorous hybrid genotypes can be selected from segregating populations instead of creating them from inbred lines.

As heterosis appears to be involved to a lesser extent in self-pollinated crops, the creation of F_1 hybrids (actually varietal crosses) is not a prominent breeding method for these plants. However, since varietal crosses offer a quick means of producing a particular combination, this method has found a limited place in some self-pollinated crops, such as greenhouse tomatoes.

Although the maximum amount of heterosis is obtained by crossing two inbreds, a number of other less heterotic combinations may be made. The various kinds of crosses that are referred to as hybrids in the trade are designated as follows.

TYPE OF CROSS	NAME OF HYBRID
inbred × inbred	single cross
F_1 hybrid × inbred	3-way cross
F_1 hybrid × F_1 hybrid	double cross
inbred × variety	top cross

Since many inbreds are relatively weak, the double cross is an attempt to produce seed on a vigorous plant. Its use has been confined to field corn. The top cross has been used in spinach, and the three-way cross is popular in sweet corn.

The genetic improvement of inbreds is a specialized type of breeding. Basically, they are treated as self-pollinated plants. However, the success of an inbred is often difficult to determine phenotypically but is related to its success as a parent. This ability of an inbred to produce good hybrids is known as *combining ability*. Combining ability is inherited, but the only way to select for it is to test it directly. Combining ability may be selected for early in the inbreeding process by crossing the plant to a tester at the same time it is selfed. The selfed seed is set aside for further inbreeding until after the results of the crossing trial are evaluated.

The Backcross Method

The backcross has been defined as a cross of an F_1 plant with one of its parents. The backcross method is a breeding technique for transferring single characters, readily identifiable, from one variety to another. Characters controlled by single genes, such as certain types of disease resistance, male sterility, and so on, are most easily transferred by this method. By repeated backcrossing of the hybrid to the parent variety that carries the most desirable characters (*the recurrent parent*), but selecting in each generation for a single character from the other parent (*the nonrecurrent parent*), a genotype will be eventually obtained that has all the genes of the recurrent parent except those affecting the selected character from the nonrecurrent parent. In the following explanatory discussion, assume that the "varieties" are of self-pollinated plants.

As regards the consequences of the backcross method, two sets of genes must be considered. One set consists of the particular gene or genes from the nonrecurrent parent that is to be transferred. The other set consists of the large group of genes making up the recurrent parent, which we do not wish to lose. The genes of the recurrent parent can be shown to be transferred by an increment of 50% in each generation of backcrossing. By selecting plants at random in each generation, we can expect the genes of the recurrent parent to not only be incorporated in the hybrid but also to become homozygous. This can be shown easily with respect to a single gene.

Assume a cross involving a single gene pair, $AA \times aa \longrightarrow Aa$. The two types of backcrosses are

$$Aa \times AA \longrightarrow 1Aa:1AA,$$
$$Aa \times aa \longrightarrow 1Aa:1aa.$$

Compare with the self

$$Aa \times Aa \longrightarrow 1AA:2Aa:1aa.$$

In backcrossing and selfing, half of the genes become homozygous. This can be generalized for any number of genes. The rate of return to homozygosity in backcrossing is the same as in selfing, but *all of the homozygous genes resemble the recurrent parent*. If backcrossing to the same homozygous type is continued for 6–10 generations, over 95% of the genes of the hybrid will be identical to the recurrent parent and will be in the homozygous condition.

If the gene transferred is dominant the procedure is straightforward. After the last backcross the gene may be made homozygous by selfing. If the character transferred is recessive, special testing must be carried on in each generation to be sure the plant selected for backcrossing is heterozygous and thus contains the desired recessive.

The backcross method has found its greatest usefulness in self-pollinated crops and in improving inbred lines of cross-pollinated plants. It is not as useful in cross-pollinated crops because backcrossing is equivalent to selfing in achieving homozygosity. This may be overcome, however, by using a large number of selections of the recurrent variety. In this way inbreeding may be avoided (Fig. 10-16).

Fig. 10-16. *Backcross breeding for scab resistance in the apple. (A) The fruits of* Malus floribunda *821, which is heterozygous for a dominant gene that confers resistance to apple scab. (B) Selection derived from cross of* M. floribunda *821 × Rome Beauty. (C, D) Subsequent backcrosses to different large-fruited types produce resistant seedlings with increased fruit size and quality. (E) Resistant seedlings are selected in the seedling stage. Susceptible seedlings are killed by the disease.*
[Courtesy J. R. Shay.]

The main advantage of the backcross method is its predictability. The improved variety is often indistinguishable from the old one with the exception of the added character. As a result, extensive testing may be avoided. But the backcross method cannot be expected to improve the variety any more than the addition of the single selected character. Moreover, unless this character is inherited relatively simply the method is difficult to use.

Controlled Hybridization

Plant breeding is concerned largely with the control of the sexual process in plants. Before two plants can be crossed they must be induced to flower simultaneously. This may not always occur naturally, hence various environmental factors such as photoperiod, temperature, and nutrition may have to be manipulated to achieve synchronization of flowering. In some varieties of sweet potato flowering can be induced only with difficulty, thus, they must be grafted to species of morning glory and then subjected to specialized photoperiods and temperatures.

The storage and shipping of pollen facilitates artificial hybridization and in some cases saves many years. Pollen is quite variable in its ability to remain viable. For example, the pollen of cucurbits only remains viable for about three hours. Apple pollen stored under low humidity and cool temperatures (30–36°F) may retain viability for over two years. A new technique of freeze-dehydration is a promising method for pollen storage.

The basic procedure in making artificial crosses involves the following practices: (1) avoidance of contamination before artificial pollination, (2) application of the pollen, and (3) protection of the pollinated flower from subsequent contamination.

In perfect-flowered plants contamination by selfing is avoided by the process of *emasculation*. This consists in removing the anthers before they have begun to shed pollen. It is done before the flower opens, and the technique varies with the flower structure (Fig. 10-17). In monoecious plants (separate pistillate and staminate flowers) the pistillate flowers must be protected before pollination from wind or insect pollination by suitable protecting devices, such as paper, glassine bags, or cheesecloth nets. In insect-pollinated plants the petals are often removed to discourage insect visitation.

The pollen may be applied by one of several methods. Often the anthers are collected the day before pollination and dried. The pollen is then applied with a camel's-hair brush, the fingers, a blackened matchstick, or

Fig. 10-17. *Preparing a rose bud for cross-pollination. The petals are cut at the base (left) and at the tip (center). Pollen is being supplied to emasculated flower with a camel's-hair brush (right).*
[Courtesy USDA.]

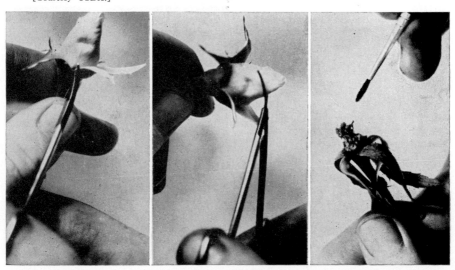

Fig. 10-18. *Pollen transfer in cross of male-fertile × male-sterile onions is achieved by caged blow flies.*
[Courtesy K. W. Johnson.]

the dried flower itself, used as a brush. The pollen should be applied in large amounts. In the greenhouse, the pollination of dioecious plants, such as spinach, may be controlled by isolating the pistillate and staminate plants to be crossed. The pollination of onions is carried out by enclosing their flower heads in mesh cages containing blow flies (Fig. 10-18).

After pollination the flower may need to be protected from contamination by cross-pollination. This is usually accomplished by enclosing the flower in paper or glassine bags (Fig. 10-19). If the petals have been left, as in peas, they may by themselves serve as the protecting device with the aid of cellophane tape. When it is only necessary to keep away insects, cheese cloth is usually sufficient. Care must be used in selecting protecting devices that do not act as a heat trap and thus prevent successful fruit set. In citrus and in apples, insects will not visit the flowers if the petals are removed, thus protection of emasculated flowers is not necessary.

Maintaining Genetic Improvement

Once a genetic gain has been achieved vigilance is still required to maintain improvement. Mutation, natural crossing, contamination, and, in vegetatively propagated material, diseases, especially those caused by viruses, tend to cause the deterioration or "running

Fig. 10-19. *A piece of ordinary soda straw protects pistil from contamination before and after pollination.*
[Courtesy G. M. Fosler.]

out" of varieties. Genetic deterioration may be reduced to a minimum by continued selection and careful propagation. In an effort to control the purity of seed many semi-public organizations and seed associations have been formed. In order to protect their reputation, seed companies and nurseries must strive constantly to keep their stocks free of contamination.

Control of Varieties

To encourage improvement of plants, United States patent laws protect the right of the originator to control the increase of new forms of certain vegetatively propagated material (white potatoes are an exception). Only the right of vegetative propagation is protected; the right to propagate by seed is not. Many varieties of gladiolus, rose, apple, peach, and pear are patented. In this way, the breeder, be he a private individual, group, or public agency, may justly profit from his discoveries, just as the inventor or chemist may be rewarded by his invention, discovery, or new process.

Although seed-propagated crops cannot now be patented, the name can be copyrighted, and the variety can be indirectly controlled in this manner. However, seed-propagated hybrids can be biologically controlled by the breeder. For example, the control of the unique sets of inbreds controls the hybrid even more effectively than does legal control. In varietal hybrids of self-pollinated plants, such as tomato, merely knowing the two varieties that are used to make the hybrid out of the hundreds available, may effectively control its production.

Selected References

Allard, R. W. *Principles of Plant Breeding*. Wiley, New York. 1960. (An outstanding presentation of the genetic foundation of plant breeding.)

Better Plants and Animals. II. USDA Yearbook. 1937. (A valuable reference for horticultural plant improvement. Together with the 1936 yearbook, this work marks a historical landmark of genetics and breeding of agricultural crops in the United States.)

Crane, M. B. and Lawrence, W. J. C. *The Genetics of Garden Plants*. Macmillan, London. 1947. (An important compilation.)

CHAPTER 11

Marketing

HORTICULTURE AFTER HARVEST

The path of horticultural products from the growing plant to the consumer is complex. *Marketing* may be defined broadly as the activities that direct the flow of goods from producer to consumer—that is, the operations and transactions involved in their movement, storage, processing, and distribution. These operations have developed into a highly specialized technology. Many production operations are a direct part of marketing. When the grower selects a particular variety to plant, he is very often making a marketing decision. Production decisions that determine ultimate quality, such as methods of disease control, may ultimately become as much a part of marketing as decisions to store or to sell or to prepack or to bulk ship. Many production and marketing operations are connected and interrelated. For example, the harvesting, grading, and packing of lettuce is combined in one field operation.

The unique aspects of marketing of horticultural products are due to their perishable nature. After harvest, the horticultural product is still alive and consequently deteriorating. The ultimate quality of the product at the consumer level, which is what determines its real economic value, hinges upon its treatment after harvest.

MARKETING FUNCTIONS

Marketing activities contribute certain increments of value to horticultural products because of the applications of *marketing function*. These have been categorized as *exchange, physical,* and *facilitation* functions. The exchange functions are those activities involved in the transfer of title to goods, that is, buying and selling. Buying in its broadest sense includes

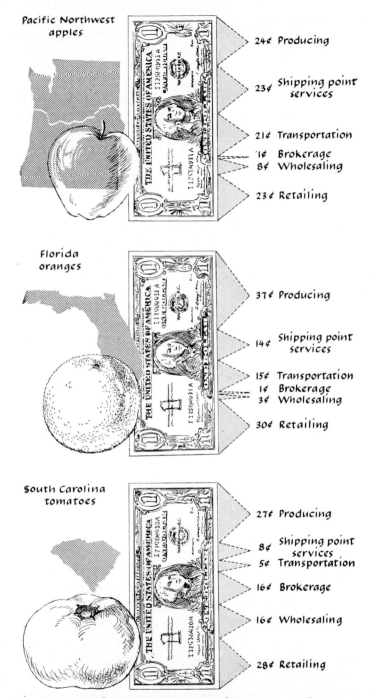

Fig. 11-1. *Marketing margins for apples, oranges, and tomatoes.*
Note that ⅔-¾ of the consumer's dollar is spent for marketing.
[Data from USDA.]

the seeking out and assembling of sources of supply. This may involve many transactions and many people at various levels of the marketing operation. Similarly, selling involves not only the transfer of goods but also includes merchandising (packaging, advertising, and promotion). The physical functions associated with marketing involve storage, transportation, and processing. These add the tangible values of prolonged availability, movement, and change in the form of the product. Finally, the *facilitating* functions make possible the orderly performance of the exchange and physical functions. They include grading, financing, risk bearing, and communication (market information). The total cost of these operations, the *marketing margin,* may greatly exceed the entire cost of production (Fig. 11-1). These are the charges of the maligned middlemen of agriculture.

This chapter is largely involved with a discussion of technological problems associated with marketing operations. The detailed structure and economic ramifications of marketing are beyond the scope of this book.

HARVESTING

The close relationship of harvesting to subsequent marketing operations makes its discussion a proper introduction to marketing technology. Harvesting is one of the crucial features in the horticultural operation. It is often the costliest production item, and its timing has a direct bearing on the final quality of the product. For example, maturity has a great influence on the subsequent storage behavior of many crops. Technological advances in harvesting have become an outstanding example of the current trend of substituting capital for labor in horticultural operations.

Predicting Harvest Dates

A number of factors must be considered with regard to the timing of harvesting: maintaining orderly production operations that make possible the maximum utilization of equipment and labor; setting up an orderly marketing sequence; and the ultimate quality and appearance of the product. For many crops, harvesting must proceed within a certain narrow time interval, for quality is a fleeting and elusive factor. Often there are a number of conflicting factors to be considered. For example, in apple harvest, storage quality is adversely affected by delaying maturity, yet on the other hand, red color tends to increase with time. Determining the optimum time of harvest is not a simple, straightforward decision.

The factors affecting the harvest date of a crop depend upon the genetic nature of the variety; planting, or bloom, date; and environmental factors that exist during the growing season. Successive harvest dates of sweet corn may be obtained by planting varieties with different maturity dates. Similarly, in tree crops, there are different varieties that mature in a definite succession every year. In the past, tremendous market gluts of peaches have been produced as a result of extensive plantings of one variety, Elberta. This has been alleviated by breeding programs that have released varieties ripening in an orderly sequence over almost a three-month period.

The harvest date of annual crops may be altered by changing the sequence of planting dates. However, a delay in planting date does not necessarily cause the same delay in harvest date. The time required to reach the harvestable stage is based largely on the crop and its temperature requirements for growth. When temperatures are below the minimum required for growth, a long delay in planting may not affect the harvest date.

In some crops the time required to reach the harvestable stage may be expressed in terms of temperate-time values called *heat units* by calculating time in relation to temperature above a minimum. For example, if the minimum temperature for growth of a particular crop is 50°F, then a day with an average temperature of 60°F would provide 10 degree-days of heat units. A day with an average temperature of 40°F would provide 0 degree-days of heat units. The harvest date can be ascertained by an accounting of accumulated heat units. In Wisconsin it has been shown that 1200–1250 degree-days are required for the Alaska variety of pea to mature if planted in the early spring. Under increasing spring temperatures it takes longer to accumulate heat units in the early part of the season than later. Assuming that all temperatures above a minimum have similar effects on growth, there would be a decreasing interval between planting and harvest dates as the season progresses.

The heat-unit system has a number of limitations. For example, soil temperatures more accurately indicate early growth than do air temperatures. Differences in day-night temperature-shifts, day length effects, as well as the differential effect of temperature on various stages of plant growth, also affect the results. In addition, temperatures above a minimum may not have a similar effect on growth, but within limits, may act exponentially, approximately doubling many physiological processes with every 18°F rise in temperature. The precise determination of harvest date by the accumulation of temperature data depends upon a knowledge of the general climate of an area and upon experience with harvest dates based upon planting dates for each crop.

For many long-season fruit crops, such as apples, the most reliable index for calculating maturity is the number of days from flowering. This value, determined from an analysis of previous data, is surprisingly consistent. It would indicate that other environmental factors besides temperature are important in determining fruit maturity.

A number of physiological criteria are used to determine harvest date. In pears the proper stage of each variety is determined by a combination of criteria, among which are pressure testing of the fruit, ground color of the skin, seed color, and percentage of soluble solids (basically sugar) of the flesh. In some crops other criteria are also utilized. These include the formation of abscission zones separating fruit from stem (muskmelons), the visible stage of development (such as degree of bud tightness in roses), color (tomatoes), sugar-acid ratio (blueberries), and even the way the fruit sounds when thumped (watermelons). A combination of methods is often used to determine the correct degree of maturity.

Harvesting Methods

Hand harvesting is still the only practical method for many high value crops that are either sensitive to bruising or that must be selectively picked (strawberries, apples). The mechanization of harvesting has proceeded in stages. Thus, we may speak of complete, semi-, and nonmechanized har-

Fig. 11-2. *Mechanical harvest of snap beans in Wisconsin. (A) Each picker harvests 8–10 acres of snap beans per day. (B) A pallet box containing about 700 lb of snap beans being lowered to the ground. (C) Tractors with hydraulic lifts loading pallets onto a truck, which is dispatched to the canning plant.*

[Courtesy National Canner's Association.]

Fig. 11-3. *Mechanical harvest of sweet corn and potato.*
[Photograph at top by J. C. Allen & Son; photograph at bottom courtesy Purdue Univ.]

vesting. For example, in Arizona muskmelons are harvested by hand but are placed on conveyors, where they are graded, and are packed in the field on moving machines. Similar operations are used for cabbage, peppers, cauliflower, and broccoli.

The harvesting of many crops is completely mechanized, although it is done in a number of separate steps. For example, when grown for processing, pumpkins and squash are raked into windrows and are loaded by conveyor in another operation.

For other crops, harvesting is completely mechanized; all operations are performed by a single machine in a single step. Thus, potatoes are harvested by a combine which digs, removes vines, and loads tubers. A somewhat similar operation is used to harvest radishes, beets, carrots, and floral bulb crops. Snap beans (Fig. 11-2) and sweet corn (Fig. 11-3) are mechanically harvested; canning peas are now picked, vined, and shelled in the field. Tomato and asparagus harvesters are in advanced experimental stages.

Fruit crops present a somewhat different problem in that the plant itself must not be destroyed. Cranberries were the first fruits to be machine harvested; the principal of operation involves the combing of the vine Equipment for shaking plums, clingstone peaches, blueberries, and nuts onto canvas have been developed. Grape and raspberry harvesters are in experimental forms.

In general, machine harvesting must proceed hand in hand with breeding to develop machine-compatible plants. Such plants must usually possess high uniformity, a concentration of ripe fruit, and enough firmness to resist excessive bruising, although, when perfected, the machines often perform a more satisfactory job than hand harvesting. Machine-harvested potatoes show a decrease in defects due to bruising. The culture of many crops must be adjusted to the machine. For example, the pickling cucumber harvester combs the same vine a number of times. Thus, the vines must be trained in one direction. The problem of uniformity in many vegetable crops is facilitated by the use of F_1 hybrids.

Post Harvest Alterations

The desirability, or quality, of the horticultural product refers to many different things, depending on the commodity. For processing tomatoes, it implies freedom from cracking and good internal red color. On the other hand, in the Delicious apple, desirability connotes a particular flavor, shape, and pattern of external red color. Desirability of nursery stock refers to viability, form, and size, plus the proper proportion and packaging of roots and soil.

For the sake of precision, the general term *quality* is best divorced from the meanings suggested by the terms *condition* and *appearance*. In food crops the word quality is best used with reference to palatability. This implies a pleasing combination of flavor and texture; flavor resulting from taste and smell, and texture perceived as "mouth feel." Quality can also properly be used to describe nonedible products such as seed or nursery stock. Used in this sense the term refers to the physiological state of the material, connoting high viability and trueness to type. *Condition* refers to the presence of, or freedom from, disease, injury, or physiological disorders. Although we associate good condition with high quality, this is not always the case. *Appearance* refers to the visible attributes of the product. It includes color, conformation, and size. Unfortunately appearance is not always a reliable index of quality.

A number of physiological and biochemical processes occur in the harvested, nonprocessed horticultural product that contribute to change (Table

11-1). This may result in the deterioration of quality, condition, and appearance in some crops, and in the improvement of quality and appearance in

Table 11-1. *Changes that occur in harvested produce.*

CHANGE	PROCESS	EXAMPLES AND SIGNIFICANCE
Water loss	Transpiration Evaporation	Unattractive appearance, texture changes, weight loss, "shriveling"
Carbohydrate conversion	Enzymatic	Starch to sugar; detrimental in potatoes, beneficial in bananas and pears Sugar to starch; detrimental in sweet corn and most edible crops
Flavor	Enzymatic	Usually detrimental. May be beneficial (persimmons, pears, bananas)
Softening	Pectic enzymes Water loss	Usually detrimental. Beneficial in pears, bananas
Color	Pigment synthesis or destruction	May be detrimental or beneficial
Toughening	Fiber development	Detrimental in celery
Vitamin	Enzymatic	May be gain (vitamin A) or loss (vitamin C)
Sprouting Rooting Elongation	Growth and development	Detrimental in potatoes and onions Detrimental in asparagus
Decay and rot	Pathological Physiological	Detrimental

those crops that complete ripening after harvest. For most commodities the objective is to maintain the product as close to harvest condition as possible. The horticultural product must be maintained in the living state because death causes irreversible biochemical changes. These may involve gross deterioration and drastic differences in flavor, texture, and appearance.

GRADING

Owing to the inherent variability of horticultural products at harvest, and to their differences in value, it is necessary to grade them according to some objective standard. Grading is the basis of long-distance trade. It permits the description of products in terms that are understandable to both buyer and seller. Without a system of grading, all products would have to be individually inspected. Grading thus adds a tangible value to horticultural products.

Grading has two distinct functions. The first is to eliminate completely all obviously unsatisfactory items. This is extremely important in packaging, since diseases spread rapidly in the suitable environments of packages. Furthermore, one poor item visually detracts, out of all proportion to its bulk, from the appearance of a larger sample. The second function of grading is consolidation. This may include variety, size, appearance, defects, and, where possible, quality. Because of inherent differences, certain crops (for example, apple and pear) are grouped and identified by variety. Within a variety, size is the most obvious gradable factor (Fig. 11-4). Various size characteristics may be used: stem length (roses), stem diameter (trees),

Fig. 11-4.   *This fruit grader sizes fruit on a weight basis. The fiber cartons are tray-packed.*
[Courtesy Food Machinery and Chemical Corp.]

spread (shrubs), weight (watermelons), and diameter (most fruit). Grading for appearance may be based on the absence of defects, conformation, and the amount and intensity of color. Various techniques have been used to objectively evaluate palatability, such as the determination of oil content (avocados), firmness (tomatoes), sugar-acid ratio (oranges), specific gravity (white potatoes), and various maturity criteria.

One of the factors that determines the quality grade of the processed product is the quality of the raw product. Raw product grades for processing must take into account particular demands of the industry. Some factors assume greater importance, whereas others assume less. For example, apple skin color is of small importance, since the skins are removed in processing, but large fruit size is extremely important because of the limitations of mechanical peelers. Special quality features for processing have been determined, for example, total solids (tomatoes), tenderness (peas and corn), and sugar content (grapes for wine). Defects, texture, and internal color become very important.

Inspection and grading is backed by federal law. The most comprehensive recent piece of legislation is Title II of Public Law 733, known as the Agricultural Marketing Act of 1946, which directs the Secretary of Agriculture:

> To develop and improve standards of quality. . . . To inspect, certify, and identify the class, quality, quantity, and condition of agricultural products when shipped or received in interstate commerce, under such rules and regulations as the Secretary of Agriculture may prescribe . . . to the end that agricultural products may be marketed, to the best advantage, that trading may be facilitated, and that consumers may be able to obtain the quality product which they desire. . . .

Most federal standards for horticultural products are permissive; that is, they are officially recommended but are not compulsory, but if federal grades are used to describe the product, they must be complied with. Mandatory grades do exist in special conditions, however, as in the export of apples and pears. Most of the grade standards for fruits and vegetables are designed for wholesale trading, and are not directly carried over into retail trading.

Federal grading regulations are complemented by state laws. This has created confusion and disorder where state regulations differ widely from each other and from federal standards. The inspection of fresh fruits and vegetables at shipping points is performed by the combined efforts of federal and state agencies.

MARKET PREPARATION

Most horticultural crops require special preparation after harvest. They are usually cleaned, trimmed, or especially treated in some manner. Root crops must be cleaned to remove adhering soil and debris. Muck grown potatoes are at a serious disadvantage unless the extremely fine black soil is removed. Washing or brushing of fruit is done to enhance appearance. The outer leaves of lettuce and cabbage are routinely removed, as are the tops of beets and carrots. Leaves of many florist crops, such as chrysanthemums and snapdragons, are stripped by the grower at harvest. Strawberry plants are "cleaned" by removing the dead leaves and runners.

Many products are waxed to prevent water loss and to improve appearance (turnips, citrus fruits, and cucumbers). Waxing is now a standard practice for dormant nursery stock, especially rose plants. Bananas are dipped in solutions of copper sulfate to control storage and shipping rots.

Curing

Curing is a postharvest treatment used to prolong the storage life of certain commodities, e.g. white potatoes, sweet potatoes, and bulb crops. Curing involves exposing the product to specialized temperature or humidity conditions. White potatoes are "cured" at 55–60°F during the first 2 or 3 weeks of storage. The humidity is kept very high during this period to prevent shrinkage due to the loss of water. Since the tubers are dormant, sprouting does not occur. Curing brings about the healing of cuts and bruises that occur in harvest. Two physiological processes are involved: *suberization*, the deposit of a fatty material by the tuber, which produces a fairly effective barrier to the loss of moisture; and *active cell division* of the periderm, which produces a new "hide." After the curing period, temperatures are lowered for prolonged storage to prevent sprouting. A similar curing treatment is involved in the storage of sweet potatoes, although higher curing temperatures are involved (around 80°F).

In bulbs curing involves the removal of water from the outer scales and neck. This was formerly done in the field, but the trend is toward the use of artificial drying in storage. Proper curing prevents rot by eliminating the favorable environment for organisms on the bulb itself. No active cell division is involved.

Packaging

Packaging affords protection, convenience, economy, and appeal. The changes in packaging have had great impact on the horticultural industry. Before World War I a tremendous variety of wooden containers was used (barrels, boxes, crates, and baskets of varying shapes and dimensions). By World War II a certain amount of standardization was reached, and the wooden bushel basket and box became the principal packages used for a great variety of vegetables and fruit. These containers originated as a grower pack and were also used by the retailer. The wooden bushel basket has proved unsuitable in many crops. It is bulky, relatively heavy, and costly. It is also expensive to fill, since it must be faced. Nor is its shape particularly suitable for packing; stacking them wastes space and badly bruises the contents, especially the top layer. Furthermore, the bushel is no longer a convenient retail package, since it would necessitate completely repacking the contents into refrigerated display cases now in common use.

The materials used for packing differ with the product. Wooden packages are still being used for many products, such as melons. This has been especially true for products that are hydrocooled. Lighter weight fiber cartons are now replacing wood for many packages (Fig. 11-5); some are specially coated to give them wet strength. Plastics, paper, and cloth are now commonly used as packaging materials.

Fig. 11-5. *Different packages for apples.*
[Courtesy Purdue Univ.]

The term *prepackaging* has been used for the process of putting produce in a consumer unit package at some point before it is put on display in the retail store. The rise of the self-service supermarkets has irrevocably altered packaging of horticultural commodities, although perishable commodities were the last to be prepackaged. In 1960, over one-quarter of all fruits and vegetables were prepackaged before they reached the retail store.

The prepackaging of fruit and vegetables has been made possible by the creation of satisfactory films. Polyethylene has proved to be extremely versatile. It is strong, transparent, moisture-resistant, and can be made permeable for gas exchange. The natural appeal of products in transparent bags with a minimum of printing has proved to be a selling attraction. At present, carrots and radishes are nearly always prepackaged. Apples are commonly retailed in five-pound "poly" bags packaged in fiber cartons. Polyethylene films have had a great influence on the perennial plant business by eliminating the need for heavy moisture carriers such as peat. In general, specialized films are being created to suit individual products. Other materials such as cardboard, paper, cloth, and plastics have proven useful for particular commodities.

The prepackaging of produce has put a premium on uniformity. This has eliminated customer handling and has prevented much in-store damage. Prepackaging has also reduced premiums usually paid for large size because by selling a fixed quantity the customer has shown a preference for receiving a particular number of items. Prepackaging has not in any way eliminated refrigeration, though it has in many cases increased shelf life by improving moisture retention. In general, prepackaging has improved quality levels.

The question of who should do the prepackaging has not yet been settled. There is controversy over whether prepackaging is best handled at the shipping point or at the distribution point. Although different crops have been handled in different ways, there is a trend with many commodities for grower packaging. As producers have increased in size, buying organizations have dealt directly with growers and have specified package requirements. The producer, if large enough, often finds it profitable to assume the packaging operations.

PRECOOLING

Precooling refers to the rapid removal of heat from freshly harvested fruits and vegetables in order to slow ripening and reduce deterioration prior to storage or shipment. The rate of deterioration depends on many factors: temperature, the natural respiration rate of the crop, the moisture content, the presence of natural protective barriers to water loss, and the presence of decay organisms. The major effect of precooling consists in reducing the respiration rate. Precooling also slows deterioration and rot by retarding the growth of decay organisms, and reduces wilting and shriveling, since transpiration and evaporation occur more slowly at low temperatures. The internal temperature of horticultural products (such as a peach) harvested on a hot day may be 20°F above air temperature. The removal of field heat, to reduce the temperature of the harvested product to 32–40°F, must be as rapid as possible; consequently, a great deal of energy is required. Hence, the harvesting of many perishable crops is now done at night or early in the morning to avoid excessive field heat. With the field heat removed, considerably less energy is required to maintain low temperatures, since the respiration rate at temperatures of 32–40° is relatively slight. The special techniques developed to precool vegetables and fruits are: *contact icing*, *hydrocooling*, *vacuum cooling*, and *air cooling*.

Contact icing refers to the use of crushed ice placed in or on the package to effect cooling. The major advantage of ice is that it does not dry out the food in cooling it. Another advantage is that produce may be shipped immediately after treatment, since cooling takes place in transit. Although icing requires relatively small outlays of special equipment, a large weight of ice must be shipped. Furthermore, after the ice has melted the package is left only partly full. When lettuce was precooled by icing, a packed crate would contain 60 lb of lettuce and 30 lb of ice. The use of ice spread mechanically over the produce after loading (*top icing*) has eliminated the slack pack, but cooling is not as efficient. Contact icing is being replaced by hydro- and vacuum cooling.

Hydrocooling refers to the cooling of fruits and vegetables with water (Fig. 11-6). The water (usually iced) flows through the packed containers and absorbs heat directly from the produce. The high efficiency of the system is due to the large heat capacity and high rate of heat transfer of water. The time required is related to the thickness of the individual product, as well as the internal temperature at the beginning of the cooling process, in relation to the desired temperature drop. Fungicides such as calcium hypochlorite at concentrations of 50–100 ppm are used to prevent the spread of decay organisms. One of the chief advantages of hydrocooling is that it prevents the loss of moisture during the process. The crops most commonly hydrocooled are peaches, sweet corn, and celery. The system requires large-volume usage to operate efficiently.

Vacuum cooling utilizes the rapid evaporation (actually boiling) of water

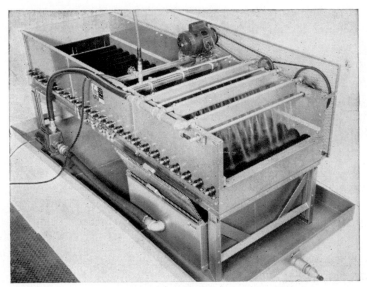

Fig. 11-6.   *A hydrocooler in which the fruit may be brushed as it is cooled.*

[Courtesy Food Machinery and Chemical Corp.]

at reduced pressures to effect cooling. In a reduced atmospheric pressure of 1/165 of the normal 14.7 lb/in², water will boil at 32°F. This rapid evaporation takes up heat directly from the crop. The crop must have a large surface area in proportion to its volume to cool quickly without excessive drying of the surface layers. Lettuce and other leafy crops are ideally suited to vacuum cooling. Sweet corn may be vacuum cooled if it is moistened beforehand. The expensive equipment for vacuum cooling makes it feasible only for large growers or organizations, although portable vacuum coolers are in use.

Air cooling, the basis of most refrigeration systems, operates by the movement of refrigerated air. For rapid cooling special equipment is needed to effect the high air circulation required. Air must be as cold as possible but must not freeze the produce. To prevent drying, produce must be removed from the air blast after it is cooled. Solanaceous fruit crops, beans, and berries can be efficiently air cooled. Leafy crops, however, are not satisfactorily precooled by this method because of desiccation.

TRANSPORTATION

Marketing depends upon short-haul movement and handling by the growers and upon large-scale, long-haul transportation facilities. One of the revolutions in horticultural marketing has been the bulk handling of produce. Great savings are made possible by the synchronization of harvesting and hauling operations to minimize handling. The harvesting container has increased in size to conform to machine power rather than manpower. For example, the bushel field crate is being replaced as the harvesting unit. Automatic potato and onion harvesters unload directly into truckbeds. Hand-picking operations, as in apple and pear, unload into 30-bushel pallet boxes, which may be stored directly or shipped to processing plants where they are automatically unloaded (Fig. 11-7). Industrial management techniques in packing and storage layout have been utilized to facilitate bulk handling. This has made centralized grading, storage, and packing operations particularly efficient. Thus, a

Fig. 11-7. *An automatic pallet unloader in a canning factory.*
[Courtesy Gerber Products Co.]

large portion of the fruit production in the Northwest is handled through the centralized facilities of grower organizations.

Long-haul shipment of horticultural products is handled principally by truck, railroad, and boat. Special railroad cars have been constructed to transport potatoes by bulk directly from the harvesting operation. This has materially decreased bruising, an important cause of trouble in potato storage. Air shipment of certain high-value perishables, such as flowers and strawberries, is increasing. Long-haul transportation contributes storage as well as movement and necessitates specialized packaging, packing arrangements, and environmental controls for the reduction of in-transit spoilage.

STORAGE AND PRESERVATION

The demand for most horticultural products is continuous. Owing to their seasonal production and the rapid deterioration of horticultural products after harvest, preservation and storage are essential in order to insure an extended supply. The principle involved in extending the supply of any horticultural commodity consists in retarding the natural physiological deterioration that occurs inherently in living systems and in preventing decay by microorganisms. The method used depends on the product, its use, and the necessary time interval involved. The imposed limitation is that the product be acceptable after storage. As regards plant parts used for reproduction (seeds, bulbs, whole plants) the overriding factor is viability. For fresh fruits, vegetables and flowers, the maintenance of acceptable quality is dependent upon preserving the natural, living state, although reproductive viability is not necessary. For the extended storage of certain food crops a number of processes have been developed that stop the life functions but maintain edible quality even though the product may be materially altered from its harvest condition. This change in form involved in food processing (for example, tomatoes to ketchup) may result in a new product that has utility far beyond its preservation function.

Storage of Perishables

The storage of perishable plant products in their natural state may be accomplished by means of environmental control. The major principles involved in prolonging the life of a product are to slow down respiration in order to retard microbial activity and to prevent excessive water loss. Respiration and microbial activity may be regulated by the control of temperature and of oxygen and carbon dioxide levels. Water loss may be prevented by controlling humidity.

The storage life of produce depends not only on the storage condition but on the natural rate of respiration. This may depend upon the plant part, the maturity level, and the degree of dormancy. Bruising and decay must be considered because of adverse pathological and physiological effects (increased respiration, discoloration).

Temperature Control

For best results the storage temperature must be held constant, since the optimum temperature range for many products is narrow. For example, most apple varieties keep best and longest when held at a constant temperature of 30–32°F. Temperature increases of as little as 5°F hasten ripening in proportion to the duration of the increase.

The evolution of heat by respiration must be considered as a factor in storage-temperature control. The heat evolved may be calculated from the respiration rate, which increases with temperature (Table 11-2). The respiration rate of produce varies considerably. The respiration rate of spinach is high enough such that, even if stored at 40°F its temperature could in-

Table 11-2. *The relationship between temperature and heat evolved due to increasing respiration.*
[Adapted from Agricultural Handbook No. 66, USDA.]

TEMPERATURE (°F)	HEAT EVOLVED PER TON OF FRUIT PER 24 HOURS (B.T.U.)	
	LEMONS	STRAWBERRIES
32	480–900	2730–3800
40	620–1890	3610–6750
50	1610–3670	7480–13,090
60	2310–4950	15,640–20,280
70	4050–5570	22,510–30,160
80	4530–5490	37,220–64,440

crease to over 100°F in 5 days if no heat escaped. This is a real problem in shipment if adequate ventilation is not provided within the package.

The lower limits of storage temperature must be determined for each item. In general, most products undergo some injury when frozen, although the degree of injury differs with the product. Some commodities are severely damaged by even slight freezing, whereas others less susceptible may undergo a number of successive freezes and thaws without perceptible permanent injury. Storage temperatures are usually kept above the point at which the commodity freezes, although strawberry plants are often stored in the frozen condition.

Injury can occur at temperatures considerably above freezing in the storage of many commodities. This injury is known as *chilling injury* in contrast to *freezing injury.* Chilling injury interferes with the ripening sequence in tomatoes and bananas. Chilling injury affects appearance and may result in actual breakdown.

Oxygen and Carbon Dioxide Level

In addition to being temperature dependent, respiration is also directly affected by the oxygen and carbon dioxide levels. The atmosphere normally contains about 78% nitrogen, 21% oxygen, 0.03% carbon dioxide, and small percentages of several inert gases. Since respiration is an oxidation process, a reduction in the amount of oxygen reduces the respiration rate. Although slight variations of the carbon dioxide levels show little effect on respiration, high concentrations may inhibit or prevent respiration.

The response of respiration to oxygen and carbon dioxide levels is utilized in the storage of fruit. In a gas-tight room filled with freshly harvested "living" apples, the respiration of the fruit will consume the oxygen and at the same time give up equal concentrations of carbon dioxide. When the oxygen is exhausted the carbon dioxide level will reach the original level of oxygen; that is, 21%. At this point anaerobic respiration begins, and alcohol is formed in the fruit. However, if at some intermediate point fresh air is introduced, the amounts of oxygen and carbon dioxide may be kept at compensating levels. The CO_2 concentration may be further decreased by passing storage air through an "air scrubber," usually a sodium hydroxide solution. This may eliminate the detrimental effect of the high concentration of carbon dioxide observed with some apple varieties.

If respiration rate is reduced through the control of oxygen and carbon dioxide levels, then storage temperatures may be kept higher than normally required. In the "controlled-atmosphere" storage of apples, storage temperatures may be maintained at 37–45°F rather than 30–32°, eliminating disorders of certain varieties associated with low temperature.

The principle of modified atmosphere may be utilized by using sealed film liners that are differentially permeable to carbon dioxide and oxygen. This creates a micro environment one bushel in size (Fig. 11-8). Poly-

ethylene film is about five times more permeable to carbon dioxide than to oxygen. When apples are placed in sealed polyethylene film liners, the oxygen in the liner is reduced, and the carbon dioxide is increased as a result of respiration. The final concentration depends on the storage temperature and the permeability of the film. In general, increasing the film thickness decreases permeability, which results in lower oxygen and higher carbon dioxide concentrations. Film density also influences permeability; for example, a film of density 0.928

Fig. 11-8. *Polyethylene film liners create a modified-atmosphere storage having a 1-bushel capacity. Film liners are available for 30-bushel pallet boxes.*
[Courtesy Purdue Univ.]

transmits oxygen and carbon dioxide at one half the rate of film of density 0.910.

Film liners have made possible an improved method of storing some varieties of apple. Golden Delicious shows excellent results, although Grimes Golden does very poorly. The high humidity inside the liner is an asset, but temperature must still be controlled closely.

Organic Volatiles

A number of organic volatiles are produced in ripening fruit. Among these are acids, alcohols, esters, aldehydes, and ketones. The relative proportion of these substances varies with the species and with maturity, and is reflected in differences in aroma and flavor. In general, the influence of these compounds on respiration is slight. An exception to this statement is ethylene, an organic volatile produced by many fruits during the ripening phase. Ethylene is an unsaturated hydrocarbon (C_2H_6), which is nonpoisonous and has a sweetish odor. It is generally produced in greater amount than the other organic volatiles, usually accounting for two-thirds of the total carbon lost in volatile form. In apples it may be present in an amount 10–50 times that of other volatiles.

Ethylene gas has a profound effect on the ripening phase of many fruits, although its exact physiological role is not clear. Ethylene applied externally to immature fruits influences the respiration and ripening but has no effect on ripe fruits. A certain minimum concentration and minimum time of exposure triggers an irreversible stimulation of respiration. Forty ppm is sufficient to stimulate ripening in honeydew melon. A 24-hour exposure is sufficient if temperatures are high enough.

Ethylene gas has been used commercially to effect other processes. For example, oranges may be "degreened" by ethylene gas. This involves destruction of chlorophyll associated with the peel. This effect was first observed from the use of kerosene heaters in shipment. Ethylene gas is not produced naturally by citrus fruits, but it may be produced from a *Penicillium* mold that is often associated with them. Ethylene is used commercially in banana ripening rooms to produce uniform ripening or to accelerate ripening. At high concentrations ethylene has been used to defoliate rose bushes. It is also used incidentally in dehusking walnuts, inhibiting potato sprouting, and inducing flowering in pineapple.

Ethylene gas adversely affects growing plants. Thus, neither plants nor cut flowers can be stored with apples. Scion wood stored in apple storages may show severe damage as a result of bark peeling and splitting.

Humidity Control

The control of humidity is directly related to the keeping quality of many horticultural products. In general, low humidity is likely to result in desiccation and wilting. On the other hand, high humidity favors the development of decay, especially if temperatures are too high. Humidity control has become an important feature of modern storage facilities.

The amount of moisture in the air can be expressed as *absolute* or *relative* humidity. *Absolute humidity* refers to the amount of moisture per cubic foot of air. It is expressed as grains of water (one grain equals 1/7000 pound). However, the amount of water vapor that can be held in a given space decreases with decreasing temperature. *Relative humidity* is the water-vapor content of the air expressed as a percentage of the amount it is capable of absorbing at the same temperature. The ability of a storage to dry out products is related to relative humidity and temperature. This "drying power" of air is proportional to the water vapor deficit below saturation. At high temperatures small differences in the relative humidity represent large differences in drying power. At low temperatures the reverse is true. Relative humidity may be increased in storage by either adding moisture, as by the use of fine mist, or by lowering the temperature. However, in refrigerated storages if the differences in temperature between the refrigeration coils and the room is very large, water will condense as ice on the coils and will effectively lower the humidity. This may be avoided by keeping the coil temperature within 2–4°F of the room temperature. Thus, the refrigerant system must be large enough to maintain proper temperature. Humidity control becomes more difficult as the rate of air circulation increases.

For the storage of leafy vegetables and root crops the optimum relative humidity is 90–95%, but for most fruits and vegetables a relative humidity of 85–90% is desired. On the other hand, seed is best stored at relative humidities of 4–8%.

Ripening

Although most horticultural products ripen on the plant, there are a number of commodities that only ripen to optimum quality when off the plant (for example, bananas, pears, avocados). Pears are picked "green" and although stored at 30–31°F, must be ripened at 60–65°F for optimum quality. The length of the storage period depends on the variety. When ripened on the plant, bananas become mealy, lack flavor, and are subject to splitting and subsequent decay. When green, bananas can be stored at 56°F. They are best ripened at temperatures of about 64°F with 90–95% relative humidity until the fruit is colored. At this point the humidity can be reduced to 85%. Ripening can be hastened by holding initial temperatures at not more than 70°F for the first 18–24 hours and at 66°F thereafter. Prolonged high temperatures increase deterioration and decay.

Tomatoes ripen both on and off of the plant, but since they do not ship or store satisfactorily when ripe, the fruit may be picked in the "mature" green state and ripened artificially. Tomatoes will ripen at temperatures above 55°F (preferably at 60–65°F), although the ultimate quality is often less than that of vine-ripened fruit.

Storage Types

Common storage refers to facilities in which the temperature of the atmosphere is utilized and which are adaptable only where naturally occurring temperatures are low enough. Temperature is regulated by insulation and natural circulation. The most primitive type takes advantage of the reduced temperature fluctuations of the soil. Thus, in the fall, natural trenches or mounds may be used for storing vegetables or plant material. Caves and unheated cellars provide more usable room, but above-ground structures, properly insulated and provided with sufficient ventilation, may be satisfactory in cooler climates. During warm weather, cooling is accomplished by the intake and circulation of the cool night air. Humidity may be kept high with earthen floors. Although common storage is cheap, the lack of precise temperature and humidity control often makes it economically unsound for many horticultural crops.

In *cold storage*, temperature and humidity are regulated by refrigeration. Many of the present structures are converted common storages, but large structures with better insulation and convenience features are now being constructed especially for storage purposes. The basic refrigeration and ventilation system involves forced air circulation. The structure must be sufficiently insulated to conserve power.

Controlled atmosphere storage involves the regulation of oxygen and carbon dioxide levels as well as the regulation of temperature. These storages are divided into rooms that are sealed in order that all gaseous exchange can be controlled. The rooms are closed after fruit is stored and remain sealed until fruit is removed. Temperature, humidity, and gas concentrations must be controlled automatically.

Food Processing

Relatively long term preservation of food may be achieved by physical and chemical processes that sterilize the food or render it incapable of supporting the growth of microorganisms. These processes include drying, canning, freezing, fermentation and pickling, raising the sugar concentration, and irradiation.

Drying

Drying is one of the most ancient methods of food preservation. The process consists in removing water from the tissues, which results in a highly concentrated material of enduring quality (Fig. 11-9). The natural deterioration of the product by respiration is stopped because of enzyme inactivation. The lack of free water protects the dried products from decay by microorganisms.

Horticultural products may be naturally dried (*sun drying*) or artificially dried (*dehydration*). Sun drying is relatively inexpensive in locations where summers are sufficiently warm and dry. Dehydration, although a more expensive process, has a number of advantages: the process can be carried on independently of climate, drying time is reduced, and quality may be improved. The yield of dried fruit from a dehydrator is slightly higher than from sun drying because sugar is not lost as a result of continued respiration and yeast fermentation. Furthermore, sun drying requires considerable land and presents sanitation problems.

Dehydration is typically accomplished by hot-air drying. Air both con-

Fig. 11-9. *Dehydrated snap beans and the reconstituted product.*

[Courtesy Quartermaster Food and Container Inst.]

ducts heat to the food and carries away the liberated moisture vapor. Many types of equipment are used for fruits and vegetables. After being sorted, washed, peeled, and trimmed, fruits to be dehydrated may be treated with sulfur dioxide fumes, which act as a bleaching agent in lighter colored fruits and as a chemical aid to preservation. Safe drying temperatures are near 140°F. The moisture content of fruits is reduced to 15–25%. In the dehydration of vegetables, enzyme systems are first inactivated by heating in boiling water or steam (*blanching*). Many vegetables are also more stable if given a sulfur treatment. For satisfactory storage the moisture content is reduced to 4% because of the lower sugar content of vegetables as compared to fruits.

A greater quantity of fruit is preserved in the world by drying than by any other method of preservation. Among the important dried fruits are raisin, prune, apricot, date, fig, banana, peach, apple, and pear. In contrast, the amount of dried vegetables on the market is relatively small. Potatoes are the most important dried vegetable. Most successful dried vegetable products are used as flavoring ingredients (for example, onion, celery, parsley, and their powders). Some dehydrated vegetables are sold in soup mixes; others are used in remanufacturing canned products.

A recent technological development called *freeze-dehydration* may increase the use of drying preservation. Through the use of a high vacuum, quick frozen food can be dehydrated. The quality of the reconstituted product is greatly improved over ordinary dehydration. The storage period of dried materials is extended at cool temperatures. At high humidities mold growth may occur.

Canning

Canning is a method of preservation that consists in heat sterilizing food in an air tight container. Heating destroys the human pathogenic and food spoilage microorganisms, and inactivates the enzymes that would otherwise decompose the food during storage (Fig. 11-10). The sealed container prevents reinfection of the food after it has been sterilized, and prevents gaseous exchange.

The application of sufficient heat to sterilize food and inactivate enzymes results in alterations in color, flavor, texture, and nutritive value of foods. Quality is therefore the limiting factor in canning. The quality of canned products may be increased by prompt dispatch of high quality raw products through the processing plant and proper attention to processing procedures. This involves a precise relationship between processing time and temperature control. In general, the reduction in processing time, brought about by increasing temperatures, increases the quality of the product. The

Fig. 11-10. *Canning cherries. The fruit is being cooked in stainless steel tanks under a constant spray of syrup and color ingredients. The fruit is artificially colored and flavored to make a new product, Maraschino cherries.*
[Courtesy S&W Corp.]

precise time and temperature required for each commodity is based largely on the natural acidity of the food. There are basically two groups: a *low-acid* group (*p*H 4.5–7.0), which includes most vegetables, and an *acid* group (*p*H below 4.5), which includes fruits, berries, tomatoes, and fermented and pickled foods. Low-acid foods require relatively severe heat treatment, since they can support growth of *Clostridium botulinum*, a bacteria that causes food poisoning. A millionth of a gram of the toxin produced by this organism will kill a person. Thus, all foods capable of sustaining growth of this organism are processed on the assumption that the organism is present and must be destroyed. Since this organism is extremely heat resistant the high temperatures required often reduce quality.

The storage life of the canned product decreases as the temperature increases. For extended storage (over 5 years), storage temperatures should be below 50°F. At storage temperatures above 120°F certain heat-loving bacteria (*thermophiles*), which are not ordinarily all killed by the sterilization process, will continue to grow, causing spoilage. In humid regions, and especially in coastal areas, where salt concentrations are high, storage life is limited by the life of the container, which may be shortened due to corrosion of metal cans or of the metal lids on glass containers.

Freezing

Freezing protects food from spoiling because microorganisms cannot grow at temperatures below 32°F. The freezing process stops most enzymatic activity and is not in itself destructive to nutrients. Some enzymatic activity of certain products must be stopped by heat treatment (blanching) to keep full flavor and color intact during storage.

The rate of freezing is an important factor in the quality of the thawed product. Under slow freezing relatively large ice crystals develop, which fracture the tissue cells; then, upon thawing, the foods lose cellular fluid, resulting in a soft texture. If freezing occurs rapidly many small fine crystals are formed (about one-hundredth the size of those formed during slow freezing). Because these crystals are tightly packed, fewer cells are ruptured.

The basic principle of rapid freezing is the speedy removal of heat from foods by methods utilizing cold air blasts, direct immersion in a cooling medium, contact with refrigerated plates, and liquid air, nitrogen, or carbon dioxide. Freezing in still air is the slowest method. As living plant cells contain much water, most plant foods freeze between 25° and 31°F. The temperature of the food undergoing freezing remains relatively constant at its freezing point until it is almost completely frozen. Quick freezing is described as a process in which the water in food passes through the zone of maximum ice crystal formation in thirty minutes or less. This usually involves refrigerant temperatures of −20° to −40°F.

The success of freezing as a method of preservation depends on the continuous application of the process. Some nutrient loss as well as deterioration in color, texture and flavor may occur during frozen storage, depending on the temperature. Best results are obtained at a temperature of −10°F, although most storages are kept at 0°F. Temperatures must be kept uniform. Frozen foods must be packaged to protect them from dehydration during freezing and subsequent storage. Sublimation of ice occurs in unprotected food, resulting in a freezing disorder called *freezer burn*, which irreversibly alters the color, texture, flavor, and acceptability of frozen foods.

Fermentation and Pickling

Although microorganisms are commonly associated with decay, microbial action may be utilized in food preservation. The action of certain bacteria and yeasts in decomposing carbohydrates is known as *fermentation*. The decomposition may be accomplished by a number of different organisms, the end products varying with the organism. These end products include carbon dioxide and water (complete oxidation), acids (partial oxidation), alcohols (alcoholic fermentation), lactic acid (lactic fermentation), and others. When built up to sufficient concentrations, some of these fermentation products create unfavorable conditions for other organisms, including the original one. They act as preservatives by retarding enzymatic deterioration and impart flavors that are regarded as desirable. Fermentation may be controlled by conditions which favor growth of one type of organism. This is done through the regulation of pH, oxygen availability, and temperature and through the use of salt.

Fermentation is an important processing method for some horticultural crops. The fermentation of the juice of grapes or other fruits produces wines. The further fermentation of alcohol to acetic acid is the basis of vinegar production. When used in combination with salting fermentation is called *pickling*. This term is used especially for cucumbers but applies to other commodities, such as olives and many vegetables (onions, tomatoes, beans, cauliflower, cabbage, watermelon rind). Fermented cabbage (sauerkraut) involves a number of distinct fermentation series. Pickling may be accomplished without the direct use of microorganisms by placing food in organic acids (for example, vinegar, citric acid). For extended storage of pickled products the enzyme systems must be inactivated. This is usually done by canning.

Sugar Concentrates

Acid fruits, concentrated to at least 65% of soluble solids, may be preserved with mild heat treatment if protected from air. The high concentration of sugars, and low water content, preserves the food. Depending on the recipe used to make it, the product may be called jelly (made from fruit juice), jam (made from concentrated fruit), preserves (made from whole fruit), fruit butter (a semisolid, smooth product made from high concentrations of fruit), or marmalade (made from citrus fruit and rind). The making of candied or glacéed fruits involves the slow impregnation of tissues with sugar. Storage of these products at high temperatures reduce quality. Appearance is spoiled by nonenzymatic browning caused by reactions of organic acids with reducing sugars.

Chemical Preservation

In addition to the natural preservatives, such as salt, vinegar, spices, and so on, there are a number of chemicals that, when added to food, prevent or retard deterioration. These are usually used in conjunction with other methods of preservation. Some of the chemical preservatives used in food preparation are inorganic agents, such as sulfur dioxide and chlorine; others are organic agents, such as benzoic acid, certain fatty acids (including sorbic acid), ethylene and propylene oxides (fumigants), and various anti-biotics. Each has a special use in the preservation of fruits and vegetables. For example, sulfur dioxide is widely used in the drying of fruits and vege-tables. Chlorine compounds are used in hydrocooling and in processing. Potassium sorbate and sodium benzoate are useful in preventing growth of yeasts and molds in such fruit products as fresh cider. Ethylene oxide has been used in the sterilization of spices and flavoring compounds.

Chemical preservatives have a legitimate place in food processing. They are not, however, in the best interests of the public if used to deceive or if there is any danger in their use.

Radiation Preservation

Although radiation is not at present used to preserve horticultural foods, there is experimental evidence indicating possible usefulness (Table 11-3).

Fig. 11-11. *Inhibition of potato sprouting with irradiation. A dose of 7500 r permits some varieties of potatoes to be stored at 50°F for two years.*
[Courtesy Quartermaster Food and Container Inst.]

Table 11-3. *Radiation effects on fruits and vegetables.*
[Data courtesy N. R. Desrosier.]

DOSE ABSORBED (RADS)*	CHEMICAL AND PHYSIOLOGICAL ALTERATIONS	POTENTIAL HORTICULTURAL APPLICATIONS
10^1	Interferes with sensitive enzyme systems (Auxin, DNA)	
10^2		Treatment of seed potatoes for storage at room temperature
10^3	Injures many growth processes	Sprout inhibition of potatoes
10^4	Termination of growth processes	Sprout inhibition of bulbs Accelerate pear ripening
10^5	Destruction of 90–99% of micro-organisms	Surface sterilization of fruits and vegetables to increase shelf life. Increase storage of strawberries and soft fruits five fold
10^6	Hydrolysis of carbohydrates; Termination of respiration Destruction of enzymes, proteins, viruses	Sterilize fruits Sterilize vegetables Sweeten peas Tenderize asparagus
10^7	Complete tissue deterioration	

* 1 Rad = 100 ergs/g of moist tissue. The energy of radiation supplied must be below 2.2 mev (million electron volts) to prevent induced radiation. Cobalt 60 emits radiation below this energy level.

Some of the possible uses are the extension of storage life of perishables by low level irradiation (for example, fresh strawberries) and the inhibition of such growth processes as sprouting in potatoes (Fig. 11-11). Radiation also has potential use in certain unit operations of the food industry, such as the aging of wine, sweetening of peas, and tenderizing of asparagus. Before such methods can be adopted, however, conclusive proof must be obtained regarding possible noxious effects and the nutritional adequacy and acceptability in terms of flavor, texture, and appearance of irradiated food. So far there has been no direct evidence of toxic effects, but there are indications of the destruction of vitamins and other nutrients similar to that produced by heat treatment.

DISTRIBUTION

Marketing channels refer to those agencies that handle the commodity in its course from producer to consumer, the actual physical route as well as the route of title. In general, horticultural commodities travel from producer to wholesaler to retailer to consumer. The concentration of goods by whole-

Fig. 11-12. *Principal marketing channels for fruits and vegetables.*
[Adapted from USDA.]

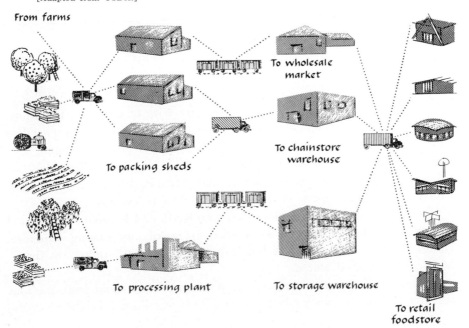

From farms

To wholesale market

To chainstore warehouse

To packing sheds

To processing plant

To storage warehouse

To retail foodstore

MARKETING CHANNELS FOR NURSERY CROPS, 1949

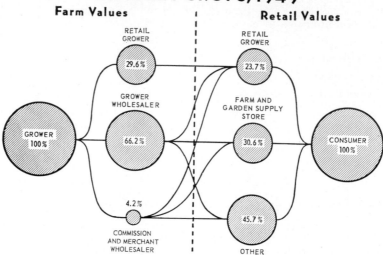

Fig. 11-13. *Marketing channels for nursery crops.*
[Courtesy USDA.]

salers and the corresponding dispersion into retail outlets are diagrammed in Fig. 11-12. Storage and preservation tend to equalize uneven production with relatively constant demand. The exact marketing channels differ with each commodity and change in pattern over the years. Figure 11-13 diagrams the principal marketing channels for nursery crops in 1949.

Wholesaling

The wholesaling of horticultural crops vary with commodity. The transactions involved in wholesaling are performed by *middlemen* who specialize in the sale of goods, moving commodity from producer to consumer.

Merchant middlemen act as representatives for buyers or sellers; they are called *commission men* when they actually handle the product and are called *brokers* when their relation to the product is less direct.

Speculators take title to products but merely attempt to profit from market fluctuations. Their effect on the market is mainly on pricing structure. Potato "futures" are the chief horticultural commodity traded by speculators in the United States.

A number of organizations such as *flower exchanges* and *fruit auctions* are involved in the wholesaling process. They establish procedures at the market and may contribute services such as storage or grading. They operate from fees and assessments paid by those who use the facilities.

Some processors of horticultural products also perform wholesaling functions by acting as their own buying and selling agents. Large processors advertise their own products to build up brand loyalties among consumers. On the other hand, smaller processors distribute their food through food brokers and commission agents. At the present time processors are large customers for other forms of processed food products. For example, canners are becoming large buyers of frozen foods. Thus, the marketing channels involving processors are becoming quite complex.

Retailing and Merchandising

Retailing, the final outlet for horticultural goods, is the most expensive marketing operation. It accounts for almost 50% of the total marketing cost for fruit and vegetables. In recent years great innovations occurring at the retail level have created a revolution in marketing that has been felt throughout the horticultural industry, namely, the almost complete shift to the self-service "supermarket." Mass selling, although adaptable to processed products, was not possible with the older methods of retailing fresh fruits and vegetables. The self-service idea has created the packaging concept, which has emphasized better grading and increased standardization. This has also affected ornamentals. At present, nursery stock and perennial plants are being sold in this manner.

The self-service trend, and the wide variety and form of products available to the consumer has resulted in competition that is influenced greatly by promotion and advertising. Different commodities compete for quantity and quality of space in the supermarket. Moreover, certain commodities from one region compete with the same commodities from other regions. This struggle has encouraged producers to organize on the basis of crop and region to facilitate the marketing of their product. Probably the best example of this kind of organization is the California Fruit Growers Exchange, which markets citrus under the Sunkist label. Smaller groups such as the Michigan Blueberry Association, Idaho Potato Growers, and Ocean Spray, Inc. (a cranberry grower cooperative), are molded after this pattern. The combined resources of many producers make it possible to promote their crop and at the same time guarantee a more standardized product.

The marketing of flowers is an exception to this retailing trend. Because of the large service that is sold with flowers in the form of arrangements, florists have retained their identity as retail units. However, retail florists have organized through the Florist's Telegraph Delivery and the Telegraph Delivery Service.

Integration

The marketing channels may be integrated horizontally or vertically. Vertical integration is the combination of firms under one management that controls two or more steps in the production, handling, processing, distribution, and sales of a commodity. A large canning company such as Dole Pineapple is a good example. Horizontal integration is the combination of firms for the performance of a similar function; a co-op that markets fruits or vegetables from a given area is a good example. Chain stores illustrate both types. They are vertically integrated in that they control their own wholesaling organization. They are not as yet involved in production. Their organization of retail units constitutes horizontal integration. The degree of integration in marketing does not eliminate the main thoroughfares of the marketing channels, although it may streamline them. All the marketing operations, such as grading, storage, or packaging, must still be performed.

Selected References

Desrosier, N. W. *The Technology of Food Preservation.* Avi, Westport Connecticut. 1959. (An excellent treatment of the subject.)

Kohls, R. C. *Marketing of Agricultural Products.* Macmillan, New York. 1960. (An introduction to agricultural marketing.)

Marketing. USDA Yearbook, 1954. (The story of marketing written for the layman.)

United States Standards. USDA Agricultural Marketing Service. (Standards and grades are issued and revised periodically by the USDA.)

PART III

The Industry
of Horticulture

CHAPTER 12

Horticultural Geography

The commercial production of horticultural crops is not evenly distributed over agricultural regions, but tends to be concentrated in limited areas of the world. Horticultural geography deals with the distribution of the industry, and is concerned with the environmental, economic, and social factors that determine its location and development.

CLIMATE

The physical environment of plants involves many factors whose actions and interactions must be considered. Climate, the summation of an area's weather, involves temperature, moisture, and light effects. It largely determines where, when, and what plants will grow. Thus, vegetation is one of the obvious differences in appearance between climatic regions. A map of the earth's climatic regions is also an approximation of natural vegetation. Climate, as the fundamental force in the environment also shapes the soil and to a lesser extent the configuration of the earth's surface.

The pattern of climate is a result of the circulation of the atmosphere. Solar radiation falling more directly on tropical than on polar regions warms the equatorial air, causing it to flow poleward. The resultant pressure produces a return ground flow of cold polar air. The flow pattern does not follow a simple direct line from the pole to the equator but is deflected as a consequence of (1) the easterly rotational spin of the earth, (2) the seasonal effect, (3) the differential cooling of land and water masses, (4) the altitude and the configuration of the land, and (5) the storms and winds resulting from the interactions of cold and warm air masses. Other extraterrestial factors, such as sun spot activity, may affect the weather but are little understood.

MICROCLIMATE

Microclimate refers to the climate of a "small area." The climate at the ground may differ considerably from that at thirty feet above the ground. These climatic differences are of vital importance to man and his agriculture. We become cognizant of the microclimate as we drive in and out of pockets of fog on a chilly morning. The orchardist who loses the crop on the lower half of his trees as a result of frost becomes painfully aware of microclimate.

Whereas *location* refers to a geographic and climatic area, the term *site* implies microclimatic influences within a specific location. The ultimate success of horticultural enterprises depends to a great extent on proper location and site. Microclimatic variations are due to exposure, slope, vegetation, and thermal capacity and conductive characteristics of the soil. These will be discussed along with the climatic elements: temperature, moisture, and light.

CLIMATIC ELEMENTS

Temperature

The temperature at any point on the earth's surface depends on the geographic ordinates of latitude and altitude, season and time of day, and the mediating influence of microclimate. The major factor that determines temperature is the amount of solar radiation received, which depends upon both the intensity and the duration of radiation. The more vertical the sun's rays, the less atmosphere they must penetrate. In addition, vertical rays provide a greater concentration of energy per unit area than do the oblique rays that reach the poles. The duration of the solar radiation is affected both by the day length, which imposes an absolute limit on the amount of solar energy received, and on the variable effects of cloud cover. Furthermore, there is a decrease in temperature with an increase in elevation. This averages 3.6°F for every 1000 ft of elevation, approximately 1000 times the rate of temperature change in latitude. The reason for this is that much of the atmospheric thermal energy is received directly from the earth's surface and only indirectly from the sun. In addition, the lower tropospheric air contains more water vapor and dust and is a more efficient absorber of terrestrial radiation, which explains the snow-capped mountains on the equator, such as the famous Mt. Kilimanjaro.

The variation in temperature reported at the earth's surface is enormous and ranges over 200°F, from a record −96°F at Verkhoyansk, Siberia to

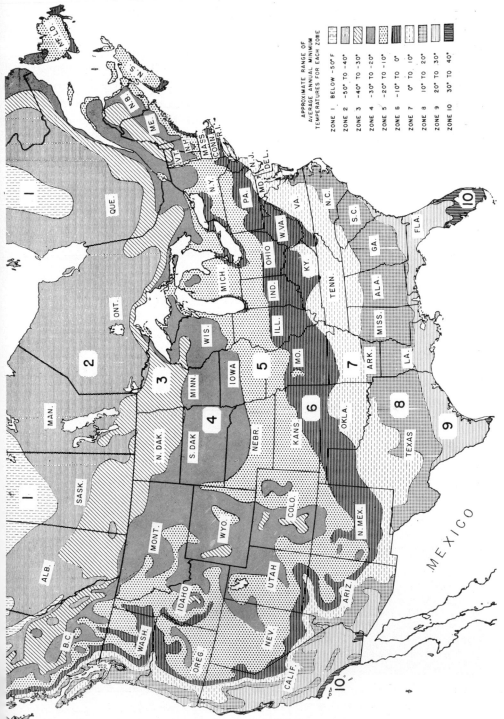

Fig. 12-1. *The zones of plant hardiness in the United States and Canada.*
[From USDA Misc. Publ. 814.]

136°F at Azizia, Libya. The mean annual temperatures range from an estimated −22°F at the South Pole (elevation 8000 ft) to a record 86°F at Massawa, Eritrea, Africa. In annual crops the important temperature values are the mean and extreme temperatures as well as the length of the "growing season." Perennial plants are affected by the temperature values during the whole year. Both seasonal variation and average temperature must be considered in relation to plant growth. Peaches, for example, require a long growing season and warm summer temperatures. Their northern distribution is limited by their degree of hardiness; temperatures below −12°F cause flower bud injury. Their southern distribution is limited by their chilling requirements. A map of the expected minimum temperatures of the horticulturally important areas of the continental United States and Canada is presented in Fig. 12-1.

Frost

Frost is a thin layer of ice crystals deposited on soil and plant surfaces as a result of freezing temperatures. Two types of weather conditions produce freezing temperatures: (1) rapid radiational cooling, which results in a *radiational frost*, and (2) the introduction of a cold air mass with a temperature below 32°F, which produces an *air mass freeze*. Frost is common under conditions of clear calm skies; freeze, on the other hand, may occur

Fig. 12-2. *Frost is a serious hazard in the orchard during the bloom period.*
[Photograph by J. C. Allen & Son.]

with an overcast sky, and usually involves considerable wind. Both frost and freeze involve temperatures at or below the freezing point. Because of its local nature, frost may occur when the so-called official temperature (taken relatively nearby, and usually at a height of six feet) is above freezing.

The earth radiates energy, as do all bodies. At night the earth receives no solar radiation, thus there is a net loss of radiation. Frost occurs when the loss of heat from the ground permits the temperature to drop to or below the freezing point.

Frost is of vital horticultural concern. It defines the season for annual crops in the middle latitudes and is potentially extremely destructive to perennial fruit crops, which flower in the early spring. The danger of frost is usually not due to actual tree damage but to injury of temperature-sensitive flower parts (Fig. 12-2). The year's crop is thus at the mercy of spring frost.

Frost Conditions

Conditions favorable for radiational frost are those that are conducive to rapid and prolonged surface cooling. For example, the introduction of low-temperature polar air followed by clear, dry, calm nights will facilitate upward radiation. The presence of cloudy, humid air causes reradiation back to the earth and thus prevents frost conditions. The main effect of fogging in the control of frost is the creation of an artificial reradiating surface, although there is some release of heat as the fog droplets cool. Strong evaporation after rainfall, especially on plant cover with a large surface area, will

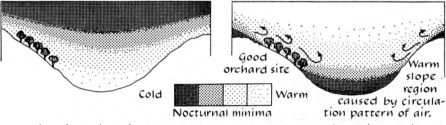

Good orchard site

Warm slope region caused by circulation pattern of air.

Cold Warm

Nocturnal minima

Except in an inversion, air temperature decreases with height. (Darker tones indicate cooler air.)

A temperature inversion sets in when cool air is trapped under warm layer. The normal temperature gradient is reversed in the inversion layer.

Fig. 12-3. *Schematic representation of the origin of a thermal belt as a result of a temperature inversion on a hillside.*

[Adapted from Geiger, *Climate Near the Ground,* Harvard Univ. Press, Cambridge, Mass., 1957.]

increase cooling. The absence of wind leaves the coldest air undisturbed and next to the ground.

Frost conditions are usually quite variable, since local conditions modify radiation. Site is an important factor in frost. For example, slopes are protected by "air drainage." Since cold air is denser than warm air, it moves downhill. The circulation pattern of the displaced warm air produces a relatively warm area, or *thermal belt,* on the slope itself. It is this microclimatic factor that makes slopes good sites for fruit plantings. Low areas, on the other hand, collect cold air and become "frost pockets." This results in a phenomenon referred to as *temperature inversion,* in which air temperatures increase with altitude (Fig. 12-3). Artificial wind machines prevent frost damage by mixing in the upper warmer air (Fig. 12-4).

Fig. 12-4. *Wind machines protect citrus from frost by mixing the warmer upper air that exists under conditions of temperature inversion.*

[Courtesy Food Machinery and Chemical Corp.]

The frost protection afforded by large bodies of water is due to the high specific heat of water as compared to that of the land; water absorbs and gives up heat slowly. Solar radiation penetrates water more deeply than land, and the continuous internal movement of water results in heat distribution throughout the water mass. Thus, large bodies of water become heat reservoirs in the fall, and cold reservoirs in the spring. Because of their great heat capacity, large bodies of water moderate temperatures. In the winter and early spring the influence of water keeps temperatures moderately low and prevents premature plant growth. In the late spring it may provide enough heat to prevent frost. Similarly, in the fall there is a warming influence that tends to delay the advent of frost conditions. This temperature lag is felt mainly along the windward side of large bodies of water.

Many factors affect frost. Anything that prevents the accumulation of radiation during the day will increase frost. For example, vegetation that shades the soil will reduce the amount of heat stored in the day. Thus, a sodded or mulched area is more liable to become frosted than one under "clean cultivation." The necessity for controlling frost is one of the main reasons why peaches are not grown under permanent sod. The exposure of the slope also affects the amount of radiation received. In the Northern hemisphere, southerly slopes receive considerably more radiation than northerly slopes.

Heat from the lower layers of the earth moves up by conduction. Consequently, the conductivity of the soil will affect frost at the surface. Frost on muck is a serious hazard because organic soils tend to be poor conductors of heat as compared to mineral soils. More important than soil type in the occurrence of frost is the amount of soil moisture. By replacing air (a poor conductor) with water (a better conductor) the danger of frost can be reduced. Thus, frost damage may be prevented in muck areas by flooding.

The *white frost* commonly seen in the morning results from frozen dew (Fig. 12-5). Its occurrence depends on the *dewpoint*—the temperature at which relative humidity reaches 100%. When the air temperature is below the dewpoint but above 32°F, water vapor condenses in the form of dew. White frost occurs when the air temperature is below the dewpoint and below 32°F. If the humidity is low, frost damage may occur when the air temperature is below 32° F but above the dewpoint. This is known as a *black frost* because the only visible indication of it comes when the vegetation turns dark due to cold injury.

The change in state from water to ice results in the release of energy, the *heat of fusion*. Consequently, if temperatures do not get too low, the freezing of water or the occurrence of a white frost actually protects vegetation from lower temperatures. This phenomenon is

Fig. 12-5. *Frost is frozen dew. Hoarfrost results when sublimation occurs over several hours, leaving heavy ice crystal deposits in the form of scales, needles, feathers, and fans.*

[Photograph by J. C. Allen & Son.]

exploited in the use of sprinkler irrigation as a method of frost protection. The ice forming on the plant releases heat and acts as a protective buffer against cold injury!

The techniques that have been discussed to prevent frost involve either the cutting down of heat loss through radiation or the addition of heat. Radiation loss is prevented by such practices as fogging, hot caps, or the use of cold frames. Heat may be obtained from the earth by improving the conduction characteristics of the soil, or it may be obtained from the air by disturbing the temperature inversion. Heat may be added directly from smudge pots or indirectly by sprinkler irrigation or through techniques that increase the daytime absorption of insolation.

Moisture

Moisture, with respect to climate, refers to both precipitation (rain and snow) and atmospheric humidity. Rainfall is directly related to the circulation pattern of the atmosphere. It results from the cooling of warm humid air forced upward by the convergence of air currents. The record total precipitation varies on the earth's surface from 1 to 900 in./year. Owing to topographical variation, a marked difference in rainfall may occur between points relatively close together. This may result in the close proximity of desert and rain forest. A map of average annual precipitation is presented in Fig. 12-6.

Of greater agricultural significance than average precipitation is the *effective precipitation*, the water that is not lost by runoff or evaporation and which is consequently available to plants. The percentage of precipitation that is "effective" is higher where temperatures are low. Thus, cool areas require less rain for plants than do warm areas. The natural vegetation of an area is the most satisfactory measure of effective precipitation.

The extremes of precipitation result in drought and flood. Drought may be predictable in some areas on a seasonal basis; in others, it appears to reoccur over a longer cycle. Unless irrigation is practical, drought areas effectively restrict horticultural crop production. Although methods exist for the efficient utilization of existing water, there is no substitute for sufficient water in intensive crop production. Horticultural crops require a plentiful supply of water as compared to grain or grassland farming. Flood, on the other hand, is equally injurious (Fig. 12-7). Except for such water-loving plants as cranberries, which are grown in boggy areas, an excess of water results in extensive damage. Much of this is due to root damage from lack of soil oxygen. Excessive moisture also results in disease problems, since high humidity favors the growth of many fungi. Many crops (tomato, peach, apple, cherry) show abnormal splitting and cracking of the fruit as a consequence of excess moisture at periods of fruit ripening. Flooding

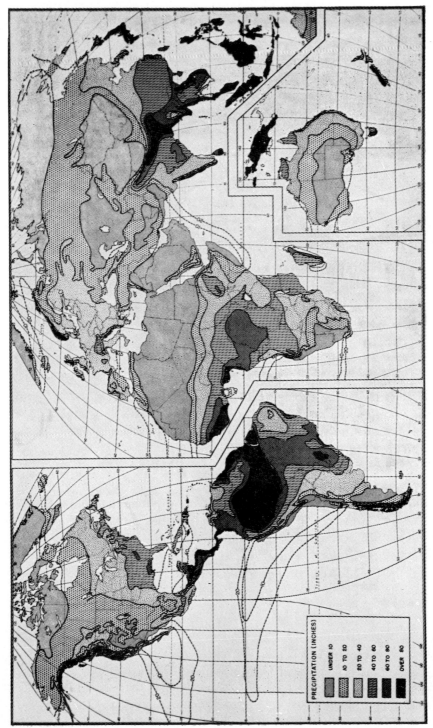

Fig. 12-6. *World's average annual precipitation.* [Courtesy USDA.]

PRECIPITATION (INCHES)

UNDER 10
10 TO 20
20 TO 40
40 TO 60
60 TO 80
OVER 80

Fig. 12-7. *Spring flooding and erosion.* In a dry year farmers complain of starvation; in wet years farmers starve—*folk proverb.*
[Courtesy J. C. Allen & Son.]

can be overcome by proper drainage in some locations. Tiling and proper soil management do much to alleviate the problem.

Light

Quantity of light is an important climate feature and is a significant part of the plant environment. Day length is the most obvious difference between climates. In the tropics the day is close to twelve hours long throughout the year. At the polar regions the summer day length goes up to 24 hours. Consequently, long-day plants cannot reproduce sexually in the tropics. Thus, the world distribution of plant species is greatly determined by their photoperiodic response. It is useless to attempt to grow long-day plants for flowers or fruit in the tropics, for they will remain vegetative indefinitely. In addition to daylength the quantity of light is affected by atmospheric conditions such as the number of sunny versus cloudy days during the growth season. The amount of sunlight greatly affects quality in many crops (for example, grapes, apples).

SOIL AND CLIMATE

The chemical, physical, and biological changes that determine the soil profile are all affected by long-term climatic conditions. The major difference between soils is a result of climate operating through soil-forming processes and vegetation. Thus, climate directly affects soil formation through weathering processes and indirectly through vegetation.

The distribution of the major soil groups can be interpreted through broad climatic types, based on weathering and vegetation. The major zonal soil types, grouped on a climatic basis, are (1) the strongly leached, red soils supporting tropical rain forests in areas of hot, humid climate, (2) the unleached light-colored soils in areas of hot desert climate, (3) the dark-colored soils supporting native tall grasses in areas of subhumid, temperate climate, and (4) the acid, light-colored soils supporting coniferous forests in areas of cool, moist climate. Unfortunately, the climates best suited for plant growth do not always coincide with the areas of naturally fertile soils.

CROP ECOLOGY

Ecology is the study of life forms in relation to their environment. Plant ecology deals largely with natural plant communities, and is concerned with the causes responsible for the course and pattern of plant development, succession, and distribution. It is concerned with the relationship between climate, soil, and biological interaction.

By definition, horticulture deals with cultivated plants. However, the crop plant community is subject to many of the same ecological responses as is the natural plant community. These plant responses determine to a great extent the ability of a region to successfully support a particular crop and define the specific problems of land use and crop management.

Climatic environment, rather than geography in its topographical sense, determines the course of plant development. It is the extremes of temperature (Table 12-1), rainfall, and light rather than their yearly means that determine the status and define the limitations of agriculture. The inappropriate utilization of agriculture in areas of marginal climate results in more "poor years" than "good years." Unfortunately, the occurrence of unusual periods of "good" weather often results in overextension of an unsuited agriculture, with disastrous consequences when the more normal pattern resumes.

The effect of climate upon quality and appearance plays an important role in the location of the horticultural industry. For example, high light intensity favors maximum development of red color in apple fruits. The prominence of the central valleys of Washington State as an apple-producing area is due to their dry climate, which is brought about by a favorable

Table 12-1. *Classification of common fruit crops by temperature requirements.* [*]

TROPICAL	SUBTROPICAL	TEMPERATE	
		MILD WINTER	SEVERE WINTER
coconut			
banana			
cacao			
mango			
pineapple			
papaya			
coffee			
date			
fig			
avocado			
	citrus		
	olive		
	pomegranate		
		almond	
		blackberry	
		grape (European)	
		persimmon (Japanese)	
		quince	
		peach	
		cherry	
		apricot (blossoms tender)	
		strawberry ⎱ (very hardy with	
		blueberry ⎰ snow cover)	
		raspberry	
		cranberry	
			pear
			plum
			grape (American)
			currant
			apple

LOW-TEMPERATURE SENSITIVE	SLIGHTLY FROST TOLERANT	TENDER	WINTER-HARDY
NONCOLD REQUIRING		COLD REQUIRING	

[*] Variation in tolerance depends to a large extent on species, variety, plant part, and stage of growth.

combination of altitude and mountain ranges that results in bright, cloudless summers.

CLIMATIC REGIONS

There are a variety of ways of classifying climatic regions. We are all familiar with the climatic classification by temperature into tropical, temperate, and polar zones. A more useful classification takes into account both temperature and moisture to include seasonal patterns. In this regard the natural vegetation may be used as a meteorological instrument to integrate the climatic elements. Using precipitation effectiveness* and temperature efficiency,† Thornthwaite has divided climate into regions associated with a characteristic vegetation (for example, desert, steppe, grassland, forest, rainforest) (Fig. 12-8).

A widely used method of classifying climates is the Köppen system, which is based on annual and monthly means of temperature and precipitation. The temperature and precipitation boundary lines are selected by natural vegetation and crop responses rather than by atmospheric circulation patterns (Fig. 12-9). The classification discussed here is derived from Trewartha's modification of the Köppen classification.

Tropical Rainy

The tropical rainy region lies in an irregular belt 20–40° wide that straddles the equator. Its most typical feature is the absence of winter. The difference between average day and night temperature exceeds the annual temperature range. The temperature boundaries of this region have been arbitrarily placed at the average minimum monthly temperature of 64°F. This coincides with the poleward limit of plants requiring continuing high temperature, as various tropical palms. Although rainfall is abundant (rarely less than 30 in. per year), its distribution serves to produce two subclimatic types. One type has ample rainfall throughout the year, and although there is a seasonal difference, no less than $2\frac{1}{2}$ in. of rain falls in any month. The other subclimate is distinguished by distinct wet and dry seasons.

* Precipitation effectiveness is the summation of monthly precipitation divided by evaporation.
† Temperature efficiency is the summation of monthly mean temperature minus 32°F divided by 4.

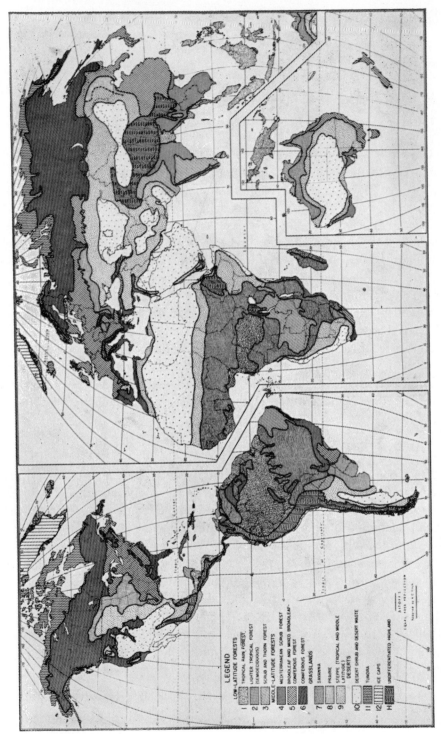

Fig. 12-8. *World's natural vegetation.* [Courtesy USDA.]

LEGEND

LOW-LATITUDE FORESTS
1 TROPICAL RAIN FOREST
2 LIGHTER TROPICAL FOREST (SEMIDECIDUOUS)
3 SCRUB AND THORN FOREST

MIDDLE-LATITUDE FORESTS
4 MEDITERRANEAN SCRUB FOREST
5 BROADLEAF AND MIXED BROADLEAF-CONIFEROUS FOREST
6 CONIFEROUS FOREST

GRASSLANDS
7 SAVANNA
8 PRAIRIE
9 STEPPE (TROPICAL AND MIDDLE LATITUDE)

DESERTS
10 DESERT SHRUB AND DESERT WASTE

11 TUNDRA
12 ICE CAPS
H UNDIFFERENTIATED HIGHLANDS

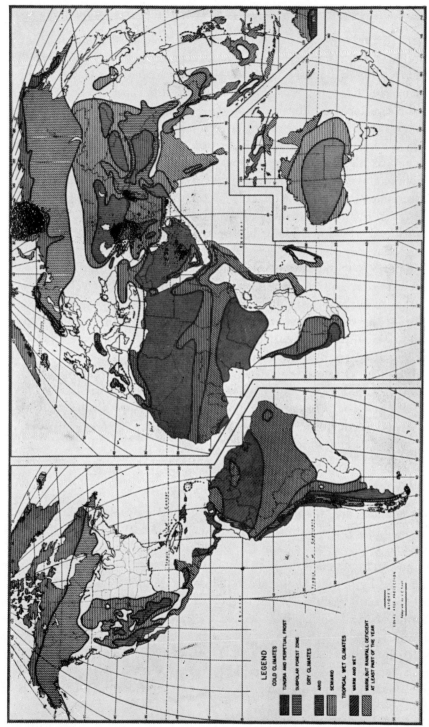

Fig. 12-9. *The world's climates.* [Courtesy USDA.]

Tropical soils are notoriously unproductive under continual cultivation. The rapid destruction of organic matter results in a soil structure that deteriorates under intensive crop use. The low native fertility, a result of constant leaching, makes them responsive to fertilizer application.

In the continually rainy areas of the tropics the natural vegetation is lush and varied. No other area can compare with its diversity of plant species. The natural vegetation is broadleaf and evergreen and has no dormancy requirement. In the seasonally wet and dry areas of the tropics the dominant vegetation is coarse grass, which goes dormant under dry periods; hence the name *savanna climate*. The number of trees is related to the duration of the wet season.

The chief horticultural plants of the tropics grow continuously and have no dormancy requirement. As a group they are quite sensitive to any extended periods without moisture. Thus, tropical horticulture is generally confined to the continually wet areas. The wet-dry tropical climate is utilized agriculturally principally as grazing land unless irrigation is available during the dry season. Although many tropical horticultural crops are known principally in their native areas (mango, yam (*Dioscorea*), papaya), many important crops of world-wide significance must be grown in tropical or subtropical climates exclusively. The separation of plant agriculture into horticulture and agronomy is less meaningful in the tropics. Although sugar and rice are considered as agronomic crops, the distinction of such crops as palms (for oils), jute and rubber as horticultural is justifiable because of their intensive culture.

Dry

Dry climates are those in which the potential evaporation through soil-surface and vegetative transpiration exceeds annual rainfall; rainfall is scarce and unpredictable; there is often a water deficiency. As evaporation and transpiration increases with temperature, the boundaries of dry climates are affected by both rainfall and temperature. The dry climates are roughly distributed on either side of the tropical rainy climates.

The dry climates are subdivided on the basis of moisture and temperature into *arid* (*desert*) and *semiarid* (*steppe*). Steppe is a transitional zone between humid and desert climates. These dry climates may also be subdivided into tropical and subtropical regions on the basis of a coldest temperature of 32°F. Thus, there are four general regions—hot and cold desert, hot and cold steppe.

Although natural vegetation is meager, the abundance of areas with dry climates (26% of the earth's surface) makes it a widespread agricultural resource. The steppe areas support low-growing, shallow-rooted grasses, thus their chief agricultural use is grazing.

Since the soils of dry climate are subject to minimum leaching, they are high in nutrients. Although the desert soils tend to be sandy and unsuitable for agriculture, the steppe soils are superior. The grass roots provide con siderable organic matter. Here, irrigation provides an abundant agriculture, transforming the land into an ideal horticultural area. The irrigated lands of our Southwest provide a splendid example of this. There, subtropical horticultural crops such as melons, figs, and citrus are produced, and temperate-climate vegetables such as carrots and lettuce are grown in the cooler season. The agriculture of this area, provided with water, resembles the oasis agriculture of naturally moist areas (deltas, flood plains, and alluvial fans) within dry climates.

Humid Temperate

The climate of the middle latitudes is characterized by a distinct seasonal rhythm; winter, spring, summer, and autumn have real meaning. The chief factor influencing plant dormancy is low temperature, rather than drought. The humid, temperate climates are subdivided into mild-wintered (mesothermal) and severe-wintered (microthermal). This distinction is based on an average coldest month temperature of 32°F. This can be empirically found on the basis of a durable winter snow cover.

Mild Winter

The mild-wintered temperate zones are found in the lower latitudes and in marine locations on the westerly side of continents. Within the mild-wintered temperate zone there are three important climatic types: (1) *Mediterranean*, (2) *humid subtropical*, and (3) *marine*.

MEDITERRANEAN CLIMATE. The Mediterranean climate has a subtropical, dry-summer climate. It represents a most important "horticultural region." It is characterized by dry, warm to hot summers and mild winters with adequate rainfall. The high proportion of fog provides some summer moisture. The inland areas have hotter summers than the coastal areas. Because of its delightfully mild winters, bright sunny weather, and strong horticultural associations, it is one of the best known climates. The Mediterranean region, central and coastal California, central Chile, the southern tip of South Africa, and parts of southern Australia make up less than 2%

of the land. However, these climates provide a large portion of the world's horticultural products, especially subtropical fruits (citrus, figs, dates, grapes, olives).

The Mediterranean soils are variable. The natural vegetation consists of mixed trees and stunted woody shrubs. Typical leaves are thick and glossy, designed to prevent excessive transpiration. The growing season lasts practically the whole year. However, during the winter months frosts do occur. These may be extremely dangerous to horticultural crops that are marginal for that area, such as out-of-season vegetables and citrus. Although rainfall is fairly moderate (15–20 in.), the effective precipitation is high, since the bulk of the rain comes in the cool winter, making much of it available for plant growth. Summers are distinctly dry. This has resulted in a double dormancy in native vegetation: one due to low winter tempera-tures; the other, to summer droughts. The dry heat of the summer is ideal for fruit drying. It is here that this method of fruit preservation originated, and this area still provides dried figs, dates, plums (prunes), and grapes (raisins).

Flower seed production is an important part of the horticultural industry of this part of California. Under irrigation an extensive fruit and vegetable canning industry has developed. Cool season crops are shipped almost ex-clusively from California during the winter months. For example, the Im-perial Valley provides most of the United States' winter supply of lettuce.

HUMID SUBTROPICAL. The humid subtropical climates are typically on the eastern side of continents (for example, the cotton belt of the United States). The precipitation is usually abundant (30–65 in.) and well dis-tributed over the entire year. The summers are hot and muggy. Although winters are generally mild, freezing temperatures occasionally occur. There is, however, considerable variation; in the United States the South ex-periences more severe winters than do the humid, subtropical areas of South America, Australia, or China.

The natural vegetation includes forest (mixed conifers and broad leaf, both deciduous and evergreen) and grassland, depending on precipitation. The soils are deep, owing to continuing weathering, but are typically low in fertility as a result of constant leaching. The grassland soils are more productive.

The humid subtropics are rich vegetable-producing lands. For example, the long growing season and high summer temperatures of the south-eastern United States allow such crops as sweet potatoes, dried beans, and melons to be grown. The relatively mild spring and fall allow two crops of such garden vegetables as spinach, mustard greens, radishes and snap beans. Tomatoes, peppers, and celery are grown as spring crops. A large industry based on the growing of vegetables and flower transplants for shipment to Northern states is located in this area. Only those fruit crops having a low winter chilling requirement can be grown. Thus this area is more important for growing peaches than it is for apples. In sites where spring frost hazards are minimal, peaches are a particularly important crop. This is particularly true of the gulf states. Strawberries and blueberries, which have a wide range of adaptation, are common horticultural crops. The nursery industry is expanding along the northern edge of this area.

MARINE. Marine climates are found on the western side of middle latitude continents and extend into the high latitudes owing to the ocean's influence. The extent to which it penetrates depends on topographical features. In North and South America and in Scandinavia the marine climates are narrow owing to the parallel range of mountains along the coast. In Western Europe extensive lowlands serve to carry the ocean's influence inland.

In contrast to Mediterranean and humid subtropical climates, the marine summers are cool. The warmest months typically average 65–70°F. Winters are exceptionally mild considering the latitude, the average cold month temperature being above freezing. The growing season is long. Frosts are frequent, however, and winter is generally long enough to produce a dormant season.

There is adequate rainfall in all seasons, although precipitation varies greatly, from over 100 in. in the Pacific Northwest to 20–30 in. in parts of Western Europe, which is surprising considering the amount of rainy weather. Sunshine is limited; fog and mist are abundant. About half the days per year are cloudy.

The natural vegetation is forest, deciduous in Europe and coniferous in the Pacific Northwest. The soils are variable though generally deep. The gray forest soils of this area have excellent structure, and although the natural fertility is moderate, it is higher than in other forest soils. In addition, there are areas of organic soils (peat-bogs), areas of thin, stony glacially deposited soils (Scandinavia), and sandy coastal plains (Germany and Denmark).

Horticulture in marine climates is not the predominant agriculture but it is extensive. Apples and pears are well suited to this area, as is the ubiquitous strawberry. Cool season vegetables, peas, lettuce, and crucifers do especially well. There is not enough heat, however, for outdoor plant-ings of some crops, such as melons. For example, cucumbers and grapes are commonly grown under glass in Holland, Belgium, and England. The long spring extends the flowering season. Bulbous flowers (tulips, daffodils, hyacinth) grow well. As a result this area is a large bulb-producing area and an important "garden country."

Severe Winter

The severe-wintered climates of the humid temperate regions are charac-terized by a distinct though shorter summer than the mild-wintered climates. This climate, which is located in the interior and poleward in North America and Eurasia, is dominated by large land masses. It is bounded in the north by *polar* climates. The main climatic distinction within this climate is temperature. The climate is divided into areas of warm summers (U.S. corn belt), cool summer (Great Lakes area, Western and Central Russia), and subarctic (North Canada, Alaska, Siberia). The insulation provided by permanent deep snow cover serves to prevent excessively low soil tempera-tures (although winter air temperatures become extremely low in the higher latitudes and greatly vary). Precipitation is generally greater in the sum-mer owing to the influx of warm, humid air from the south, as compared to the winters, which are influenced by cold polar air. This is significant in regards to plant growth. Although yearly precipitation is moderate, ample moisture is usually available during the growing season. Under this relatively high effective precipitation the cool- and warm-summered climates support an abundant agriculture.

The natural vegetation consists of forests (in which conifers predominate) at the northernmost margins, and tall-grass prairies in the subhumid in-teriors. The gray-brown deciduous forest soils are good, but the highly acid *podzol* soils of the cooler, more northerly coniferous forests are poor. The prairie soils are excellent in structure and in fertility and make these lands particularly suitable for corn and wheat despite the somewhat lower and less reliable rainfall. Although these prairie soils are limited in extent, they make up the finest agricultural lands in North America. Glaciation has molded many of the topographical features in this climate (for example, the rocky New England hills).

The warm-summered climates are ideal for such horticultural crops as melons and tomatoes, which require high temperatures. The cool-summered climate more typically supports extensive plantings of hardy fruits, such as apples and pears, although cherries and peaches can be produced in protected sites as are found in the Great Lakes area. This climate is known for cool-season vegetables, such as white potatoes and peas. Sweet corn is an important canning crop in the northern part of the United States, where cool summer temperatures tend to prolong the period of good quality for harvesting. The nursery industry has taken advantage of the deep prairie soils; bulb crops, strawberry plants, and nursery shrubs are grown extensively in this region. For example, Iowa, located in the heart of the corn belt, is an important center for the mail order nursery business specializing in deciduous plants. These ship well when in full dormancy.

The subarctic regions of the severe-wintered, temperate climates support only a limited horticulture. The long summer days compensate for the cool temperatures and lower light intensity. Here, summer frosts become a serious hazard. The frost-free season may last only 50–75 days. The important horticultural crops are root crops (potatoes, turnips, beets, carrots, parsnips) and crucifers (cabbage, cauliflower). As a result of breeding programs in Alaska some adapted strawberry varieties are now available.

The polar climates are found in the high latitudes and at high altitudes. The boundary is set by a mean annual temperature of 32°F, with the average warmest monthly temperature being 50°F. There is no horticultural activity in this climate.

ECONOMIC FACTORS

In addition to such environmental factors as climate and soil a number of economic considerations strongly affect the complexion of the horticultural industry. These include land costs, availability of labor, distance to market, and transportation facilities. The general level of the economy is also an important factor. A highly developed industrial economy is able to afford an abundance of horticultural products. In the United States an increase in the standard of living results in an increase in the consumption of fresh fruits and leafy vegetables. In addition, the perishable nature of many horticultural crops necessitates advanced technology for movement, storage, and processing. In an agricultural society the actual production of horticultural products for local consumption is diversified and is largely based upon home grown products. As a result the total variety and value of horticultural products decreases.

Horticultural crops differ as to their adaptability. In general, long-season crops, biennials, and perennials must be restricted to areas where weather remains favorable for extended periods of time; many months are required for long-season annuals, and many years are required for tree fruit production. This greatly restricts their location, especially in a highly competitive market. On the other hand, annual crops of comparatively short season often appear to have a wider range of adaptation. This is also true for biennial plants (carrots, onions, cabbage) that are grown as annual crops. Actually it is their adaptability as a crop that is large. They may produce a marketable crop in a short time. Seed may be produced elsewhere under more favorable conditions.

The wide adaptability of annual horticultural crops makes them responsive to local economic advantages. Increased quality and local market preference account for some of this. With technological advances in the long-distance movement of horticultural crops these local advantages decrease in importance. The trend is for annual crop production to be situated in optimum climatic locations, especially those favorable to off-season production. Nevertheless, the great cities are still ringed by relatively small market gardens that grow fresh produce for local consumption. However, their number is decreasing. With the increase in processing and the increase in centralization of the chain stores' marketing operations, the demand for the products of local growers has dwindled to an insignificant level in many areas.

Land Costs

Land cost includes not only land prices but local taxes as well. Horticultural crop production is often intensive enough to justify the use of expensive agricultural land but cannot long survive in urban areas. The horticultural enterprises originating on the outskirts of large cities may be literally overrun by urban expansion. High urban taxes soon make any agricultural operation unprofitable. Although "selling out" may result in an immediate profit to individual land owners, the horticultural industry is destroyed, and valuable agricultural land is often lost forever. Potato farming in Long Island, New York, and the citrus industry around Los Angeles, California are examples of this loss.

Labor Supply

Many horticultural operations require at some point—usually during harvesting—an abundant supply of labor. Because of the extensive requirement of hand work in the past, the horticultural industries have been dependent upon a plentiful supply of low-cost labor. The relative compactness of horticultural areas has set up routes utilized by migrant workers who move from crop to crop as the season progresses. In some areas, "nationals" are brought in from other countries. The organization of this labor, or Federal and State legislation involving minimum wages and standards, will increase the cost of production. This need for transient labor has created great problems and has encouraged the automation of such operations as transplanting, weed control, and harvesting. Nevertheless, many operations will, in the near future, depend upon large seasonal labor resources.

The recent move of the greenhouse industry away from large centers of population to more rural locations is due to labor costs as well as to taxation. Cheap labor, however, is not a dependable resource. The solution to extensive labor requirements undoubtedly lies in labor-saving devices and technological innovations.

Market Advantage

Historically, the commercial horticultural industry originated close to the large centers of population. The perishable nature of most horticultural products gave a distinct advantage to market proximity by virtue of a monopoly on quality. As transportation and storage facilities have improved, this advantage has steadily diminished. Rapid, refrigerated transportation facilities operating over great distances have equalized the quality differential. The integration of railroad and motor truck systems have further increased transportation efficiency. Recent advances in the air shipment of high-priced horticultural products such as flowers and strawberries have reduced the advantages of market proximity to growers of these highly perishable commodities.

Transportation costs have remained relatively constant over the years and do not explain the decrease in the industry's dependence on market proximity. Other factors that determine the distribution pattern are market price, season of shipment and cost of production. Transportation costs, however, are still a significant cost factor (Table 12-2). However, when the reduced cost of production of a different region offsets excessive transportation costs, the industry is bound to move.

One of the chief factors in market advantage has been out-of-season production. Thus, early strawberry production in Louisiana and winter production of vegetables in warmer southern and western climates have created an important horticultural industry, notwithstanding poor soils and frost dangers.

The consolidation of marketing operations by large food chains, which

Table 12-2. *Transportation costs for Delicious apples, 1955–1957.*

[Data from *Agricultural Marketing Service*, USDA.]

ORIGIN	CITY MARKETED	RETAIL PRICE PER LB (CENTS)	TRANS-PORTATION COST PER LB (CENTS)	TRANS-PORTATION COST IN PERCENT OF RETAIL PRICE
Washington	Los Angles, Calif.	20.5	1.4	7
Washington	Chicago, Ill.	20.6	2.3	11
Washington	New York, N.Y.	20.0	2.8	14
Hudson Valley, N.Y.	New York, N.Y.	15.7	0.5	3

deal directly with growers, favors larger operators located in favored climatic areas of production. For example, less than 200 buying concerns handle 60% of the nation's fruit. The trend is toward the centralization of the industry in response to climatic factors.

Cultural Factors

In addition to environmental and economic factors, there are a number of cultural factors that have played a significant role in the distribution of the horticultural industry. In many cases the development of the industry in the United States can be traced along with the history of certain national groups. For example, the greenhouse industry was brought to America primarily by the Dutch immigrants, and is reflected today in the large percentage of people of Dutch descent who still engage in the commercial production of vegetables under glass in the Midwest. This is also true of the onion set industry located around Chicago. Similarly, the Japanese flower and vegetable growers are prominent in West Coast horticulture.

Many local horticultural enterprises of considerable scale relate to a particular family or firm. A single grower in Wisconsin produces a significant percentage of the horse radish used in the United States. The success of the Hill Nurseries, the largest rose center in the United States, has brought a large floricultural industry to Indiana, although there are better adapted areas in terms of light and temperature. The carnation industry in New England traces its origin to a few private conservatories of wealthy estates.

Market preferences have greatly affected the horticultural industry. For example, collards and mustard greens are typical southern dishes. The population shifts of people from the South to Chicago industry has resulted in a new crop for market gardeners located in this area. Similarly, the large number of "Chinese restaurants" in the East has stimulated specialized vegetable enterprises in Long Island to serve this trade. In general, these unique markets tend to decrease in importance in the United States as the mobility of population increases. However, national habits involving food preferences change relatively slowly. The preference for wine versus beer has a profound effect on a nation's horticulture.

Selected References

Climate and Man. USDA Yearbook. 1941. (A broad, popular treatment.)

Dansereau, P. *Biogeography.* Ronald, New York. 1957. (An advanced text on plant ecology.)

Geiger, R. *The Climate Near the Ground.* Harvard Univ. Press, Cambridge. 1957. (A revised translation of an outstanding work on microclimate.)

Klages, K. H. W. *Ecological Crop Geography.* Macmillan, New York. 1942. (A discussion of the factors determining the distribution of crop plants.)

Trewartha, G. T. *An Introduction to Climate.* McGraw-Hill, New York. 1954. (An elementary but comprehensive text.)

Wilsie, C. P. *Crop Adaptation and Distribution.* Freeman, San Francisco. 1962. (A general treatment of the principles of crop ecology.)

CHAPTER 13

Horticultural Enterprises

The commercial horticultural industry is made up of those enterprises concerned directly with the production, handling, and maintenance of horticultural crops. The many allied enterprises that handle horticultural crops in a more or less direct way, such as the storage, processing, and marketing organizations, as well as the maintenance and service enterprises connected with horticultural plantings will only be indirectly discussed. Horticulture is, ultimately, the study of the individual crop, the basis of the industry. Notwithstanding the diversity of horticultural plants, the production enterprises can be properly grouped into a number of distinct areas based on the traditional divisions of horticultural crops, namely, fruits, vegetables, and ornamentals.

Horticultural production is characterized by extensive expenditures for capital and labor. The size of the operations varies greatly. In the tropics and subtropics, much of horticulture is run typically on a plantation basis, and in many instances is integrated with extensive processing operations (for example, pineapple, cocoa). In contrast, greenhouse production in the temperate climates may be extremely small with respect to land utilization, although highly specialized and requiring much capital.

Accurate world production figures for all horticultural crops are not available. This is due in part to the absence of international communications and in part to poor statistical records. Production statistics may be incomplete or may be computed differently in different countries. For example, some countries report only commercial production; others report total production. The lack of reliable data is especially noticeable for crops that may be of local importance but that do not enter significantly in world trade. This tends to underestimate the more highly perishable horticultural crops, even those that may be grown extensively in home or local gardens. World production figures of the major crops, shown in Table 13-1, indicate the importance of horticulture.

414

Table 13-1. *Comparison of world production* of some major crops.*
[Data from *Production Yearbook* 1959, F.A.O., 1960.]

CROP	1958 PRODUCTION (MILLIONS OF METRIC TONS)†	
All grains		856
Rice	254	
Maize	189	
Wheat	180	
Oil seed**		68
Cotton		8
Sugar (noncentrifugal cane)		7
Potatoes		185
Sweet Potatoes and Yams		104
Dried Legumes		25
Fruit Crops‡		107

* USSR excluded.
† 1 metric ton = 1.1 English tons.
** Soybeans, peanuts, cottonseed, linseed, rapeseed, sesame, sunflower seed.
‡ Grape, apple, citrus, banana, olive, pear, plum, peach, pineapple, fig, date, cherry, apricot.

The economic level of horticultural crop production is in large part related to the general agricultural situation. At present the limitation to agricultural progress has been the slow rate of economic development in many parts of the world. The striking increase in productivity that we have seen brought about by advances in agricultural science have not benefited all countries. In much of the world, such advances will depend not upon increased information but upon eliminating rural poverty and the insecurity of farm tenure as well as increasing the availability of reasonable credit. In many areas, farm prices are unstable and discourage the investment required for an intensive mechanized agriculture. In addition, marketing channels are often inadequate for handling perishable crops.

The production of many horticultural crops has shown an upward climb over the last decade (Table 13-2). This reflects not only the increase in world population but also the increase in world trade and the expansion of the processing industries, especially in many European countries. The broadening of the marketing season by variety selection and application of improved distribution technology has increased the availability of horticultural crops over the year. The following broadcast of the British Broadcasting Company, aimed at the English housewife, illustrates this nicely.

Table 13-2. *World production figures (in thousands of metric tons)* *for selected horticultural crops.*
[Data from *Production Yearbook* 1959, F.A.O., 1960.]

	YEAR	EUROPE	NORTH AMERICA	LATIN AMERICA	NEAR EAST	FAR EAST	AFRICA	OCEANIA	WORLD TOTAL
FRUITS†,**									
Grape (total)	1948–52	23,160	2740	2650	2210	50	2360	461	33,600
	1957	21,040	2390	2780	2960	120	3070	563	32,900
	1958	28,560	2790	3200	3880	120	2920	543	42,000
Oranges	1948–52	1690	4500	3340	710	750	720	130	11,800
	1957	2260	4400	4030	1070	1330	1180	140	14,400
	1958	2300	5220	4060	1240	1450	1070	160	15,500
Grapefruit	1948–52		1470	70	50	40	20	10	1700
	1957		1410	130	70	50	40	10	1700
	1958		1560	130	80	40	30	10	1800
Lemons and Limes	1948–52	410	440	320	90	310	30	20	1600
	1957	490	630	370	170	290	50	20	2000
	1958	570	640	380	180	300	40	20	2100
Apples (includes cider)	1948–52	9600	2710	360	130	430	50	230	13,500
	1957	5060	2900	420	170	870	—	350	9900
	1958	15,910	3100	610	250	890	—	—	21,700
Bananas	1948–52	222	4	7800	70	2870	310	140	11,400
	1957	283	4	10,600	110	2540	550	150	14,200
	1958	284	4	10,600	120	2630	550	180	14,400
Olives and Olive Oil	1948–52	4100	45	45	435		485		5100
	1957	5100	34	55	350		460		6000
	1958	4000	64	70	720		870		5700

Pears (includes perry) 1948–52	2400	670	150	80	110	20	76	3510
1957	1440	730	170	110	205	35	121	2810
1958	3710	680	160	120	220	—	92	5010
Plums and Prunes 1948–52	2240	535	85	65	45	40	25	3040
1957	1860	530	—	90	50	40	27	2710
1958	2650	345	—	90	40	—	—	3280
Peaches 1948–52	610	1370	240	20	50	40	59	2390
1957	1030	1410	330	75	150	65	77	3140
1958	950	1620	260	80	155	60	65	3190
Pineapples 1948–52		680	420		140	40	40	1320
1957		711	540		330	100	75	1750
1958		—	570		—	—	95	1850
Figs 1948–52	870	90	25	205	2	170	1	1370
1957	870	70	25	245	—	170	1	1390
1958	960	75	—	260	—	180	—	1500
Dates 1948–52	7	15	4	850	80	190		1150
1957	9	21	10	1100	85	190		1420
1958	10	18	10	1090	—	—		1400
Cherries (sweet and tart) 1948–52	890	220	8	45	5		6	1170
1957	790	230	—	55	5		6	1100
1958	1140	190	—	55	5		—	1400
Apricots 1948–52	200	188	14	150		35	35	620
1957	390	179	20	180		50	40	860
1958	240	103	18	175		50	30	620

Table 13-2. (*Continued*)

	YEAR	EUROPE	NORTH AMERICA	LATIN AMERICA	NEAR EAST	FAR EAST	AFRICA	OCEANIA	WORLD TOTAL
VEGETABLES									
Potatoes	1947–52	218,540	12,830	4800	1000	17,400	820	580	256,000
	1957	230,920	12,900	5660	1710	28,500	1000	750	281,400
	1958	217,480	13,930	5440	1720	31,070	890	650	271,200
Sweet Potatoes	1947–52	200	980	2500	20	49,500	16,900	110	70,200
and Yams	1957	150	790	2800	70	80,700	18,660	120	103,200
	1958	160	790	2720	60	81,200	18,490	120	103,500
Cassava	1947–52			15,520	—	8700	27,700	70	52,000
	1957			18,430	—	13,140	30,600	120	62,300
	1958			17,830	—	14,090	31,060	—	63,100
Tomato	1947–52	3650	3990	780	545	210	215	100	9490
	1957	5360	4200	990	880	260	300	142	12,140
	1958	6150	5110	1040	986	270	320	142	14,020
Onion	1947–52	2020	1000	380	770	570	95	60	9490
	1957	2320	1150	620	1060	1030	100	—	12,140
	1958	2440	1130	600	980	1070	—	—	14,020
LEGUMES									
Dry Beans†	1948–52	750	820	2040	145	2460	535	1	6500
(*Phaseolus vulgaris*)	1957	910	740	2430	180	3010	620	—	7500
	1958	850	920	2540	215	3280	645	—	8500
Chick Peas†	1948–52	230		100	140	4680	200	—	5500
	1957	230		130	140	7130	150	—	7300
	1958	230		140	130	5790	140	—	6400

Dry Peas†	1948–52	750	165	105	5	3595	390	50	5100
	1957	620	185	95	5	3725	340	50	5000
	1958	480	145	95	5	3745	350	—	4900
Broad Beans (Vicia faba)	1948–52	750		130	330	2970	200	2	4400
	1957	960		110	330	3120	150	—	4700
	1958	900		130	290	3120	160	—	4600
Lentils†	1948–52	70		50	160	385	95		760
	1957	80		30	240	280	80		710
	1958	70		30	160	260	80		600
BEVERAGE CROPS									
Coffee	1948–52		3	1880	5	70	285	2	2245
	1957		4	2475	6	124	540	2	3150
	1958		7	2790	5	130	570	2	3505
Cocoa	1948–52			246		4	499	4	755
	1957			285		5	456	8	752
	1958			301		6	566	9	882
Tea	1948–52			2	5	600	19		626
	1957			4	9	784	34		832
	1958			4	10	843	40		898

* 1 metric ton = 1.1 English tons.
† Excluding the USSR.
** Excluding mainland China

Extract from "Shopping List," broadcast by the B.B.C., February 13, 1959

Fruit

If you're looking for luxury this week-end this is undoubtedly the time to buy a pineapple. Those superb large pineapples from the Azores—normally very expensive—are being sold in a number of shops at less than their usual price. There's no catch in it—they are of excellent quality; it just happens that the market price has fallen. Look for bright color on the skin and fresh looking foliage.

If the price is still above your budget, or if you can't find any in your local shops, there are plenty of smaller, far cheaper, pineapples, from South Africa and Jamaica. Their flavour is not as full as that of the Azores ones, but for a fraction of the price they're pretty good all the same.

The first of the blood oranges from Spain and Morocco will already be in a few shops this week-end. Their flavour is pleasant—they're very rarely sharp—and the bright red mixed with the orange colour is attractive.

Israeli oranges, too, are excellent now. And I see the Manchester report is recommending for value large oval oranges imported from Turkey. Another best buy listed in nearly all areas is bananas.

There has not been a heavy crop of South African peaches this year; although there's been a relatively big arrival this week. But you can't expect any low prices. Gaviota plums too—they're the yellowish-orange ones—are not cheap but they're large juicy fruit.

South African grapes—black and white—are now in most areas.

Here's something unusual for this time of year; there have been fresh arrivals of remarkably good quality chestnuts from Italy.

Vegetables

The Bristol report says there are improved supplies of leeks. Also well worth buying are carrots and all the cabbage family, including savoys and spring greens. There are more parsnips now and generally their quality has improved.

I've been getting some well flavoured, reasonably priced tomatoes. And I see the report from Glasgow agrees that Canary tomatoes are in good condition now. But you need to see that they are firm.

There are some home-grown cucumbers in a few shops, and if you think they're expensive, I'm told they are not as high in price as usual at this time of year.

The report on Wednesday was of lower prices of home-grown potatoes. There is also a bewildering variety of imported ones, the latest arrivals coming from the Canary Islands; these aren't cheap, but they do include some which can be scraped.

In contrast to many of the staple agricultural crops, the world prices of nearly all horticultural crops are freed from price controls. However, in many countries there are stringent import controls. This restrictive trade provides protection for domestic horticultural production.

FRUIT PRODUCTION

Taken together, the production of fruit compares favorably with the world's staple agricultural crops. World fruit production is steadily increasing, although government programs have tended to favor grain and oil crops. Horticultural crops tend to be expensive in terms of calories. Although the permanent nature of fruit crops tends to stabilize production over the long run, there may be great differences in production from year to year. This is due in part to their concentration and sensitivity to environment. Compare, for example, the variation between European apple and pear production in 1957 and 1958. The low 1957 production was due to cold weather during the winter and spring of 1956–1957. The heavy crop of fruit buds subsequently produced resulted in a bumper crop in 1958.

Grapes

Grapes are the most important fruit crop, accounting for almost half of the fruit production of the world. Grapes are grown throughout the temperate regions and especially in the warmer, sunnier climates with mild winters. In Northern Europe, especially in Belgium and the Netherlands, there is significant production of grapes under glass. About 54% of the world's crop is pressed into wine, 45% is consumed fresh, and 1% is dried. Specific varieties are grown for each purpose. The combination of soil type, climate, and grape variety accounts for the differences in wines produced throughout the world. In the United States, grape production is largely located in California, although a sizable grape industry exists in the Great Lakes region. In California, the European grape, *Vitis vinifera,* is grown for fresh fruit, raisins, and wine. Of the entire California crop, 20% of the grapes grown are wine varieties, 20% are table varieties, and 60% are raisin varieties. In the past, raisins and other dried fruit made up the bulk of our fruit exports, but this market has been decreasing. In the Great Lakes region the more severe winters limit the culture of *vinifera* grapes, thus the American grape *V. labrusca* is grown almost exclusively. The basis of the industry is the Concord variety, whose "foxy" flavor is prized for nonfermented grape juice. Grape juice is usually canned, although frozen concentrate is achieving exceptional market acceptance.

Apples and Pears

Apple and pear, the pome fruits, are important tree fruits of the temperate climates. The fruits are closely related botanically and their culture is similar. Both crops are often grown in the same orchard.

The apple is the most important individual species of tree fruits in the world. It is widely adapted and is grown in temperate regions that have a distinct cold period. Although the United States is the largest single producer, the bulk of the world's crop is grown in Europe. The majority of the European varieties are predominantly cooking and cider apples. Cider, which is sold with an alcoholic content of about 6–8%, is quite popular in England and Northern Europe. Recently there has been a trend away from cooking apples to dessert types, with increased emphasis on the more attractive red varieties.

Although apples are grown throughout the United States, the largest concentrations are on the West Coast (Washington, California), in the Great Lakes area (New York, Michigan), and in the Appalachian area (Virginia, West Virginia, Pennsylvania). The Western orchards must be irrigated, but the low humidity reduces the disease problem, and the climate is uniquely adapted for the production of fruit of high "finish" and attractiveness.

About 10 varieties account for over 90% of the United States crop. The trend over the last fifty years has been toward a great reduction in the number of varieties and a change to the red sports of the more popular varieties, such as Delicious, Rome, Jonathan, McIntosh. The small "farm orchards" have disappeared, and production has concentrated in more adapted locations. Although tree numbers have shown a gradual decline until recently, yields are going up. The export market, which has decreased from pre-World War II levels, is now stable. The net effect of the increase in population, along with a decrease in per capita consumption, has been a stabilization of the apple consumption in the United States over the past decade.

Production technology in the apple industry has shown great changes. In the United States there is a trend toward greater use of dwarfing rootstocks particularly of the "semidwarf" types such as EM II and EM VII, but seedling rootstocks are still the most prominent. The use of controlled atmosphere storage makes it possible to obtain high quality apples the year around. As this technological advance increases in use, it promises to bring significant changes to the pattern of apple marketing. It already has interfered with the movement of early summer varieties. Probably the most significant advance in production technology has been the increased use of organic fungicides and insecticides in the spray schedules. Most Northeastern orchards use high concentrate speed sprayers but dusting is more prominent in the West.

The world's pear production is about a third of the world's apple production. The major world production is located in Western Europe. Over 40% of the European crop goes into the production of perry ("pear cider"); the rest is practically all consumed fresh. In the United States, pears are relatively less important, and total production represents only about one-fourth that of apples. The United States industry is based largely on the Bartlett variety, which accounts for about 80% of the total production. Bartlett is used for fresh consumption and processing. The Bartlett pear is becoming one of the most important varieties in Europe, where it is known as Williams or William Bon Chrétien. Almost 90% of the United States production is located in the states of Washington, Oregon, and California. Of the total crop, about half is processed by canning.

Although the pear is not quite as hardy as the apple, the limiting factor to pear production has been the bacterial disease fireblight, which has eliminated commercial pear production from the warmer humid regions of the United States. The disease had been confined to the Western hemisphere but has recently appeared in England. Recently a disorder called pear decline has severely hampered western pear production. The trouble is severe on varieties grafted onto oriental rootstocks.

Citrus Fruits

The citrus group of evergreen fruits are native to the subtropical regions of Eastern Asia. They are now the major fruit crop of the subtropical climates, and rank in importance with apple and pear. Although the crop can be grown in the tropics, fruit quality is inferior. The main centers of world production are the United States, Brazil, Spain, Japan, Italy, Mexico, and Israel. The United States is far and away the highest producer, although the industry is located in relatively small areas in the states of Florida, California, and Texas.

The citrus group contains a great number of edible species. Of the commercially grown types, the sweet orange is the most important. California orange industry is based primarily on two varieties, the Washington Navel, which is relatively seedless, and the Valencia (Fig. 13-1). The Florida industry is made up of a number of thin-skinned varieties, of which the most important are the Valencia and the Pineapple. Mandarin oranges, a different species than the sweet orange, are typically rough skinned, and are loosely united, having easily separated segments. (Deep orange-red mandarins are called tangerines.) Mandarins are widely popular in Japan and have achieved considerable importance in the United States.

A number of artificial hybrids within the citrus group have been produced. Among these are the tangor (tangerine × sweet orange) and the tangelos (tangerine × grapefruit). The most important of these hybrids is the temple "orange," which is believed to be a tangor. The temple orange has achieved importance in Florida. Grapefruits, lemons, and limes are the other major citrus crops.

Fig. 13-1. *Valencia oranges in California.*

[Photograph by J. C. Allen & Son.]

The high concentration of citrus production in the United States has led to grove management on a contract basis by cooperative or caretaking organizations. The size of individually owned groves is commonly as small as 20 acres, although the Florida enterprises tend to be larger. The great increase in the citrus industry in the United States is due to a number of factors, including low production costs (low as compared to apples, for example), efficient marketing, joint industry advertising and promotion, and the rise of citrus as an important processing crop. A major part of the Florida citrus crop is utilized as frozen concentrate.

Bananas

Bananas, originating in the tropical regions of southern Asia, represent one of the earliest of cultivated plants (Fig. 13-2). They are a true tropical fruit and require temperatures that do not fall below 50°F or rise above 105°F. Although there are many edible species, the most important are the seedless selections of *Musa sapientum*, exemplified by the variety Gros Michel. In Asia there are many starchy cooking types of bananas known as Plantains (*M. paradisica*). Bananas have become one of the most important fruits of the world, and are the best known of the tropical fruits. The leading producing countries in the Western Hemisphere are Honduras, Costa Rica, and Panama, whereas the leading Asian countries are India, Malaya, Formosa, and the Philippines. The present export in-dustry is located largely in the Caribbean countries and is con-trolled by a few companies, of which United Fruit is the largest. The main limitation to production in Central America have been two devastating diseases, the "Panama disease," a root wilt caused by a *Fusarium oxysporium cubense* and Sigatoka, a leaf spot caused by *Cercospora musae*. At present the only economical way of controlling Panama disease is to move plant-ings to new wilt-free locations.

Stone Fruits

Species of the genus *Prunus* con-stitute the so-called stone fruits and include the plum, peach, cherry, and apricot. The stone fruits re-quire a cold period to break their rest period, but are subject to win-ter killing and frost injury and thus can be grown profitably only in re-stricted locations.

Plums and peaches are the most important of the stone fruits. There are a great number of plum varie-ties and species, with a correspond-ing wide range of adaptability.

Fig. 13-2. *The banana plant. As the stem elongates, the blossoms unfold. The fruited stalk, or bunch, consists of many clusters of flowers called hands. Each female flower develops into a fruit—the "finger." Male flowers are produced to-ward the apex end of the stem.*
[Photograph by J. C. Allen & Son.]

Plums that have a high sugar content and can be dried are known as prune-type plums, or simply as prunes. The great bulk of the world's plums are grown in Europe. The leading countries are Yugoslavia, Rumania, and Ger-many. In the United States the West Coast accounts for almost the entire commercial crop, of which a large proportion is dried and sold as prunes.

The United States is the most important peach producing country. About half of the crop is grown in California. Two-thirds of the California crop are clingstone peaches. These are "rubbery fleshed" peaches and are all processed by canning. The remaining California production, and the rest of the United States production, is devoted to freestone peaches. These have "melting flesh," and the pit more or less separates from the flesh when ripe. Probably the most famous freestone peach is the Elberta, which is still the standard variety. A number of breeding programs have produced peaches that ripen over a two-month period at most locations. Nectarines, which are smooth-skinned peaches, are produced almost exclusively in California.

Cherries are an important European fruit. They are relatively less popular in the United States. European production consists mainly of sweet cherries (*Prunus avium*), whereas more than half of the United States production consists of tart cherries (*Prunus cerasus*). The variety Montmorency is the basis of the tart cherry industry in the United States. The production of sweet cherries is concentrated on the West Coast, whereas tart cherries are grown most abundantly in the Great Lakes region. The United States commercial production of apricots is almost completely confined to California. The bulk of the crop is processed by canning or drying.

Fig. 13-3. *The blueberry has become an important small fruit crop, transforming many of the supposedly worthless acid soils into valuable cropland.*
[Photograph by J. C. Allen & Son.]

Small Fruits

The small fruits include the grape, strawberry, the brambles, currant, gooseberry, cranberry, and blueberry (Fig. 13-3). Except for grapes, the most important (and perishable) small fruit is the strawberry (Fig. 13-4), which is followed in turn by the brambles (blackberries, raspberries, dewberries). These crops are widely adapted, although expansion of the West Coast strawberry indus-

Fig. 13-4. *The strawberry is one of the most widely adapted fruit crops. Present-day varieties descend from hybrids of Fra-garia virginiana, native to the east coast, and F. chiloensis, native to the Pacific coastline of North and South America.*
[Photograph by J. C. Allen & Son.]

try has reached the point where California accounts for almost half of the United States crop. In California the acreage devoted to this crop increases and decreases in response to price changes.

The high labor costs associated with small fruits have limited the expansion of this crop in the United States. Although production has stabilized, yields per acre have steadily gone up with the increased care of improved varieties and with the adoption of better cultural practices. The use of virus-free plants has increased the productivity of many small fruit varieties. In strawberries irrigation has played an important role in increasing performance. Irrigation is also widely used to control spring frost. The development of the freezing industry and the experimental success of harvesting machines in the brambles would indicate future expansion of the industry.

VEGETABLE PRODUCTION

The vegetable industry has been characterized by flexibility. Most vegetables are grown as annuals, hence shifts in variety and crop can be readily made. In the past, a good portion of the vegetable enterprises was diversified, and no great long-term investments were required. It was always relatively easy to go into or out of the vegetable business. This is becoming less true as irrigation, specialized equipment, and storage and packing facilities are becoming an integral part of vegetable enterprises. The vegetable industry in the United States may be classified into *home garden, market garden,* and *truck garden.* In addition to these categories, there exist a number of specialized parts of the vegetable industry, such as plant growing, greenhouse forcing, seed production, and mushroom culture.

The *"home garden"* involves the production of vegetables for home consumption and is still the most important source of vegetables in many countries. It is still a considerable factor in vegetable production in the rural United States, although the garden appears to be becoming almost more important as an outlet for recreation than as a source of food. In times of national peril, home gardens become an important part of a country's food supply. *"Market gardening"* developed from local gardens and involves intensive production of many kinds of vegetables around larger centers of population. Market gardening is disappearing in the United States as a result of increasing land costs and improvement in food distribution. The remaining market garden areas have succeeded due to the extremely intensive cultural practices of skilled growers who produce high yields and good quality. The large-scale production of vegetables, commonly less diversified than market-gardens production, is known as *"truck farming"* (from the French "troquer," meaning "to barter"). Truck farming, which is based on suitable season, climate, and soil rather than market

Fig. 13-5. *An irrigated lettuce farm in the Hawaiian Islands.*
[Photograph by J. C. Allen & Son.]

proximity, has become the most important part of the modern vegetable industry (Fig. 13-5). Truck crop production may be destined for fresh market consumption or for processing. The rise of the processing industry has made many individual vegetable crops part of the general rotation of farm crops. For example, tomatoes and sweet corn have become an important "cash" crop in many midwestern general, or grain, farms.

Tomatoes

The tomato is native to South America, and was introduced into Europe prior to 1544 via the Spanish conquistadores. Superstitions concerning presumed poisonous qualities discouraged its use in many European countries with the exception of the Mediterranean regions until the late eighteenth century. Tomatoes did not become popular in the United States until the latter part of the nineteenth century, although they had been introduced from Europe over a hundred years earlier.

Although the plant is frost susceptible, the tomato is one of the most widely cultivated plants, and is grown from the equator to as far north as Fort Norman, Canada (65° lat.). The tomato is also grown largely under glass in Northern Europe. In the United States it is the most important greenhouse vegetable and ranks as the most popular home garden food plant. The leading countries in terms of production are the United States, Italy, Spain, and Egypt. The United States accounts for about one-third of the world's production. In 1960, California, Florida, and Texas were the leading states for fresh market production.

Fig. 13-6. (*Above*) *Plant breeders examine dwarf tomato plant developed for mechanical harvesting.* (*Below*) *Roma, a paste tomato, was developed by the USDA to provide a high-solids product for processing.*
[Courtesy Purdue University and J. C. Allen & Son.]

Tomatoes destined for fresh consumption are picked in the pink stage, from which they ripen naturally off the plant. Tomatoes can also be picked green, stored, and artificially ripened. They are then referred to as "green

wraps." California, Indiana, and Ohio are the leading states in the production of tomatoes for processing. Tomatoes are canned whole and, in
order of increasing consistency, as juice, puree, sauce, catsup, and
paste.

Tomatoes, although a perennial plant, are grown as an annual. The usual
method of planting is by transplants, although direct seeding is increasing
in popularity due to the effectiveness of chemical weed control. The
mechanical harvesting of tomatoes has been developed and promises to
effect great changes in the industry (Fig. 13-6).

Potatoes, Sweet Potatoes, and Yams

The major starchy vegetable crops of the world are three unrelated
"underground" crops. Two are native to South America, and both are referred to as "potatoes." *Solanum tuberosum*, the white (or Irish) potato,[*] is
a cool-season, temperate-zone crop, whereas *Ipomoea batatas*, the sweet
potato, is a warm season crop that is more adapted to the tropics and
subtropics. Although some varieties of sweet potatoes, especially those with
a moist, soft texture are referred to as yams, the true yam belongs to the
genus *Dioscorea*, an important tropical root crop of Asia that is relatively
unknown in the Western Hemisphere.

The white potato is one of the most important food crops of the world
and is especially adapted to the northern United States, southern Canada,
and northern Europe. A temperature of 70°F is optimum for tuber formation. At higher temperatures the increased respiration rate reduces the
amount of stored carbohydrates and consequently reduces yield and quality.
Although adequate rainfall is essential, excess rain has been feared as a
result of severe infestations of the late blight disease caused by *Pytophthora
infestans*. This is the same disease that was partially responsible for the
famines in Ireland in the 1840's. Potatoes are also an important animal
feed in Europe. Because of their bulk they have never become important
in international trade.

In the United States, potato production is concentrated in the North
(Idaho and Maine are the highest producers), although early-maturing
varieties are widely grown as fall and spring crops in southern latitudes.
Even though acreage has sharply decreased, average yields more than
doubled between 1940 and 1960. As a result, the United States production
has stabilized, although per capita consumption has shown a steady de-

---

[*] The names white potato and Irish potato are unfortunate choices. *Solanum tuberosum* originated in South America, and there are also yellow-fleshed types.

crease since the 1900's. Recently this trend has reversed. This is due in large part to the use of processed potato products, mainly chips and other "snack-type" foods.

Onions

The onion and the other pungent species of the genus *Allium* (leek, garlic, and chives) are among the most ancient of cultivated vegetables. These are all biennial bulb-form-ing plants of the Lily family. The onion, the most important of this group, is grown in all temperate climates (Fig. 13-7). The most important onion producing coun-tries are the United States, Japan, Romania, Italy, and Turkey. In the United States the crop is widely grown, with California, New York, Texas, and Michigan being the chief producing states. Onions require cool temperatures during early growth and require long days and high temperatures for bulb formation. Green onions, or scallions (the nonbulbous stage of onion) are an important winter crop in the southern United States.

Fig. 13-7. *Onions are among the most ancient of vegetable crops.*
[Photograph by J. C. Allen & Son.]

In the northern states onions are commonly planted from seed in the spring; in the southern states plantings are made in the fall or winter from seed, seedlings, or onion sets. The pro-duction of onion sets, which the small bulbs produced by crowding, is a specialized industry in Michigan, Illinois, and Wisconsin. Fall onions are stored for sale in the winter. A relatively small percentage of the crop is processed as flavorings for use in other products.

Crucifers

The important vegetables of the family *Cruciferae* include cabbage, cauliflower, broccoli, Brussels sprouts, Chinese cabbage, kale, collards, and mustard. These are all species of the genus *Brassica*, and are known collectively as *cole crops*. The radish (*Raphanas sativa*) is a Crucifer, but it belongs to a different genus. The cole crops are cool-season, hardy plants. Except for cauliflower and broccoli, which are annuals, they are biennials, requiring a cold treatment to flower.

The cole crops are grown widely in Europe, where they constitute the major "green" vegetables. In the United States, cabbage is the most important cole crop, and, in the past, was a common winter vegetable, since it is easily stored. The production of cabbage has sharply declined, however, reflecting a general consumer shift to other vegetables. About 10% of the present acreage is grown for the production of sauerkraut. The production of broccoli, although minor as compared to cabbage, has increased in importance, and has become increasingly popular as a frozen vegetable.

The cole crops are usually set as transplants. In the north, they are set out in the spring; in the warmer climate of the south, they are planted in the fall or winter. Insect control is particularly important. In general, soils with a pH above 7 are used to control clubroot, a serious root disease caused by *Plasmodium brassica*. However, resistant varieties are becoming commercially available.

Edible Legumes

The edible legumes, or *pulse crops*, include many genera of the *Leguminosae*. These crops represent important sources of protein and are especially important in Asia and South America, where they constitute a key part of the diet. In the United States the most important of the edible legumes are the common bean and pea. (Soybeans, although edible as a vegetable, are grown in the United States as an oil crop.)

The common bean (*Phaseolus vulgaris*) is a warm-season annual that is quite sensitive to frost. This species and the lima (or butter) bean (*P. lunatus*) are both native to South America, although they are now extensively grown over the world. The bean is edible in various stages of growth, but various varieties are now grown for each type. The edible podded types are called snap, or stringless, beans (formerly string beans!) and may be either the climbing ("pole beans") or bush type. Beans are also used in the green or the dry-seeded stage. Dried beans are a substantially larger crop than "snap beans" and account for about ten times the acreage. Various types of dried beans are grown in the United States, among which are the navy (or pea bean), red kidney, pinto, great northern, marrow, and yellow eye.

The garden pea, in contrast to the common bean, is native to Asia and is a cool season crop. It is used in the green or dry-seeded stage although there are varieties that are edible in the podded stage. Almost the entire commercial green pea crop is now produced for processing. At present, peas are one of the most popular frozen vegetables, but the bulk of the crop is still canned. The important producing areas are the northern states of Wisconsin, Washington, Minnesota, and Oregon. Dried peas, almost as large a crop as green peas, are produced mainly in Washington and Oregon.

Cucurbits

The cucurbits, or vine crops, include the cucumber, muskmelon, watermelon, pumpkin, squash, and the chayote. They are all warm season crops and are very susceptible to cold injury.

The cucumber, probably native to Asia, has been in cultivation for thousands of years. In Europe it is an important greenhouse crop; the extremely large fruits, grown in the absence of pollinating insects, develop without seeds. In the United States the majority of the acreage is devoted to the production of pickling cucumbers. The crop is widely planted; Michigan and Wisconsin are the leading producing states. Mechanical harvesting machines have recently been developed, but these are only partly successful.

Muskmelons, native to Iran, are a relatively recent crop in the United States. (The term cantaloupe, although widely used in the United States, is a misnomer.) California, Texas, and Arizona are the chief producing states. There are many types of melons in addition to the netted, musky type. The most important of these is the late-ripening *winter melon,* of which the most common variety is the Honey Dew, a white-skinned, large-fruited type.

Watermelons make up the bulk of the United States acreage. Although watermelons are native to Africa, they have achieved their greatest popularity in the United States. The bulk of the planting is in the southern states, although there are important areas as far north as Iowa. The types range from large 30-lb fruits to small round "icebox types" weighing between 5 and 10 lb (Fig. 13-8). There are also yellow-fleshed types, but the red is the most popular. The seedless watermelon, a triploid fruit first created in Japan in the 1940's from crossing tetraploids and diploids, has become quite important in Japan, where it accounts for about one-third of the watermelon acreage. The seedless watermelon is still just a novelty in the United States.

Pumpkins and squash are native to the New World. The distinction be-

Fig. 13-8. *Various patterns and shapes of the watermelon.*
[Courtesy E. C. Stevenson.]

tween pumpkin and squash is a loose one. Some would use the word pumpkin only for species of *Cucurbita pepo,* referring to *C. maxima* and *C. maschata* as squash. However, the fast-growing types of *C. pepo* are commonly called summer squash. It would seem that the orange, large-fruited, smooth types will continue to be called pumpkins regardless of species. Squash represents an important food crop in South America, ranking next to maize and beans. The flowers, flesh, and seeds may be eaten. The chayote (*Sechium edule*), practically unknown in the United States, is an important South American plant. It is customarily trained on trellises.

Sweet Corn

Sweet corn, a sugary-seeded type of maize native to South America, has only been popular since the last century. Although maize is a well-known crop in many parts of the world, the popularity of sweet corn is confined to the United States.

Sweet corn is a warm-season crop, but is produced mainly in the Northern States. This is because of the short period at which quality can be maintained in extremely hot weather. About two-thirds of the acreage is grown for processing chiefly in Wisconsin, Minnesota, and Illinois, but sizable acreage for fresh-market production has built up in Florida and Texas.

The transitory nature of quality in sweet corn is due to the rapid conversion of sugar to starch. Experimental combinations of other genes, in addition to the common sugary factor (*su*), produce not only a higher sugar content but a less rapid conversion to starch. These types will no doubt extend commercial sweet corn production to areas of hotter climates.

ORNAMENTAL PRODUCTION

Although flowering bulbs and flower seed represent an important component of agricultural production for the low countries of Europe, and for the Netherlands in particular, ornamentals are relatively insignificant in world trade. As a result, world statistics for most of these crops are unavailable. In the United States, rather complete statistics on ornamental horticulture have been obtained by special censuses taken in connection with the 1890, 1930, 1950, and 1960 Censuses of Agriculture. In 1960 the value of ornamentals amounted to almost a quarter billion dollars.

Flowers

The largest part of the florist industry in the United States is based on cut flower production, of which chrysanthemums, roses, carnations, gladiolus, orchids, and snapdragons account for 85% of the wholesale value. The cut flower industry is based on artificial control of the environment. This involves structures incorporating glass, plastic, lath, or shade cloth, as well as artificial heating and cooling. Recent technological advances in the industry, such as injection fertility, evaporative cooling (mist, fan, and pad), plastics, and organic pesticides have increased the complexity of the business and favored the highly specialized organizations. The business is highly competitive, and with the increased erosion of the profit margins only the larger organizations can survive economically.

In spite of the immobility of individual organizations, there is a decided tendency toward movement away from Eastern urban areas of high taxes and labor costs to locations having lower tax rates and a rural labor pool, as well as a more favorable climate (milder temperatures and greater sunlight). As a result, the florist industry is moving west and south. The development of air freight has emphasized interregional competition. Flowers can be shipped great distances by air and arrive in fresh condition to compete with locally grown products. This has eliminated many of the smaller Midwestern and Eastern producers.

Chrysanthemum

The chrysanthemum, long cultivated in Asia, has become the largest cut flower crop in the United States. It is considered a "warm temperature" crop and performs best at about 65°F. The great number of varieties is

usually classified into two types: *standards,* or large-flowered types, and
Pompons, or sprays. Pompons, small-flowered types, may be globular or
daisy-like, and are largely used as fillers in floral arrangements.

The main stimulus to chrysanthemum production has been the ability to
produce continual flowering by the manipulation of photoperiod. The plant
is a perennial and will bloom perpetually, but is grown as an annual crop.
Chrysanthemums are grown under glass in the northern and midwestern
states, under plastic in California (the center of production), and under
cloth in Florida.

Rose

Roses have long been one of the major cut flower crops. The industry
is largely based on the hybrid tea, a perpetually blooming, long-stemmed
rose whose pedigree incorporates many species of *Rosa.* In greenhouse culture, the plants are budded or grafted onto *Rosa Manetti,* a vigorous rootstock. Under proper management the plants bloom continuously, although
the intensity of production is affected by temperature and fertility. Production can be manipulated by pruning (referred to as pinching) and
temperature control to take advantage of favorable marketing periods.
The plants are usually kept from 4 to 7 years, depending on their vigor.

The ideal growing temperature is 60°F. Commercial rose growing has
been restricted to areas north of Lexington, Kentucky, but some establishments are found in the higher altitudes of North Carolina. Evaporative
cooling is being utilized to reduce daytime temperatures farther south,
but, in general, areas that have night temperatures above 65°F for extensive periods of the year are not suitable for roses. Most of the rose
production is carried out under glass, although there is a trend toward
semipermanent construction utilizing lath and plastic, as in the San Francisco area.

The high capitalization for rose culture has generally limited production
to establishments not smaller than 10,000 ft². The importance of novelties,
as well as the better keeping qualities in the hybrid teas, has made hybridization an important part of many rose growing establishments. The
most widely grown forcing variety, however, is "Better Times" orginated
in 1931 by Hills Brothers Nursery of Richmond, Indiana.

Carnation

Carnations require cool temperatures (48–50°F) and high light intensities
for maximum quality production. The cut flower industry is based on
perpetual flowering types, and production proceeds the year round. Plant-

ings are established from cuttings and are maintained from 1 to 2 years. Production of carnations is greatest in California and Colorado, although a sizable industry exists in Massachusetts. The production of carnations has shown a spectacular increase from 1950 to 1960, mainly as a result of expansion in the western states.

Although there are many carnation varieties in production today the Red Sim and White Sim varieties are the most popular (Fig. 13-9). These varieties and their sports are characterized by vigorous growth, heavy production, and long stems. Their chief disadvantage is a tendency towards calyx splitting, a disorder not well understood but felt to be accentuated by large differences between night and day temperatures. Recently, artificial dyeing of carnations has become popular. The dye is taken up from the cut end of the stem

Fig. 13-9. *The White Sim carnation is a periclinal (hand-in-glove) chimeral sport of the Red Sim. The internal tissues carry genetic factors for red color. The White Sim carnation can be identified by flecks of red tissue in the flower.*
[Photograph by J. C. Allen & Son.]

and is absorbed into the veins of the petals. This permits a wide variety of pastel shades to be achieved while only the white-flowered varieties need be grown.

Orchid

Orchid culture is a specialized part of the greenhouse industry. The main type is the showy *Cattleya* (Fig. 13-10), but *Cymbidiums* are becoming increasingly popular. Orchids are a warm-season crop with optimum growth at 65–70°F. Shade is necessary during the summer, but must be removed to maintain adequate light intensity during the winter. The plants are commonly propagated by divisions. Orchids are an aerophyte, and obtain nutrients from decomposing organic matter. They are grown either in *osmunda fiber* or in shredded white fir bark. Since repotting, one of the costliest items of culture, is difficult with osmunda, shredded bark is more widely used by commercial growers. The plants bloom once a year. The harvested flowers are usually placed in tubes of water and are relatively long lasting.

Breeding is an important part of orchid culture, for new varieties may become quite profitable. The long and exacting techniques involved in growing plants from seed have encouraged specialized enterprises that grow seedlings on a commission basis. Successful breeding methods involve hybridization of diploid and tetraploid types, since triploid orchids have proven to be extremely vigorous.

Fig. 13-10. *The cattleya orchid.*
[Photograph by J. C. Allen & Son.]

Snapdragon

Snapdragons, although perennial, are grown as annuals and are planted from seed. In the past, snapdragons have been grown only under relatively cool temperatures, but selection for varieties that perform well under hot temperatures has created a year-round program for this crop. In the Midwest, snapdragons appear to fit into a profitable rotation with greenhouse forcing tomatoes. Snapdragons tolerate low light if temperatures are cool, and can be grown during the winter, when conditions are unfavorable for tomatoes.

At present, practically the entire collection of commercial varieties consists of F_1 hybrids, which have uniformity and vigor. Artificially created tetraploid varieties have achieved some success due to their larger flower size.

Gladiolus

Gladiolus have practically disappeared as a greenhouse forcing crop. At present, almost all of them are produced in outdoor culture with the main production in Florida, California, and North Carolina. A great variety of colors and types exists (Fig. 13-11). Owing to the nature of the plant, bulb and flower production are part of the same business.

Nursery Crops

A nursery refers broadly to the establishment of young plants before permanent planting. The nursery industry involves the production and distribution of woody and herbaceous perennial plants, and is often expanded to include bulbs, corms, and herbaceous annuals (bedding plants). The production of cuttings to be grown in greenhouses or for indoor use (foliage plants), as well as the production of bedding plants, is usually considered a part of the florist industry, but this distinction is fading. Ornamental plants represent the most important nursery crop; next in importance are fruit plants and bulb crops. The most important single plant grown for outdoor culture is the rose. The types of nursery plants grown depend on location. In general, the northern areas provide deciduous and coniferous evergreens (Fig. 13-12), whereas the southern nurseries provide tender, broadleaf evergreens.

The nursery industry in the United States may be divided into wholesale, retail, and mail-order enterprises, although there may be some overlapping. The typical

Fig. 13-11. *All-America gladiolus selections. (Left to right) Thunderbird, Horizon, Ben-Hur.*

wholesale nursery specializes in relatively few crops, and supplies only retail nurseries or florists. The wholesale nursery deals largely in plant propagation. They sell young "lining out" stock of woody material to the retail nursery, which performs two basic functions: care of the plant until growth is complete, and resale to the public. Often, but not always, the retail nursery provides planting and maintenance service. Many nurseries also execute the design of the planting in addition to furnishing the plants. This is analogous to the provision by some lumber yards of architectural services. This area is a complex one, since some states license landscape architects as members of a distinct profession.

Mail-order nursery companies usually grow only a small proportion of their catalogue listings, and subcontract the rest from wholesale houses. Although some of the largest and most reputable businesses in the country deal only in mail orders, this business very often attracts the fly-by-night operator.

Fig. 13-12. *A field of container-grown evergreens.*
[Courtesy D. Hill Nursery Co., Dundee, Illinois.]

Seed Production

Seed production is a relatively small but essential part of the horticultural industry. The seed business involves not only a great many crops but literally thousands of varieties and hybrids. It involves not only plant growing but the manufacturing and processing (milling, cleaning, packaging, and storing) involved in seed production.

The principal world areas of horticultural seed production are the northern and low countries of Europe (Holland, Denmark, England), Japan and the United States. In the United States, although seed houses are located in all regions, the most important seed producing area is located in the western states. California produces practically all of the flower seeds, but a good share of the vegetable seed, especially of large-seeded crops such as beans, peas, and corn, is produced in Idaho. The actual growing of plants is often contracted out to growers, although large seed houses may produce some of their own specialties directly. There are also a number of specialty growers whose production is confined to a few crops, such as pansies or sweet corn.

The seed business itself is divided into wholesale, retail, and mail-order houses. To the majority of the American public, the commission packages are the most familiar wares of the seed industry, but these represent only a small percentage of seed sales.

There is an obvious relationship between seed growing and seed improvement. The progressive seed houses have initiated the breeding of many crops, especially flowers. The Department of Agriculture and State Agricultural Experiment Stations have also supported much of the breeding programs, and, as a result, many experiment stations have sponsored seed associations. At present, horticultural crops represent only a minor portion of this business.

Selected References

Agricultural Statistics 1960. USDA, 1961. (A yearly compilation of United States agricultural production. Includes information on vegetables and fruit.)

Childers, N. F. *Modern Fruit Science.* Horticultural Publications, Rutgers State University, New Brunswick. 1961. (A text of orchard and small-fruit management.)

Horticultural Specialties. United States Census of Agriculture. U.S. Dept. of Commerce, Bureau of the Census. 1960. (Statistics on the floriculture and nursery business.)

Post, K. *Florist Crop Production and Marketing.* Orange Judd, New York. 1949. (A splendid text for the floriculture industry.)

Production Yearbook 1959. Vol. 13, FAO. Rome, 1960. (Compiled annually. A valuable compilation on world food production.)

Schery, R. W., *Plants for Man.* Prentice-Hall, New Jersey. 1952. (An introduction to economic botany.)

Thompson, H. C. and Kelly, W. C. *Vegetable Crops.* McGraw-Hill, New York. 1957. (An excellent text and reference.)

CHAPTER 14

Esthetics of Horticulture

ESTHETIC VALUES

In addition to their utility, plants have esthetic value. Owing to particular qualities we call beauty, certain plants provide pleasure to man. Beauty is not a tangible quality that can be measured or weighed but is a value judgment unique to man. A thing is beautiful when someone decides that it is. The artist is one who can make this judgment and communicate the experience. This judgment is a reflection of man's cultural tradition. People of widely different heritage will have quite different opinions as to what is beautiful and what is ugly.

The concept of beauty depends upon our response to a visible sensation. Although a certain amount of our perception is innate, many perceptual responses are learned. To a great extent we are aware only of what we are able to interpret. For example, upon hearing a foreign language we do not actually perceive most of the nuances of sound and inflection until we have learned to imitate them; yet even a newborn baby is aware of a sudden loud noise and can distinguish between gentle and disapproving tones of voice. Similarly, the botanist learns to discern small differences in plants that may be all but invisible to the layman. So it is with beauty; we must learn to recognize it.

With reference to the concept of beauty, it is difficult to determine what part the innate psychological stimulation plays in the learned response. If any generalization can be made it is that we tend to enjoy the full exercise of our perceptive facilities. Consider, for instance, the universal preferences for color, depth, and contrast for our visual experiences. Nevertheless, the concept of beauty is basically a learned response. This explains the underlying conservatism concerning beauty. We prefer what we are used to, and tend to reject the completely strange and new. Yet we learn to enjoy small,

442

subtle differences and we can be "trained" to expect them, as the automobile manufacturers and flower breeders have discovered.

It we accept a relative concept of beauty then it is apparent that we cannot arbitrarily define it. We cannot say absolutely whether a particular object, or arrangement of objects, is beautiful or not. We must suspend judgment until we have considered the object in relation to man. Snakes, spiders, and worms are considered ugly by many people, but are considered beautiful by others. It is no coincidence that these are feared objects in our culture and that a certain fear of them is passed down by each generation. Thus, our concept of beauty is strongly affected by our emotional feelings and by our cultural attitudes toward the object. This is to say that the standards of one culture cannot in time be applied in all cases to another, for our method of evaluation—our yardstick—has been molded within a particular culture itself. Generally, the things that have been accepted as beautiful for long periods of time, and which are more or less universally admired, have a basic simplicity and harmony of form and function. In conclusion, our concept of beauty is made up of two parts: (1) a visual, or sense, stimulation and (2) a personal, cultured response to this stimulation.

Most plants have an inherent capacity to visually stimulate. Their most obvious feature is their coloring; not only the brilliant hues of flowers, fruits, and in some plants, leaves, but the muted tones of stem and bark. Green, of course, is the most common color, and it is probably more than coincidental that it is psychologically the most restful. The stimulation of plant color is enhanced by contrast and texture.

Also significant with respect to visual effects are the plant's structure and shape; that is, its form. Form can be seen not only in the plant as a whole but in its parts as well. The forms of plants are infinitely varied. But the same could be said of random stones, which are considerably less interesting. The perpetual interest in plants is a result of their ordered arrangements of parts, which involves symmetry, the repetition of parts on either side of an axis.

Symmetry can make any random shape an orderly one. The psychological satisfaction experienced in viewing symmetrical objects is probably due to their inherent order. Man exhibits a universal awareness of symmetry, which is not strange considering its common occurrence in biological forms (Fig. 14-1). Although all plants show some types of symmetry, the growth of many plants produces asymmetrical patterns. It is this deviation from symmetry that makes for visual interest. The basis of contemporary design is to achieve balance and harmony without the monotony of perfect symmetry.

With the possible exception of the Eskimo, man has developed in a plant orientated environment. Plants provide food for man and for his animals, fiber, shelter, and shade. Man's dependence upon plants has influenced and molded his esthetic consideration of them. Man needs plants, and no doubt

plants have been culturally accepted as beautiful partly because they are useful. In our present American culture, in which only a relatively few people are directly involved with the growing of plants (although we still all depend on them), all of us have traditional attachments to plant material. Horticulture has a place in all our lives.

DESIGN

Fig. 14-1. *Symmetry in the rose.*
[Photograph by J. C. Allen & Son.]

Design refers to the manner in which objects are artificially arranged in order to achieve a particular objective. Usually, but not always, this objective involves both a functional and a visibly pleasing arrangement. Designs are evaluated esthetically with regard to their *elements of color, texture, form,* and *line* by long-established, man-made value judgments called *design principles: balance, rhythm, emphasis,* and *harmony.* The importance attributed to each of these will vary with the objective of the design. When a design is successful it is usually considered appropriate, functional, and beautiful.

Elements of Design

The design elements are visible features of all objects.

Color is the visual sensation produced by different wavelengths of light. Color may be described in terms of its *hue* (red, blue, yellow), *value* (light versus dark), and *intensity* (or chroma), the saturation or brilliance.

Texture in design refers to the visual effect of tactile surface quality. Consider, for instance, the visual difference between burlap and silk or between the surface of a pineapple and a rose petal.

Form refers to the shape and structure of a three-dimensional object (sphere, cube, pyramid). However, when we view these forms in a plane, they may appear two-dimensional (as a circle, a square, and a triangle, respectively). In design we are concerned not only with the form of the individual objects but with the larger forms made up by their arrangement.

Line delimits shape and structure. The concept of line in design involves the means by which form guides the eye. Line becomes a one-dimensional interpretation of form. Emotional significance has been attributed to line, as shown in Fig. 14-2.

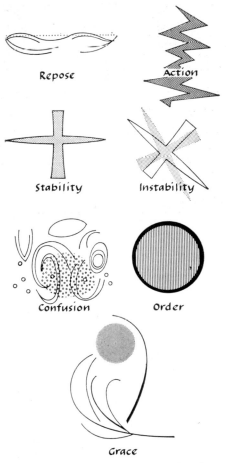

Principles of Design

The principles of design (*balance, rhythm, emphasis,* and *harmony*) apply to each of the design elements as well as to their interrelationships. Thus, we speak of balanced color as well as of balanced form. The artistic application of these principles is the basis of esthetic success, as measured by beauty and expressiveness.

Balance implies stability. Our eye becomes accustomed to material balance, and as a result we become uneasy about objects that appear unstable or ready to topple over. This concept is carried over to arrangements in which balance refers to the illusion of equilibrium around a vertical axis. Balance is

Fig. 14-2. *Line conveys emotional responses.*

achieved automatically by the symmetrical placement of objects around a central vertical axis. It is also achieved in nonsymmetrical arrangements (utilizing the lever principle) by the coordination of mass, distance, and space (Fig. 14-3). It should be emphasized that in design we are concerned with illusion rather than with actual physical balance.

Rhythm, in the auditory sense, refers to a pulsating beat. Similarly, rhythm in the visual context refers to the pattern of "spatial" beats that our eye follows in any arrangement of objects. Rhythm leads and directs the eye through the design. Rhythm suggests movement; design without rhythm becomes uninteresting. Its proper use makes for expression and excitement.

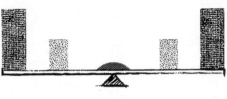

Symmetrical balance

Asymmetrical balance

Fig. 14-3. *Graphic representations of symmetrical and asymmetrical balance.*

Emphasis in design serves to lead the eye and focus its attention on some dominant aspect of the design. By accenting and emphasizing various elements (for example, a particular form, a strong horizontal line, or a brilliant color) the separate parts of the design can be drawn together. Emphasis, properly made, coordinates the design elements and creates an orderly and simplified arrangement.

Harmony refers to the unity and completeness of the design. This quality is seldom achieved except by proper planning and organization. It relies principally on scale and proportion, the pleasing relationship of size and shape. The separate components lose their identity to become part of an idea, the basis of design.

GARDENS

The origin of the garden is rooted in man's desire to surround himself with plants. The great variety of plants permits man to select, in addition to the useful, the esthetically pleasing. Their pleasant fragrance, as well as their beauty, plays a role in this selection. With respect to plants that become culturally significant as fruit trees, it is often difficult to separate the purely functional from the esthetic.

The first gardens of record appear in the ancient cultures of Egypt and China. It was in these cultures that the two opposing traditions in gardens originated, namely, *formalism* and *naturalism*.

Formalism and the Western Tradition

The Egyptian gardens (Fig. 14-4), originating at the edge of the deserts, where the natural vegetation is sparse, represented the development of an artificial oasis. The enclosed garden is cool and leafy, typified by water and shade. The dry climate demands irrigation, which results in small, formal, orderly, arranged plantings. The garden became man's triumph, as it were, over nature.

The Egyptian garden, copied everywhere though changed by local variation in land, plants, and climate, spread to Syria, Persia, and India, and ultimately to Rome. It can be traced through the remains of Egyptian paintings, Persian rugs, and Roman frescoes. This concept of the garden as a separate outdoor room is by no means outdated. The tradition has remained relatively unbroken in the Western world through the cloister gardens of the Dark Ages and the courtyard gardens of the Arab cultures to the present-day patio gardens.

During the Renaissance, the grand period of the West's cultural revival, the concept of the garden was transformed from relative in-

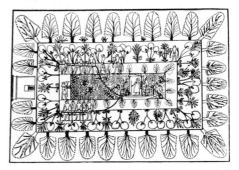

Fig. 14-4. *A formal Egyptian garden containing doum palms, date palms, acacias, and other trees and shrubs. A statue is being towed in the lotus pool toward a pavilion (from the tomb at Thebes, about 1450 B.C.).*

[From Singer, *History of Technology,* Oxford Univ. Press, London, vol. 1, 1954.]

significance to magnificent splendor befitting the age. The grounds design became the important concept, whereas the plant was treated rather impersonally as merely an architectural material. The plant was pruned, clipped, and trained to conform to the plan. Even architecture became subservient to the landscape plan, the garden engulfing and dominating the stately palaces. The resultant "noble symmetry" included courtyards, terraces, statuary, staircases, cascades, and fountains. The emphasis was on long, symmetrical vistas and promenades. The small, enclosed garden remained, but only within the walls of the buildings, as a component part of the grand plan. Formalism reached its peak in the age of Louis XIV. The master architectural gardens of André Lenôtre still remain unsurpassed examples of this concept of design over nature.

Naturalism and the East

Naturalism as a concept in gardens can be interpreted as an attempt to live with nature rather than to dominate it. The desired effect is the appearance of a "happy accident of nature," although it is achieved through methods fully as artificial as those of formalism. Although the separation between garden and landscape in formalism is severe, the separation in naturalism is vague and indistinct. The landscape blends into the garden. If Formalism is the severe lines of geometry, Naturalism is the free curve.

The Naturalism concept has been traced to China although it has also originated independently in the West. In the Eastern tradition plants have symbolic significance. This concept is carried over to the arrangement of plants and miniature landscapes and to the development of the whole landscape. The fusion of Eastern Naturalism and Western Formalism took place in eighteenth century England, where the influx of Chinese culture coincided with an internal revolt against formalism. The marriage was not always a happy one. The English gardens became interspersed with Chinese pagodas amid fake antique Gothic ruins. This brand of Naturalism remains today in our use of curved walks, artificial wishing wells, and herbaceous borders.

The trend of contemporary gardens is to develop a meaningful design for living. Freed from the confines of "naturalism" or "formalism," the modernist strives to reach esthetic expression through the capacity for abstraction. Plants and man, as in the past, make good companions. We have turned full circle to the concept of the "garden" as a vital need in our society and not merely as an esthetic mix.

LANDSCAPE ARCHITECTURE

Landscape architecture in its broadest sense is concerned with the relationship between man and the landscape and as such is concerned with all aspects of *land use for man*. The profession deals with site development, building arrangement, paving, grading plantings and gardens, playgrounds, and pools. It is concerned with the individual home and the whole community, with parks and parkways. If the landscape architect first must be an artist, he must also be a horticulturist and a civil engineer. Although landscape architecture was in the past intimately associated with architecture, they have become, unfortunately perhaps, distinct professions. The objectives of the landscape architect have been to integrate, functionally and esthetically, man, building, and site. The main tools at his disposal are plants and space (Fig. 14-5).

Fig. 14-5. *The landscape architect integrates plants, structures, and space for use by man.*
[Courtesy T. D. Church.]

Plant Materials and Design

Although the materials of the landscape architect also include stone, mortar, and wood, the main ingredients are the plants of the horticulturist, who propagates, grows, and maintains them. Unlike the materials of the painter or sculptor, plants are not static, but change seasonally and with time. The design is in living material; the composition is a growing one. These plants, along with the structural components (paving, walls, and buildings), form the elements of the landscape design. Let us consider plant material in relation to the design elements.

Color

The changing color of plant material—foliage and bark as well as flower and fruit—must be considered through the seasons in relation to the landscape. Although the material is stationary, the patterns and color contrasts are transient. Compare, for instance, the way birch trees appear in the winter with the way they appear in the spring, or compare the spring brilliance of flowering crab apple trees with their scarlet October fruit. The horticultural palette is a rich one, and variety is available for many tastes and effects. The delights of color can be planned by the allocation of space for herbaceous material (for example, bulbs, annuals, and succulents). Home landscape planning makes room for gardens to provide cut flowers for decoration within the home.

Texture

Although the variation in textural quality of plants is large, the use of plants next to structural forms (brick, stone, wood) achieves striking contrast—for example, trees in front of brick; grass and flagstones; ground cover against paving; or flowering stocks within stone walls. Deciduous trees and shrubs offer changing textural patterns from winter to summer.

Form

Plant material naturally duplicates most of the common forms of solid geometry as well as the more complicated and more interesting forms. Ground covers can be made to form any two-dimensional pattern. Forms can be created by massing plants. Care must be taken, however, to consider plants in terms of their mature forms.

Line

Line is created, as is form, by the arrangement. The dominant vertical lines are created with trees; the horizontal lines, by grading, using the ground itself. The use of individual "specimen" plants, by virtue of their own interesting "line," creates focal points—visual interest centers—within the landscape design.

Functional Use of Plant Materials

The terrain without plants is not a fit place for man (Fig. 14-6). The owner of a new home located on a raw piece of ground will readily testify to this. The primary problems are mud and erosion, lack of privacy and a need for protection from sun and wind. Equally dissatisfying is the uninteresting outlook on the wounds of construction. These are problems that can be beautifully solved with plants.

Ground Cover

The surface of the ground may be successfully protected from erosion by covering it with plants. Living ground cover serves to disperse the force of the driving rain, but, more important, it entangles and holds the soil with roots. Grass, shrubs, trees, and vines all act as successful erosion controls even in steeply sloping terrain. Perhaps too much cannot be said to extoll the virtues of grass sod as a landscape material (Fig. 14-7). It makes an ideal surface for recreation; it is cool and free of dust and glare. Grass, as a living floor, is beautiful, remarkably efficient, and relatively easy to maintain.

Fig. 14-6. *A home before and after landscaping.*
[Courtesy Ford Motor Co., Tractor and Implement Div.]

although it must be cut. In areas where less maintenance is desired, such as on slopes or in inaccessible areas, vines and spreading material (myrtle, Japanese spurge, ivy, etc.) make excellent ground cover. Herbaceous annual plants will also serve as surfacing materials, but they are only efficient for half the year in temperate climates.

Enclosure

Shrubby plant material that is high and dense serves to insure privacy by restricting movement and vision. Where space is limited, plants may be used in combination with structural fences to restrict intrusion (Fig. 14-8). By screening areas with plants, the view may be controlled. Screening thus permits a planned vista. Objectional features of the landscape (garbage cans, incinerators, clothes lines, parking areas) may be successfully blocked from

Fig. 14-7. *Sodding a lawn.*
[Courtesy Ford Motor Co., Tractor and Implement Div.]

view by plant material. Screening also serves as protection from the elements. Windbreaks are important for unprotected areas in colder regions. Garden enclosures are the sides of the landscape and as such create the feeling of space. Depending on their composition and arrangement they can produce the feeling of seclusion or grandeur.

Shade

Protection from the heat and glare of the sun becomes a vital function of plants. Shade trees are not only important to outdoor living but greatly affect the indoor temperature. Care must be taken that trees do not offer

Fig. 14-8. *Structural and plant material may be used to achieve enclosure and privacy.*
[Courtesy American Association of Nurserymen.]

potential hazards to buildings. Well-placed trees provide a ceiling to the outdoor room. Deciduous trees further offer the advantage of shade in summer and sun in winter.

Home Landscape Design

The well-designed home landscape is planned to meet the needs and desires of the family (Fig. 14-9). It is concerned with establishing a functional and esthetic relationship between building and site. It is more than the placing of shrubs around the building, although foundation planting is certainly part of it. The successful design treats the house and the surrounding area as a single home unit—"two sides of the same door." The practical plan must by its very nature be a compromise on a number of conflicting desires. This involves the distribution of space, maintenance considerations, and to most of us, expense.

Houses in their simpler forms naturally subdivide a rectangular lot into areas—front, back, and side yards. The problem of home landscaping is to transform this space into living areas. How many uses are required depends upon the family. However, most homes need at least three general areas: (1) public access, (2) service and work, and (3) family living.

The area of public access is usually the front yard. This is the portion of the house that is on view to the public, the passerby as well as the welcomed guest. It creates the setting and tone of the home, and should appear large enough to set off the house from the street (Fig. 14-10); it must offer safe access to the automobile; it should be hospitable.

The service area accommodates garbage cans, trash disposal, clothes drying, vegetable gardens, dog houses, lawn mowers, sandboxes, storage facilities, and other messy items. The problem is one of screening and yet maintaining ac-

Fig. 14-9. *Backyards are also for children. A circular course makes this back-yard fun for the younger set.*
[Courtesy T. D. Church.]

cessibility. In this regard, the service area is often split into two locations, and the side yard usually accommodates one of them. The disappearance of the alley and the change from back door garbage collections to the

Fig. 14-10. *A handsome lawn and a generous set back make an attractive setting for this home.*
[Courtesy Purdue University.]

front have altered the simple concept of service areas in home landscape planning.

To be most functional the outdoor family living area should be an outdoor extension of the dwelling. This implies accessibility from the inside living area. It should be level, or should consist of at least a series of level areas, sloping only enough to provide proper drainage. This area should be sufficiently screened and sheltered to assure privacy and comfort, taking full advantage of shade and cooling breezes. All elements of this area should be planned to contribute to a total affect of pleasant and beautiful living space (Fig. 14-11).

Prominent in the outdoor living area is the patio, a paved area attached

Fig. 14-11. *The outdoor living area of a well-landscaped home.*
[Courtesy Purdue University.]

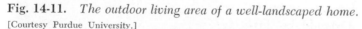

to the house, with or without a structural ceiling. Through the utilization of paving, plant enclosures, and at least one wall of the building, the patio can be made to serve as an outdoor room (Fig. 14-12). The current use of glass to separate the patio from the house helps to bring garden and house into closer harmony. A private patio that is close to or at least on the same level as the kitchen, is ideal for dining and relaxation. It is desirable, however, to have additional access from the indoor living area. When space permits, this area may be separated from other areas used for more active recreational purposes.

The relative size of the outdoor areas is a matter of need, preference, and availability of space. Where space is limited, it would seem unnecessary to waste it on the public area. On the other hand, where space is ample, and only maintenance is the limiting factor, there is no reason to skimp. Nothing is more inviting than a generous setback for the home; there is nothing as valuable to a family as space. The outdoor living area if large enough can be divided to include privacy in relaxation and spaciousness for more vigorous recreation.

Fig. 14-12. *Three sides of the house enclose this patio. Although there are relatively few plants, they are effectively placed.*
[Courtesy T. D. Church.]

That the landscaped home must be maintained is a horticultural truism. The completely paved lot is quite unappealing. The only real alternative is an urban apartment. However, the amount of maintenance may be modified with the plan. This entails minimizing lawn areas, annual plants, trimmed shrubs, or any plants that require special care. It involves increasing paved areas and planning for efficiency. The wise selection of hardy, easily grown plants of the proper mature size is necessary. The design of lawns to accommodate power mowers efficiently is an important consideration.

Urban Planning

Communities in the United States with populations over 5000 contain about 60% of the population. Ours is indeed an urban society. Yet at the same time, our cities, sprawling at the edges and decaying in the center, appear to be committing suicide by strangulation. This is reflected by the rush, by those who can afford it, to the outskirts of the city. The suburban movement is often self-defeating, since shops and businesses soon follow, and the increased stress on already inadequate public transportation further increases congestion.

Cities need not be ugly, dirty, or congested. The problems of rehabilitating the expanding modern city can be solved by planning and subsequent action. The aim is to shape the physical development of the city in harmony with its social and economic needs. This involves land use, communication and transportation control, architectural design, recreation facilities, and sometimes harbor development.

It is important as a social need for cities to be beautiful, to contain fine buildings, monuments, and parks. Beauty is a positive aim, and in this respect green living plants are a necessary part of the urban pattern. This is not to say that nature must dominate the city but only that the city should develop such that nature provides contrast and relief. Just as trees are practical for the home they are also practical for the city, to provide shade, to act as noise buffers, and to serve as windbreaks. When properly used, they contribute to the architecture, and provide visual refreshment to the drab colors of construction. The use of open space in the form of parks and gardens provides a real need for the urbanite, not only for recreational use but for esthetic fulfillment (Fig. 14-13). They are not meant as an escape from the city but as an integral part of it. Finally, open green space is an economic necessity. Blighted, congested cities lead to grave and expensive social problems.

Parks

Moreover, he hath left you all his walks,
His private arbours, and new-planted orchards
On this side Tiber; he hath left them you,
And to your heirs for ever—common pleasures,
To walk abroad and recreate yourselves.
Julius Caesar III, 2
SHAKESPEARE

Fig. 14-13. *Garden design in a backyard in New York City. Remarkable transformations are possible by imaginative planning.* [Courtesy J. Rose and the *New York Times.*]

Although open spaces in cities for the use of all citizens date from earliest times, the urban system of parks and playgrounds is a recent development. The industrial revolution has made them a pressing need. Parks and recreational areas are classified on the basis of size and use. *Squares* and *plazas* are ornamental, restful areas, the smallest unit in the park system. These become expensive, for many small units of green space create maintenance problems. *Playgrounds* and *athletic fields* are primarily recreational areas, and may or may not be part of a connected park system. *Neighborhood parks* serve areas inaccessible to large parks or are located to take advantage of local scenery. *Large parks* (over 100 acres), on the other hand, are designed to serve the city as a whole. They may provide facilities for such special recreational activities as horseback riding and golf, and where water or beach is available, swimming and boating. In addition, they often include museums, memorials, zoos, and botanical gardens (which are usually horticulturally oriented). *State* and *national parks*, although serving a greater area, become important as recreational centers for nearby cities.

The way in which parks are landscaped determines their use. At one end of the spectrum is the *wild park*, which is left almost completely natural except for the creation of a few roads or trails. This limits the use per acre of the park. Such parks are not suitable for large crowds unless they are unusually large, such as national parks and forests. The *developed park* combines increased landscape development with natural effects and allows for more intensive use. Historic Central Park in New York City is an outstanding example. Finally, *formal parks* and *gardens* offer the most intensive park use. Zoological and botanical parks are prime examples. When properly planned and designed, they are able to handle crowds gracefully.

The midway atmosphere of commercial amusement parks deteriorates the landscape. These visual vulgarities are distinguished by their lack of landscape and general unsightliness. A new trend is the large thematic amusement park (for example, Disneyland), which is landscaped and designed to give a park effect. It is hard to determine whether the effect of these places will raise the level of amusement parks or merely stimulate a host of cheap imitations.

Landscaping and Public Buildings

Public buildings, in their broadest sense, include schools, hospitals, museums, and churches in addition to national, state, and municipal buildings. They are expected to be monumental in their design and setting as compared to ordinary commercial buildings. They should represent the spirit and ideals of the city and as such require special treatment. They should be set off such that they can be seen to best advantage. The landscaping should be spacious, dignified, and distinctive.

Schools, rural and urban, deserve special consideration and the best efforts of the community. The ideal school grounds should be spacious and extensively planted to create a park-like effect. Landscaped areas should provide adequate room for free play and supervised recreation, sports events, and ceremonial outdoor programs. Rural schools in many cases have great possibilities for fine development, possessing adequate space and good soil. The development of the rural school grounds is often accomplished with community help. Natural plant materials are sometimes used to supplement nursery grown stock.

Industrial Landscaping

Factories and industrial plants are moving out of heavily congested urban areas. Many companies have begun to pay attention to esthetic considerations as part of their obligations as corporate citizens. The appearance of factories becomes an important factor in both public and labor relations. A well-landscaped industrial plant can be highly attractive (Fig. 14-14).

Fig. 14-14. *A splendid example of industrial landscaping. Note the contrast created by the exciting use of water, paving, and plant material.*
[Courtesy General Motors Corporation.]

Highways and Roadside Development

Highway design must not only satisfy the requirements of utility and safety but should satisfy esthetic considerations by including beauty in the completed structure. The landscaping objectives include the utilization of existing scenic advantages in the proposed routes. Bridges and pavement wear out but scenic values can be virtually permanent. The subsequent creation of roadside development—outlooks, picnic areas, parks, and historical marker sites—become an important factor in choosing highway routes.

Highway design should harmonize with the natural topography. Existing trees and lesser vegetation should be conserved. Plantings of material to control erosion when in harmony with the natural surroundings will accomplish a natural transition between construction and landscape. To be effective this requires an adequate right of way. Zoning is essential for control and regulation of outdoor advertising and commercial structures along the highway. Safety considerations will encourage scenic interest, the long site, gentle curves and grades.

Landscape and engineering objectives both include erosion control, economical maintenance, safety, sound construction, and conservation of natural beauty. That the public desires landscaped, well-designed highways is evident. Toll roads have become increasingly important in interstate travel. People are willing to pay for safe, restful, scenic driving. The *parkway*, a highway for noncommercial traffic located on a strip of parkland with limited access, pays for itself many times over through extensive use by the motoring public and through increased property values.

FLORAL DESIGN

Floral design bears about the same relationship to landscape design as a string quartet does to a symphony orchestra. The principles of design are the same; only the scale is reduced. Floral design, as are painting and sculpture, is one of the decorative arts, considered by some as removed from the so-called practical needs of man. This is a narrow view; any requirement outside of the sustaining necessities could be so considered.

Although arranging flowers* is a means of individual artistic expression, it is also the basis of commercial floriculture, which constitutes a large segment of the horticultural industry. All cut flowers are for ultimate use in some sort of arrangement. This may consist in simply placing a dozen roses in a vase, or it may involve the creation of a large floral float.

Planters

Planters, large containers for growing plants, are popular for indoor and outdoor use. Planters are well suited in outdoor courts and plazas. Depend-

---

* The term flower is used in its broadest sense to include all decorative plants and plant parts, especially the morphological flower.

ing on the season, a wide variety of plants may be used, including evergreen shrubs, bulbs, and annuals. Growing plants contribute to interior decoration just as they do to architecture. Because of the unavailability of indoor light, foliage plants having low light requirements such as *Philodendron, Sansevieria,* and *Ficus* are grown. Planters have become especially prominent as interior decor in lobbies, offices, and restaurants. The use of artificial foliage plants, which are becoming amazingly lifelike, is also increasing, but like all imitations they are not quite satisfactory.

Flower Arrangement

Arrangements of flowers, plants, and plant parts have long been used for decoration. In Japan, flower arrangement, or *Ikebana,* is a continuing tradition that has been an important part of cultural life for 13 centuries. Its significance in Japanese home life was established in the fifteenth century, along with the tea ceremony. In its conception, Ikebana symbolized certain philosophical and religious concepts. Today, much of the religious connotation has been lost, but the symbolism still remains a key part of the arrangement. Thus, the expression of seasonal change and the passage of time are vital parts of all arrangements, as are appropriate representations of traditional holidays and festivals. Unlike the Western concepts of floral design, the Oriental tradition emphasizes the element of line over form and color. In the classical concept, line is symbolically partitioned into the representation of heaven (vertical), earth (horizontal), and man (diagonal and intermediate). The chief aim is to achieve a beautiful flowing line, and to accomplish this end the most ordinary materials may be used. The concept of naturalism is used throughout. All symmetrical effects are avoided.

Flower arrangement is still an important part of Japanese life. There are many different styles and schools: *Ikenobo,* classical arrangements; *Rikka,* larger, ornate, upright reproductions of the landscape by means of flowers and plants; *Nageire,* simple, naturalistic arrangements; *Moribana,* expressive, scenic arrangements with greater use of foliage and flowers. These schools of flower arrangement differ in opinion and conception, but the basic principles of the art are preserved in common.

There are other typically oriental types of artistic expression involving growing plants. *Bonsai,* the culture of miniature potted trees, dwarfed by pruning and controlled nutrition, is a spectacular example of the horticultural art. Living trees, some over a hundred years old and yet only a few feet high, are grown in containers arranged to resemble a portion of the natural landscape (Fig. 14-15). *Bonseki* is the construction of a miniature landscape out of stone, sand, and living vegetation.

In Europe, flowers are readily purchased in the market and are in common use as a part of normal living. In the United States, on the other hand, the use of flowers is usually limited to special occasions such as formal dining, decoration at religious holidays, appropriate remembrances (especially birthdays, anniversaries, Mother's day), and as convalescent gifts. The ceremonial use of flowers in weddings and funerals is the backbone of the florist business. Bouquets and wreaths are standard fare for concert artists, beauty queens, openings, and derby winners. Corsages and boutonnieres become a significant part of the costume at dances, and formal occasions.

Fig. 14-15. *Bonsai. These trees are over 100 years old. The small size is maintained through pruning and by controlling nutrition.*
[Courtesy Katsuyoshi Yoshikawa, Kyoto University.]

HORTICULTURE AS RECREATION

Horticulture has long been, and will continue to be, an outlet for recreation and pleasure. Gardening is probably the true national pastime, for horticulture may be actively enjoyed at many levels. It provides either vigorous or sedentary activity, which may be pursued on any scale. The young, the strong, the aged and infirm may enjoy its respite. There is room for the innovator, the gadget-minded, the artist, and the faddist. The joys of solitude or the bustle of organizational activity are there. It yields the sweets of anticipation along with the bitterness of disappointment. Tangible rewards are available for a minimum of effort and increase in proportion to skill and persistence. All who partake of it soon acquire a keener awareness of the mysteries of life, and growth, and death. The beautiful as well as the delicious are readily available for those who seek it.

Selected References

Church, T. D. *Gardens Are for People*. Reinhold, New York. 1955. (The gardens and home landscaping of one of the leading designers in the United States.)

Eckbo, G. *Landscape for Living*. F. W. Dodge, New York. 1950. (An interesting and provocative analysis of landscape architecture.)

Lewis, H. M. *Planning the Modern City*. Wiley, New York. 1949. (The elements of city planning.)

Riester, D. W. *Design for Flower Arrangers*. Van Nostrand, New Jersey. 1959. (A beautiful book.)

Simonds, J. O. *Landscape Architecture*. F. W. Dodge, New York. 1961. (Landscape planning and site development.)

Tunnard, C. *The City of Man*. Scribners, New York. 1953. (An urbanite's approach to the city. See Chapter 10.)

Index